modern railways Dictionary
of Railway Industry Terms

John Glover

Ian Allan
PUBLISHING

CONTENTS

First published 2005

ISBN (10) 0 7110 3076 6
ISBN (13) 978 0 7110 3076 3

Published by Ian Allan Publishing

an imprint of Ian Allan Publishing Ltd, Hersham, Surrey
KT12 4RG.
Printed in England by Ian Allan Printing Ltd, Hersham,
Surrey KT12 4RG.

Code: 0511/B1

Visit the Ian Allan Publishing website at
www.ianallanpublishing.co.uk

Front cover: Gatwick Express Class 460 'Juniper' EMU
No 460007 at Clapham Junction on 18 July 2002. *John Glover*

Title page: A Virgin 'Pendolino' eases its way into London Euston
on 7 March 2005 with the 10.00 from Birmingham New Street.
The 113-mile journey has taken 94 minutes with three
intermediate stops. Euston is served also by Silverlink services
and First ScotRail. The overnight trains of the latter are becoming
the only locomotive-hauled services to use the station.
John Glover

FOREWORD

The railway has its own language, often handed down from generation to generation. Most of it consists of specialist terms which to those outside the industry are confusing. Indeed, I have spent much of my time in the industry discouraging the use of such language during on-board announcements or in other communications with customers!

As time progresses terms come and go. Whilst SPAD (Signal Passed at Danger) is now widely known, others such as MPD (Motive Power Depot) are now consigned to the history books.

I congratulate John Glover on producing this work. I am sure that it will find a place on many a railway manager's shelf.

Chris Green, FCILT
Non-executive Director, Network Rail

Top: The fortunes of the Woodhead route were built on the coal from Yorkshire pits being sent across the Pennines to Manchester, and the route could not survive the pit closures. This view of 13 June 2002 shows the blocked western portal of Woodhead Tunnel completed in 1954. To the left are the tunnels it replaced, built a century earlier. *John Glover*

Above: By 9 April 2003, the old order at Euston for Virgin Trains had little time left. Class 86 No 86233 *ALSTOM Heritage* is in more or less original livery, and is seen alongside DVT No 82140 after arrival at platforms 1 and 2. *John Glover*

INTRODUCTION

'The smooth and effective running of the railway is reliant upon the knowledge, skill and commitment of all those who work on it.'

Thus said the London, Midland & Scottish Railway's company handbook, from the far-off days of 1934. However, such sentiments are equally applicable 70 or so years later, and it is with the objective of contributing a little more to that knowledge base that this book has been compiled.

The railway as we know it today had its origins around 1830, when the Liverpool & Manchester Railway was opened. The railway, its technology, operation and marketing have been through the classic developmental and consolidation phases, while its competitive position has changed from that of a dominant monopoly to a relatively minor participant in many (but not all) markets. This has been reflected in the changing financial situation as the years progressed. Behind all this has been an evolving legislation, which for long was aimed at keeping the railway

under some kind of control, whether in the fares and charges made, or safety matters. This too has changed into finding the way in which the railway can contribute most effectively to Britain's economy.

One result has been a huge vocabulary of railway terms, which are at best only loosely recorded. Some, like those associated with horse traction and the broad gauge, are of historical interest only and will not be found here. Others are very much part of the present railway industry, which today is carrying more traffic than it has done for many years, and on a much smaller network at that.

This book sets out to record those terms which are in common railway use today, plus those which may still be found even if their main relevance is in the past. Few have fully defined meanings, and the author has drawn from a wide range of sources. There is thus a hybrid element in many of them, and for that reason few are attributed to particular sources.

To illustrate some of the difficulties involved, consider this example. The definition of a train in the Railways Act 1993, s83(1) is 'Two or more items of rolling stock coupled together, at least one of which is a locomotive, or a locomotive not coupled to any other rolling stock.' But it also defines a locomotive as 'any railway vehicle which has the capacity for self-propulsion.'

So that's clear, then. The Class 153 diesel unit fleet of single cars are all locomotives.

However, such legal definitions are there for a limited purpose, and in this case they apply to Part I of that Act only. This particular definition does not reflect common usage, and the reader will find another interpretation in this book. On the other hand, such definitions can be extremely useful, an example being that of a railway as incorporated in the Transport & Works Act 1992 and which has also been used in subsequent legislation. That one will be found, verbatim.

A word about acronyms, of which there are seemingly vast numbers. Many also change quickly. Essentially, acronyms have been omitted, other than where the terms themselves form an entry. In these cases, the acronym will be found in its correct alphabetical position and cross-referenced to the entry.

This book is an attempt to record the railway speak of the early 21st century. The author hopes that it will enlighten (and perhaps even mildly amuse) professional railwaymen and women, and observers of the industry alike. In particular, I trust that it will benefit new entrants to the industry, who may find some of the terms they come across downright baffling.

John Glover FCILT, MIRO, MPWI
Worcester Park, Surrey
July 2005

THE 21st CENTURY RAILWAY

To say that the railways of Britain have been through an unprecedented period of upheaval in the last decade or so is hardly an overstatement, but neither is it of much help to the individual in coming to terms with what has happened. The following is a brief résumé of the main events.

Until 1994, the nationalised British Railways Board (BRB) operated what became known as a vertically integrated railway, in which the provision of the infrastructure, the ownership of the trains and the operation of the services run were all functions of the Board.

Under the Railways Act 1993, these and other functions were split. The ownership of the track went to a new infrastructure company, Railtrack, which was subsequently privatised. Latterly, it became Network Rail, a not-for-profit company. All operators paid Railtrack and then Network Rail for the use of the track and signalling.

Passenger train operation was split into what became 26 separate franchises, using the BR business sector organisation as a basis. The initial franchises were mostly for a seven-year term, and were the subject of competitive bidding. Franchise awards took into account the additional service and investment commitments that the chosen franchisee would make, and whether that company required a subsidy or would make payments to the Government over the franchise term.

The passenger stations were owned by Railtrack, but apart from what are now 17 major stations, were run by the Train Operating Companies (TOCs).

Over time, many of the franchises were acquired by

Railways Act 1993

CHAPTER 43

The Railways Act 1993.
John Glover

groups active in the bus industry, notably Arriva, First Group, Go-Ahead, National Express and Stagecoach.

The passenger rolling stock became the property of three Rolling Stock Companies (ROSCOs), which then leased the stock to the Train Operating Companies. This avoided the financial problems associated with seven-year franchises and an asset life of often around 30 years.

The freight companies were also privatised, owning the locomotives themselves and those wagons not owned by their customers.

Franchising was carried out by the Office of Passenger Rail Franchising (OPRAF), and various aspects of the industry, including licensing, were overseen by the independent Rail Regulator (ORR), plus the Health & Safety Executive (HSE). The Association of Train Operating Companies (ATOC) was created to manage industry internal affairs and the Railway Forum became its public face.

The last franchises were let very shortly before the 1997 General Election, which brought a change in

The HST was one of the most significant successes of British Rail, with the train entering squadron service from 1976 and still in use today, in slightly diminished numbers. Here, a GNER set leaves Leuchars with its nearby RAF base, on 24 June 2004 with the 07.55 Aberdeen to London King's Cross. *John Glover*

Government from Conservative to Labour. Labour was concerned at the lack of overall direction and planning in the railway industry, and this resulted in the creation of the Strategic Rail Authority (SRA) in 2001 with a remit in accordance with its name. But other problems afflicted the industry, in particular the inability of many franchisees to make the financial returns they had expected, plus the level, and it turned out, the quality of investment by Railtrack. A series of high-profile rail accidents in which infrastructure shortcomings were identified turned out to be the eventual downfall of that company.

However, rising traffic levels and many more trains, either to compete or to fill the timetable to prevent new competition, led to performance problems. These became chronic after the severe restrictions hastily put in place following the Hatfield derailment of 2001. This led in turn to huge and largely justified political and media criticism of the industry.

But the cost of the railway to the public purse was rising fast, again with high-profile problems as in the projected costs of the West Coast Route Modernisation. When the Rail Regulator made his ruling at the end of 2003 on the much increased level of access charges needed to fund Network Rail to provide the infrastructure in the forthcoming five year period to 2008/09, this proved to be the proverbial straw breaking the camel's back. This would in effect be a charge to be funded by Government, since the TOCs were protected by an indemnity clause in their contracts.

The result was the Railways Act 2005. This saw the abolition of the SRA with most of its functions, including strategy, finance and the awarding of franchises, subsumed into an enlarged Department for Transport. The safety policy, regulation and enforcement functions are transferred from the HSE to the Office of Rail Regulation, while the Government sets out what Network Rail is expected to deliver for the public money it receives. Network Rail takes over the SRA's duties of monitoring TOC performance, setting timetables and directing service recovery. The access charges review process is amended, and there is a transfer of powers and budgets to Scotland, Wales and London.

Meanwhile, there have been further developments in European legislation, and this seems likely to continue. The European Commission has three central objectives for transport. These are:

To promote greater competition in the supply of transport within each mode, to reduce costs and increase quality.
To ensure competition is fair between the modes, including external costs (eg accidents, congestion and pollution), and in terms of pricing the fees for access to the infrastructure.
To provide sufficient infrastructure, especially across borders, where individual states may have insufficient incentive to invest.

At home, the junior Transport Minister Charlotte Atkins MP was emphasising the need for a long-term view. After years of underinvestment and industry fragmentation, she said, there was a need to simplify relationships, and to provide a sound footing for the next 20 to 30 years. The watchwords were to be performance, confidence and stability.

Above: Stagecoach was the first private operator to challenge the vertically integrated railway, when the company used its own vehicles to offer overnight services between London Euston and several Scottish destinations in 1992. The coaches were attached to existing trains. The venture achieved only limited success, but all parties gained experience as a result. The denationalising Railways Act followed, in 1993. *John Glover*

Right: Following privatisation, some of the initial franchises underwent changes in ownership, and in the case of West Anglia Great Northern it was subsequently split into the two component parts. On 16 September 2001, EMU No 315861 arrives at the Hertford East branch terminus with a train from Liverpool Street. Route modernisation here was well under way by this time, and the signalbox and searchlight-type colour light signals are now no more. *John Glove*

PROFESSIONAL, GOVERNMENT AND INDUSTRY BODIES

This section lists the principal bodies related to the railway industry and their functions, in alphabetical order.

Associated Society of Locomotive Engineers & Firemen (ASLEF)
The union, founded in 1880, which represents many train drivers.

Association of Community Rail Partnerships (ACoRP)
ACoRP is a national federation of over 40 such partnerships and is a not-for-profit organisation. It aims to provide impartial support, advice and guidance to anyone who is involved with rural, semi-rural and local rail services, including train operators and providers of bus, taxi and community transport services.

Association of Train Operating Companies (ATOC)
An unincorporated trade association which represents the interests of most of the national and international passenger Train Operating Companies, who are required to be members.
    ATOC acts as the official view of the passenger rail industry, providing its members with a range of services that enable them to comply with conditions laid upon them in their franchise agreements and operating licences, including:
- Revenue allocation and settlement.
- The National Rail Conditions of Carriage.
- The National Rail Enquiry Service (NRES).
- The licensing of rail appointed travel agents.
- National Railcards, the London Travelcard and Network Railcard.
- The National Rail standards.

Association of Transport Co-ordinating Officers (ATCO)
The Association was founded in 1974 to bring together local authority officers then newly tasked with transport co-ordination duties. Since then the Association has grown steadily and now has over 600 members covering almost all British authorities with passenger transport responsibilities, including bus, rail, ferry, education, community and social services transport. ATCO acts as their professional organisation, and its membership includes those from Passenger Transport Executives, Transport *for* London and the Department for Transport.

British Railways Board (BRB)
The state corporation established under the Transport Act 1962 responsible for the operation, upkeep and stewardship of the national rail network, the infrastructure and freight and passenger train services. Its functions were reallocated progressively between 1994 and 1997 as the industry was privatised.

British Transport Police (BTP)
A national police force for the railways, whose origins can be traced back to 1826. BTP, with a present complement of 2,280 officers, 221 special constables and 704 support staff, provides a policing service for rail operators, their staff and passengers. Its goal is to provide a service which delivers a safer railway environment that is free from disruption and a fear of crime. BTP reports to an independent Police Authority, the members and chairman of which are appointed by the Secretary of State. Funding is derived largely from railways sources, in the proportions of (roundly) 50% from TOCs and 25% each from Network Rail and London Underground.

Caledonian MacBrayne (Calmac)
The long-established nationalised ferry operator, which provides most of the shipping services to the Scottish islands, connecting with mainland rail services directly at Ardrossan Harbour, Wemyss Bay, Gourock, Oban and Mallaig.

(The) Chartered Institute of Logistics and Transport in the UK (CILT (UK))
Founded as the Institute of Transport in 1919, the Royal Charter was gained in 1926. Today's CILT is the professional body for individuals and organisations involved in all disciplines, modes and aspects of logistics and transport. The Institute aims to encourage the adoption of policies that are efficient and sustainable, and respond to the challenges of a changing world. Education and training is a primary objective. There are 22,000 members in the UK, part of a worldwide CILT grouping in over 50 countries.

Commission for Integrated Transport (CfIT)
The Commission was proposed in the 1998 Transport White Paper and set up in 1999. It is an independent body advising the Government on integrated transport policy. The Commission provides expert advice and carries out independent research on transport issues and the interface with environment, health, the economy and society generally.

Community of European Railways (CER)
Now the Community of European Railway and Infrastructure Companies, CER consists of 36 members from the European Union, the accession countries Bulgaria and Romania, plus Croatia, Norway and Switzerland. It is based in Brussels and represents its members' interests to the European Parliament, the Commission and Council of Members, and others.

Main Defence Rail Sites

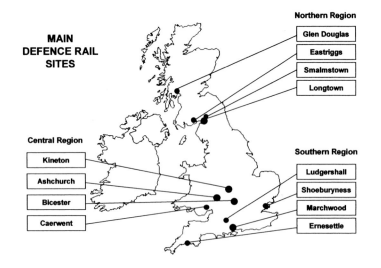

MAIN DEFENCE RAIL SITES

Northern Region
- Glen Douglas
- Eastriggs
- Smalmstown
- Longtown

Central Region
- Kineton
- Ashchurch
- Bicester
- Caerwent

Southern Region
- Ludgershall
- Shoeburyness
- Marchwood
- Ernesettle

Top: Main Defence Rail Sites map. (DRCS)

Above: Locomotive No 01510 is Thomas Hill 'Vanguard Steelman' 0-4-0 built at Rotherham in 1988. It is a military Class C four-wheel diesel-hydraulic shunting locomotive with a 335bhp eight-cylinder Cummins engine. It was originally numbered 272 when serving with Bicester Military Railway and carried the name *Royal Pioneer*. It was refurbished in spring 2003 when it gained its current DRCS livery, and was transferred to Ludgershall depot. *DRCS*

CER's main focus is promoting the development of rail as essential to the creation of a sustainable transport system which is both efficient and environmentally sound.

Community Rail Partnerships (CRP)
These are flexible informal partnerships which bring together local authorities, community groups, rail user groups, TOCs and often (but not always) Network Rail. Some include other bodies, such as national park authorities, town or parish councils, and businesses. Their objective is to promote and develop local rail services. These not-for-profit organisations, presently 43 in number, are funded mainly by local authorities and TOCs. Typically, they are staffed by a paid officer supported by a committee of stakeholders.

Convention on International Carriage by Rail (COTIF)
For goods and passengers by rail, the Convention will be incorporated in English law once it is ratified by sufficient countries. The regulations concerning the international carriage of dangerous goods by rail (RID) is a subset of the COTIF convention. There is a further convention (ADR) for the international carriage of dangerous goods by road.

Defence Rail & Container Services (DRCS)
The Defence Logistics Organisation is a body whose mission is to provide rail capability and container services. Key tasks are the provision and maintenance of rail terminal infrastructure, specialist advice on Ministry of Defence rail operational matters, overseeing the safety of MoD railway operations worldwide and the formalisation of legal frameworks for railway operations.

The strategic policy role lies with the Ministry of Defence, in terms of procurement, safety and organisation. Very broadly, this is a similar role to that of the Department for Transport in civilian life. Similarly, railway operating policy roughly matches that of the Office of Rail Regulation. Rail operating policy divides into site operations in the UK, and the main line railway contract (presently run by EWS). Internal site operation in the UK is conducted by DRCS, while two military rail operating troops (one Regular and one Territorial Army) provide the capability for overseas deployments.

Department for Transport (DfT)
The Department for Transport is the Government body responsible for the transport industry. The Department's objective is to oversee the delivery of a reliable, safe and secure transport system that responds efficiently to the needs of individuals and businesses, while safeguarding the environment. Its role is to set the policy context for the Government's transport strategy and to manage relationships with the delivery agencies.

More specifically, the Department now assumes most of the powers previously exercised by the Strategic Rail Authority on the abolition of the latter.

In previous incarnations, the DfT has been known as Department for Transport and Local Government (DTLG), Department of Environment, Transport and the Regions (DETR) and the Department of Transport (DTp).

European Conference of Ministers of Transport (ECMT)
An inter-governmental organisation established by a Protocol signed in Brussels in 1953. It is a forum in which Ministers responsible for transport, and more specifically the inland transport sector, can co-operate on policy. Members and Associates of ECMT represent 47 countries.

At present, ECMT's role consists primarily of:

● Helping to create an integrated transport system throughout Europe that is economically and technically efficient, meets the highest possible safety and environmental standards and takes full account of the social dimension.

● Helping also to build a bridge between the European Union and the rest of the Continent, at a political level.

European Railway Agency

The Agency, created in 2005, is responsible for formulating common solutions on matters concerning safety and interoperability, in order to create a safe, integrated and competitive railway without frontiers.

The role of the Agency is to give technical support to decision making, based on independent and neutral expertise, and will be an integral part of the Community system. It will be responsible for developing a harmonised format for safety certification and the implementation of the Interoperability Directives on railways.

The competitiveness of railways, especially freight, is hampered by the differences that exist between Member States as regards rolling stock, technology, signalling, types of traction currents and speed limits. The aim of the Agency's work is to reduce these disparities and establish common standards for signalling systems, telematics applications for freight services, the operation and management of rolling stock used for international freight services, and staff qualifications.

Greater London Authority (GLA)
(GLA area 2001 population 7.17 million)

Created under the Greater London Authority Act 1999. The Mayor of London, acting on behalf of the Greater London Authority, develops and implements policies for the promotion and encouragement of safe, integrated, efficient and economic transport services to, from and within Greater London. The Authority sets fares and service levels for all services provided by Transport *for* London (T*f*L). The previous power to give Directions and Guidance to the Strategic Rail Authority in relation to the provision of rail services in Greater London has been replaced by a duty on the Secretary of State to consult T*f*L when letting franchises which directly affect Greater London.

The Mayor's Integrated Transport Strategy was published in 2001, and forms the framework for projects to be promoted by the Authority. The formal agenda includes the following headings:

● Commuter services and franchise replacement

● Towards a London Metro 'turn up and go' service

● Investment in new capacity

● International links

● Security

● Integration and common standards

● Accessibility to stations

● Parking at stations

Health & Safety Executive (HSE)

The regulatory authority for health and safety, working under the general direction of the Health & Safety at Work Act, etc, 1974. Its specific railway duties were transferred to the Office of Rail Regulation under the Railways Act 2005.

Her Majesty's Railway Inspectorate (HMRI)

HMRI is the enforcement body covering health and safety on Britain's railways. That includes London Underground, metro and light rail systems, heritage railways and narrow gauge railways with a track gauge of 350mm or more.

The principal functions of HMRI are:

● To assess and approve new and altered works, plant and equipment.

● To assess and approve railway operators' safety cases.

● To carry out a programme of targeted inspections of works systems and premises to ensure compliance with health and safety legislation.

● To investigate accidents to trains, persons who are on or about the railway and significant dangerous occurrences.

● To investigate complaints made to HMRI by railway staff and members of the public and also to give advice when requested.

● To keep Ministers informed on key railway issues of concern.

● Generally to act as the Government's safety watchdog on railways.

HMRI publishes a series of manuals under the general title of Railway Safety Principles and Guidance, setting out design and operational objectives.

Institution of Railway Operators (IRO)

An Institution which provides a professional structure and qualifications for people with knowledge and experience of operating the railway, at all levels. Its formal objectives are to advance, for the benefit of the general public, the safe and reliable operation of the railways by improving the technical and general skills, knowledge and competence, and promoting the training of persons engaged in the operation of the railways in the United Kingdom.

Institution of Railway Signal Engineers (IRSE)

The IRSE is the professional institution for all those engaged in, or associated with, railway signalling, telecommunications and allied professions and is active in the UK, Europe and worldwide. Founded in 1912, the Institution aims to advance, for the public benefit, the science and practice of signalling and telecommunications engineering within the industry and to maintain high standards of knowledge of the profession amongst the membership.

InterCity

Former British Rail passenger business sector for long distance services on major routes. This covered the East Coast, Great Western, Midland and West Coast main lines, Anglia (London to Norwich), Cross Country and Gatwick Express.

International Rail Regulator (IRR)

This is a statutory office, separate from the Office of Rail Regulation. The IRR licenses the operation of certain international rail services in the European Economic Area, and access in Britain for the purpose of the operation of such services. The chairman of the ORR Board is also the present International Rail Regulator.

Local Government Association (LGA)

Formed by the merger of the Association of County Councils, the Association of District Councils and the Association of Metropolitan Authorities in 1997, the LGA has just under 500 members. These include all 238 Shire District Councils, 36 Metropolitan District Councils, 34 County Councils, 46 new Unitary Authorities, 33 London Authorities (32 Boroughs and the City of London) and 22 Welsh Authorities. In addition, the LGA represents police, fire and passenger transport authorities. The LGA is the national voice for local communities in England and Wales.

Amongst the LGA's policy priorities is integrated transport.

London Regional Transport

Functions now the responsibility of Transport *for* London.

London Transport Users Committee (LTUC)

A statutory consumer body covering the whole of London Underground, Docklands Light Railway, Croydon Tramlink, bus services, taxis and river services within Greater London, plus National Rail services within an area roundly 25 miles from Charing Cross.

The Committee has four principal spheres of activity. Consultation involves it in a continuous dialogue with the bodies which plan and operate the services. Monitoring means that the Committee keeps a close watch on the quality of service provided. Investigation is required when users are dissatisfied with any aspect of the service and when in the complainant's view the operator's initial response has been inadequate. Representation is provided by the Committee in the wider arena of public debate.

Members are appointed by the London Assembly, which funds the Committee.

National Union of Rail, Maritime and Transport Workers (RMT)

Formed as the Association of Railway Servants (ASRS) and becoming a Trade Union in 1871, it merged with the General Railway Workers' Union and the United Pointsmen and Signalmen's Society in 1913 to become the National Union of Railwaymen (NUR). Now the RMT, it is the principal union for rail staff who do not fall within the ambit of ASLEF or TSSA. Engineering staff tend to be members of the engineering union appropriate for their occupation.

Network Rail

Network Rail Ltd, a company limited by guarantee, acquired Railtrack PLC (the regulated infrastructure company) from its railway administrators in October 2002. Network Rail Infrastructure Ltd (formerly Railtrack PLC) is responsible for the operation, maintenance and renewal of the railway infrastructure com-

Network Rail

Track renewal is under way here on the Crayford loop, with the up line completely removed for re-laying and the ballast being dumped into a slowly advancing train on the down line, hauled by a Class 66 locomotive. It is the afternoon of Saturday 21 June 2003. The objective, as always, is to get the line handed back to the operators before the Monday morning peak.
John Glover

prising the track, signals, bridges, viaducts, level crossings, tunnels and stations, and of which it is the monopoly owner. The task is the delivery of a safe, reliable and efficient railway network. Network Rail operates under a licence issued by the Secretary of State for Transport and enforced by the Office of Rail Regulation.

Network Rail Ltd is a private company, run along commercial lines, but there are no shareholders. It aims to make surpluses from its operations and, instead of paying dividends, its profits are re-invested in the infrastructure.

Members take the place of shareholders; the company is run by a board of directors of whom one is appointed by Government. There are two member categories: industry and public (the majority). Members have no financial or economic interest in Network Rail; they are there to hold the board accountable for its management of the business and to ensure Network Rail is managed with high standards of corporate governance.

Network Rail Ltd is accountable to its train and freight operator customers under its licence and their access contracts which incorporate the network code. It is regulated by the Office of Rail Regulation under statute to the providers of funds (principally the SRA/DfT and the PTEs/PTAs) and the Health & Safety Executive.

The company determines its strategy for the network based on its contractual and regulatory obligations.

Network SouthEast (NSE)

Former British Rail passenger business sector covering primarily commuter travel in London and the South East.

Office of Passenger Rail Franchising (OPRAF)

Subsumed into the Strategic Rail Authority on creation of the latter on 1 February 2001.

Office of Rail Regulation (ORR)

The Office's principal function is to set the funding requirements for Network Rail Infrastructure Ltd, later amended by a need to have regard to the objectives of Ministers in the form of an output specification and their general guidance. The ORR also exercises the railway safety functions transferred from the HSE. The ORR licenses operators of railway assets (infrastructure, trains and light maintenance depots), approves agreements for access by operators to track, stations and light maintenance depots, and enforces domestic competition law in the railway context. The ORR is led by a board appointed by the Secretary of State.

Olympic Delivery Authority

A body corporate, the functions of which are to prepare for the 2012 London Olympics. Amongst its duties are ensuring that adequate arrangements are made for the provision, management and control of the facilities for transport. An Olympic Transport Plan is to be prepared.

Passenger Transport Authorities (PTAs)

The local transport authorities representing the local authorities in a metropolitan area to which the Passenger Transport Executives are responsible, funded by those local authorities.

Passenger Transport Executives (PTEs)

The seven PTEs were established between 1969 and 1973 under the powers given in the Transport Act 1968. These statutory bodies, subject to local authority control (through the Passenger Transport Authority, or PTA), are responsible for setting out local authority transport policy and expenditure plans to be allocated for public transport.

PTE powers have been limited by the Railways Act 2005, under which they co-sign the DfT/TOC franchise agreement, but would themselves need to secure the agreement of the Secretary of State for any additional services which they might wish to be provided and themselves fund.

PTEs contract for bus services which the private sector does not provide commercially, provide local transport information, are co-signatories of the relevant franchise agreements with the franchised train operators, and specify levels and standards of certain services in their areas.

- **Greater Manchester (PTE area 2001 population 2.48 million). Principal towns include Bolton, Bury, Manchester, Oldham, Salford and Stockport.**

   Following the collapse of the underground heavy rail Piccadilly/Victoria linking project, Greater Manchester PTE's efforts centred around the creation of the Metrolink light rail system. This was aimed at bringing two lines together via Manchester city centre. Subsequently extended to Eccles (new construction) with further extensions intended – in part over heavy rail lines. Potentially, will result in a residual role only for local heavy rail long term. Some new unstaffed stations have been opened.

Greater Manchester
In Greater Manchester, the linking of the railways across the centre of Manchester itself and conversion to light rail has been a key policy issue for many years. One of the first to be converted was the Bury line, seen here at Besses-o'-th'-Barn on 27 March 2003. The road immediately beneath is the A665, while the M62 motorway passes under this road in the middle distance. *John Glover*

Merseyside
There is a considerable drop to platform level at the new station at Brunswick, Merseyside, and as can be seen, this has required the construction of an equally lengthy access ramp. Like other Merseyrail stations, Brunswick is continuously staffed. This view was taken on 21 October 1998. *John Glover*

- **Merseyside (Merseytravel) (PTE area 2001 population 1.36 million). Principal towns include Birkenhead, Liverpool, St Helens and Southport.**

  Creation of the deep level loop and link in Liverpool city centre allowed rail services to be fully integrated and restored eastwards to Garston and Hunt's Cross, plus some further electrification, notably south from Rock Ferry. There are some new stations, all staffed. In July 2003, responsibility for the Merseyrail Electrics franchise was transferred from the SRA to Merseytravel, who signed a 25-year franchise agreement with Serco/NedRailways to operate the system.

- **South Yorkshire (PTE area 2001 population 1.27 million). Principal towns include Barnsley, Doncaster, Rotherham and Sheffield.**

  Some modest improvements to local services relevant to the PTE area, plus reconstructions as at Barnsley. Stations are unstaffed. The Supertram light rail system uses some former rail alignments in the Don valley.

- **Strathclyde (PTE area 2001 population 2.10 million). Principal towns include Ayr, Cumbernauld, Dumbarton, Glasgow, Motherwell and Paisley.**

  Electrification extended to Ayr and to Largs. Re-creation of an electrified cross-city link for heavy rail, on which the whole of the service pattern of the biggest suburban operation outside London is based. Some subsequent extensions to this and also new diesel services. Operator of Glasgow Underground.

- **Tyne & Wear (Nexus) (PTE area 2001 population 1.08 million). Principal towns include Newcastle upon Tyne and Sunderland.**

  Major works leading to the creation of the Metro system (wholly owned and operated by the PTE) on former BR lines, with city centre penetration. Later, services extended over Network Rail to Sunderland and South Hylton. Few conventional local rail services remain. Stations are unstaffed.

- **West Midlands (Centro) (PTE area 2001 population 2.56 million). Principal towns include Birmingham, Coventry and Wolverhampton.**

  Lichfield-Redditch line restored and electrified, Snow Hill station reopened and Leamington Spa-Stourbridge links restored. Some new stations have been built and nearly all are staffed. Services restored are Wolverhampton-Walsall and north to Rugeley. Frequencies increased. Creation of Midland Metro, mostly over old BR formation to Wolverhampton, to which extensions are planned.

- **West Yorkshire (Metro) (PTE area 2001 population 2.08 million). Principal towns include Bradford, Huddersfield, Leeds and Wakefield.**

  Frequency improvements generally, which led to the reconstruction of Leeds west end layout and new platforms. Some electrification as part of ECML scheme, but also Airedale & Wharfedale. Bradford Interchange replaced Exchange. An extensive programme of new station openings on existing lines, all unstaffed. Wakefield-Pontefract and Halifax-Huddersfield services restored.

Passenger Transport Executive Group (PTEG)

A non-statutory body bringing together and promoting the interests of the seven PTEs; Transport *for* London is an associate member.

Permanent Way Institution (PWI)

The PWI promotes and encourages the acquisition and exchange of technical and general knowledge about the design, construction and maintenance of every type of rail track, including railways, tramways, docks and harbours and the many and varied infrastructure works. The objectives of the Permanent Way Institution are to advance the knowledge of railway civil engineering, in particular track and infrastructure, and to promote, spread and exchange such knowledge amongst those who work for railways and rail systems worldwide.

Rail Accident Investigation Branch (RAIB)

The RAIB is an independent body, set up by statute, reporting directly to the Secretary of State. It operates across the UK, covering light rail and metros as well as heavy rail systems. The RAIB is required to undertake investigations into accidents and incidents with the aim of enabling lessons to be learned, making recommendations to improve safety on railways and preventing railway accidents and railway incidents. Its task is to try to determine what caused an accident, not to consider or determine blame or liability in the context of either criminal or civil proceedings.

Rail Express Systems (RES)

Former British Rail parcels and mail train operator, now part of EWS.

Rail Passengers Committees (RPCs)

The seven statutory Regional Committees established by the Railways Act 1993 to protect and promote the interests of passengers were disbanded under the Railways Act 2005. See also London Transport Users Committee.

Rail Passengers Council (RPC)

The new statutory consumers' association is a body corporate representing the interests of rail users nationally. It is resourced by the Secretary of State. Members of the Council include an appointee from the Scottish Minister, the National Assembly of Wales, the London Assembly and up to 12 others. The Secretary of State appoints the chairman. See also Consumer Representation, main text. It is anticipated that some regional duties will be delegated to local bodies.

Rail Safety and Standards Board (RSSB)

RSSB is a not-for-profit company owned by major industry stakeholders. It is independent of any single railway company and of their commercial interests. The company's primary objective is to lead and facilitate the railway industry's work to achieve continuous improvement on the health and safety performance of the railways of Great Britain, and thus to facilitate the reduction of risk to passengers, employees and the affected public.

Specifically, the company's remit includes the management of Railway Group Standards and to lead rail industry formal inquiries to ensure safety benefits are learned.

South Yorkshire
'Pacer' No 142060 sees a healthy patronage waiting as it arrives at Barnsley Interchange with a late afternoon service for Sheffield on 14 June 2002. *John Glover*

The RSSB has an extensive research programme, which is organised into seven topics and 24 research themes, as follows:

Topic	Research theme
Policy and risk	Engaging stakeholders in safety
	Safety decision making
	Risk assessment and data analysis
Management	Safety culture
	Safety management systems
	Supply chain management
	Competence
Engineering	Vehicle/track interaction
	Infrastructure integrity
	Accident survivability,
	including vehicle integrity and fire
Operations	Operations
	Abnormal and degraded working,
	contingency planning
	Safety critical communications
	Track safety and possession management
Train protection and control	Train protection and control, including separately managed workstreams on ERTMS
Public behaviour	Trespass and vandalism
	Station safety
	Personal safety and security
	Suicide
	Level crossings
Human performance	Human factors
	SPAD reduction and mitigation
	Occupational health

Railfreight Distribution (RfD)
Former British Rail business sector, now part of EWS.

Railtrack
Created as a wholly owned subsidiary of the British Railways Board on 1 April 1994 to own and develop the railway infrastructure. The company was privatised by flotation on the London Stock Exchange as Railtrack PLC in May 1996. Following a disastrous series of events, Railtrack was placed into Railway Administration by the Government (as specifically allowed for in s59-s65 of the Railways Act 1993) on 7 October 2001. It was then run by Court-appointed Administrators until it was transferred to the new not-for-profit company Network Rail on 3 October 2002.

Railway Development Companies (RDC)
Companies that can employ staff, lease or own property and undertake trading activities in a way which is not possible for voluntary groups or local government officers. They may undertake support services such as ticket selling, catering and retailing at stations or on trains, and property restoration and management. They can also provide ancillary services such as running community bus services, but do not undertake safety critical tasks. These remain the responsibility of the train operator or Network Rail. The first two RDCs are those for the Settle & Carlisle and the Esk Valley lines.

(The) Railway Forum
An industry-wide body both sponsored and paid for by most of the train operating companies including Eurostar, the rolling stock leasing companies, the Passenger Transport Executives, Network Rail, London Underground, Eurotunnel, and many manufacturing and infrastructure companies as well as other businesses connected with the railways. In all, there are over 50 members. Its key role is to act as a think tank, information exchange and point of contact for those committed to and interested in the railway industry.

Railway Group
Members are Network Rail, any train or station operator who holds a Railway Safety Case, and the Rail Safety and Standards Board (RSSB).

Railway Heritage Committee
The Railway Heritage Committee is a statutory national body operating primarily under the Railway Heritage Act 1996. It has the function of designating records and (moveable) artefacts still within the ownership of the privatised railway industry, which are historically significant and should be preserved permanently. The Committee also has to agree which institutions will hold the items no longer required by those railway businesses, and the terms under which they will be offered to them.

Railway Heritage Trust
Established in 1985, the Trust is an independent registered company, limited by guarantee, supported by Network Rail and Rail Property Ltd, on behalf of BRB (Residuary) Ltd, with the remit of:
- The conservation and enhancement of buildings and structures that are listed or scheduled, or of special architectural or historic interest owned by these organisations.
- Acting as a catalyst between outside parties and these owners on the conservation and alternative use of non-operational property, including the possible transfer of responsibility to local trusts or other interested organisations.

Railway Study Association (RSA)
The RSA's mission statement is to be the most effective forum in Great Britain for promoting a broad understanding of all aspects of the railway industry. The Railway Study Association exists for those who wish to develop and update their understanding of railway systems and technology both at home and abroad. It provides opportunities:
- To attend a unique programme of lectures addressed by experts.
- To participate in an annual Convention in a major city of significant rail interest, normally abroad.

- To attend study visits to locations not normally accessible.
- To meet informally to establish contacts and to exchange views.

Regional Development Agencies (RDA)
RDAs seek to foster regional economic development and regeneration within the context of sustainability. They prepare economic strategies for their regions and make a significant input to the preparation of such guidance and plans. Local proposals for transport and other infrastructure need to have regard for the RDA's programme of economic regeneration.

Regional Railways (RR)
Former British Rail passenger business sector for local and other services outside London and the South East. Previously known as Provincial.

RID
See Convention on International Carriage by Rail (COTIF)

Rolling stock companies (ROSCOs)
Three companies, Angel Trains, HSBC Rail and Porterbrook Leasing, who own most of the passenger locomotives and rolling stock, which is then leased to the TOCs who provide franchised services. The TOCs are thus relieved of the need to outlay large sums required for the purchase of assets whose useful life will often be much longer than that of their franchises.

Scottish Executive
The Scottish Executive is the devolved Government for Scotland. It is responsible for most of the issues of day-to-day concern to the people of Scotland, including transport. The Executive is led by a First Minister who is nominated by the Scottish Parliament, and in turn appoints the other Scottish Ministers who make up the Cabinet.

Sealink
Trading name for the railway shipping businesses operating domestic, Channel Islands, Irish and Continental routes. Sealink was sold to a subsidiary of Sea Containers Ltd on 27 July 1984.

Little known was TOPS Class 99, which was used for the Sealink train ferry vessels. The ships became pseudo locomotives, which were deemed to be hauling the wagons they contained when approaching Harwich or Dover ferry ports. The wagons themselves were listed in the same manner as in any other 'train'.

Strategic Rail Authority (SRA)
From 1 February 2001, the SRA, a non-ministerial Government body, provided strategic direction and leadership for the railway. It let and managed passenger franchises, developed and sponsored major infrastructure projects, made grants for rail freight and published an annual Strategic Plan. It was also responsible for some aspects of consumer protection. The SRA operated under Directions and Guidance from the Secretary of State for Transport.

The formal purposes of the SRA were set out in s205 of the Transport Act 2000:
- To promote the use of the railway network for the carriage of passengers and goods.
- To secure the development of the railway network.
- To contribute to the development of an integrated system of transport of passengers and goods.

The SRA was wound up under the provisions of the Railways Act 2005.

Thomas Cook
Publishers of the European Timetable and (for Africa, the Americas, Asia and Australasia) the Overseas Timetable.

Transport Committee, House of Commons
The House of Commons Select Committee on Transport is appointed by the House to examine the expenditure, administration and polity of the Department for Transport and its associated public bodies. The Committee works by undertaking inquiries and publishing reports on its findings where appropriate. Evidence is taken in sessions open to the public. Its task is to assist the House and its Committees, and not to replace them.

Transport *for* London (T*f*L)
Transport *for* London was created on 3 July 2000. Its public transport responsibilities now comprise London Rail, London Underground, buses, light rail, and river services. Directly accountable to the Mayor, T*f*L is a functional body of the Greater London Authority (GLA), responsible for implementing the Mayor's transport strategy. The main responsibilities of London Rail (a division of T*f*L) are as follows:
- To implement the rail objectives in the Mayor's transport strategy.
- To develop a Rail Plan for London.
- To work with the SRA/DfT and the rail industry to improve national rail services in London.
- To ensure progress on major new rail projects.
- To develop National Rail's contribution to an integrated public transport system for London.

Present projections are that there will be 700,000 additional people living and working in London, with the population of around 7.3 million in 2000 rising to 8.1 million by 2016.

Transport Salaried Staffs Association (TSSA)
A union for salaried staff, the clerical and managerial work force.

Union Internationale des Chemins de Fer (UIC)
International Union of Railways. The UIC (as it is commonly known) was formed in 1922 and is based in Paris. It represents most of the world's railways and sets many technical standards.

Welsh Assembly
The Welsh Assembly Government is responsible for developing and implementing policies and programmes for all issues which have been devolved to Wales. The First Minister chairs a Cabinet of eight others, one of whom is Minister for Economic Development and Transport.

RAILWAY OPERATING COMPANIES

Passenger Train Operating Companies (TOCs)

Passenger train services are provided by franchised passenger train operating companies (TOCs), which have been granted franchises to provide passenger rail services by the Strategic Rail Authority. A train operating company receives its licence to operate from the Office of Rail Regulation (ORR). The ORR also approves track access agreements between the TOCs and the infrastructure owner (Network Rail). In addition, the ORR approves the agreements for the train operators' access to stations.

Of the 34 operators, less than half of them (15) accounted for 80% of the total train km recorded. Most of the former InterCity companies are in that group, but at the top were the long distance ex-Regional Railways companies of Northern Rail, ScotRail and Central Trains, plus One and the major Network SouthEast companies south of the Thames. Notably, English, Welsh & Scottish Railway accounted for very nearly two thirds of all freight operations.

It should be stressed that this is a measure of production, not of passengers or freight carried, nor economic performance.

Table 1 shows the number of train km in the 2004/05 year as recorded by Network Rail, by operator, both passenger and freight.

Table 1: Train km by operator and proportions of total, 2004/05 year			
Operator	Train km (millions)	%	Cumulative %
Northern Rail[1]	40.44	8.5	8.5
First ScotRail	36.53	7.7	16.2
South West Trains	35.84	7.6	23.8
English, Welsh & Scottish Railway	31.25	6.6	30.4
One	29.38	6.2	36.6
Central Trains	28.00	5.9	42.5
South Eastern Trains	27.63	5.8	48.3
Virgin Cross Country Trains	26.85	5.6	53.9
Southern Trains	25.65	5.4	59.3
Arriva Trains Wales	19.21	4.0	63.3
Virgin West Coast Trains	18.25	3.8	67.1
Great North Eastern Railway	17.99	3.8	70.9
First Great Western	16.15	3.4	74.3
Transpennine Express	14.10	3.0	77.3
First Great Western Link	12.70	2.7	80.0
West Anglia Great Northern	11.55	2.4	82.4
Thameslink Rail	10.87	2.3	84.7
Wessex Trains	10.84	2.3	87.0
Midland Main Line	10.51	2.2	89.2
Silverlink	8.84	1.9	91.1
Chiltern Railways	8.10	1.7	92.8
Freightliner Ltd	7.61	1.6	94.4
c2c Rail	5.75	1.2	95.6
Merseyrail Electrics	5.53	1.2	96.8
Freightliner Heavy Haul	4.57	1.0	97.8
Gatwick Express	2.37	0.5	98.3
Nexus (Tyne & Wear Metro)[1]	2.30	0.5	98.8
Heathrow Express	1.57	0.3	99.1
Direct Rail Services	1.24	0.3	99.4
Hull Trains	1.03	0.2	99.6
Eurostar (UK)[2]	0.85	0.2	99.8
GB Railfreight	0.82	0.1	99.9
Island Line (estimated)	0.31	0.1	100
Rail Express Systems	0.04	0.0	100
Total train km operated:	**474.66**		
Passenger train km	429.14	90.4%	
Freight train km	45.52	9.6%	

[1] includes predecessor companies
[2] train km on Network Rail only

Table 2: Train Operating Companies (TOCs) franchises as at August 2005

1	c2c (London, Tilbury & Southend)	National Express
2	London Eastern Railway (One) (Greater Anglia)	National Express
3	Great North Eastern Railway (GNER)	Sea Containers
4a	WAGN Railway (now Great Northern only)	National Express
4b	Thameslink Rail	Go-Ahead
	4a and 4b to be merged in the enlarged Thameslink franchise.	
5	Midland Mainline	National Express
6	Northern Rail	Serco/NedRailways
7	TransPennine Express	First Group/Keolis
8	First ScotRail	First Group
9	West Coast Trains Ltd	Virgin Trains
10	CrossCountry Trains Ltd	Virgin Trains
	9 and 10 are separate franchises, but trade jointly as Virgin Trains.	
11	Merseyrail Electrics	Serco/NedRailways
12	Silverlink Train Services	National Express
13	Arriva Trains Wales	Arriva
14	Chiltern Railway Co	John Laing
15a	First Great Western	First Group
15b	First Great Western Link	First Group
15c	Wessex Trains	National Express
	15a, 15b and 15c to be merged as the Greater Western franchise.	
16a	South West Trains	Stagecoach
16b	Island Line	Stagecoach
	16a and 16b to be merged	
17	Southern	Go-Ahead/Govia
18	Gatwick Express	National Express
19	South Eastern Trains	SRA-owned company
	Part of the Integrated Kent franchise, including CTRL domestic services.	

Table 2 shows the Train Operating Company franchises as at August 2005.

Below left: A pair of Class 357 c2c units head along the Thames Estuary approaching Leigh-on-Sea and bound for Fenchurch Street on 15 August 2003, with No 357045 leading. Apart from freight traffic to and from the Tilbury loop, this is one of the most self-contained operations in the country. Although mainly a commuter railway, it is helped by having Southend as a sizeable commercial centre. *John Glover*

Below: Gatwick Express trains are now formed by the Class 460 units built for the job, and a down service is seen in June 2001 in the steep-sided chalk cutting on the Quarry line near Merstham. Unusually, the roofs of these units are painted red all over to attract attention from potential passengers still in the air, and also carry the company name. *John Glover*

The Central Trains franchise is to be distributed between new West Midlands, East Midlands (with Midland Mainline) and Cross Country franchises. West Midlands will include Silverlink County.

'This is the first stage in reduction in the number of franchises, and further streamlining will be necessary. It is the Government's intention that franchises are aligned as far as possible with Network Rail regions and routes in order to encourage joint working between track and train to deliver an improved service to customers, and that efficiency savings through economies of scale are maximised.' (Alastair Darling, October 2004)

Above: Smallest of the TOCs in almost any way you might care to measure it, Island Line services are now maintained by an operational fleet of six two-car sets of 1938 tube stock from London Underground. Two of these sets have been painted train red, albeit with yellow ends, and are seen here together on Ryde Pier on 21 August 2004. Island Line is also notable for being the only vertically integrated franchise. *John Glover*

Right: Southern 'Electrostar' unit No 377131 leaves the extensive junction station of Lewes with a Seaford-Brighton train on 10 April 2004. The vertical yellow strips on the sliding doors make them particularly easy to identify for those with sight problems. *John Glover*

Passenger Operators, non-franchised

Those whose operations are commercial in nature and are thus ineligible for support from public funds administered by the SRA/DfT.

Eurostar

Provides international passenger services primarily between London Waterloo International and Paris Nord, and Brussels Midi. The Eurostar service is a collaboration between three railways – SNCF and SNCB the state railways of France and Belgium respectively – and in Britain Eurostar (UK) Ltd owned by London & Continental Railways.

From 2003, there has been a single international management team responsible for Eurostar services as a whole, with Eurostar Group Ltd (owned by Eurostar UK, SNCF and SNCB) responsible for marketing.

London & Continental Railways Ltd

A private company with the concession to design, build and operate the Channel Tunnel Rail Link with some Government support. Owner of Eurostar UK Ltd, which operates passenger services primarily between London Waterloo International and Paris Nord/Brussels Midi.

Left: What now amounts to a traditional scene is this view of the west end of Reigate station showing Thames Trains (now Great Western Link) unit No 165001 passing over the busy level crossing here, on 16 September 1998. This is a Reading to Gatwick Airport service, the latter proving to be a more popular destination than the traditional one of Tonbridge. *John Glover*

Eurostar

Below left: A Waterloo International to Paris Eurostar service takes the through road at Tonbridge as it heads east on 21 September 1998. The completion of the Channel Tunnel Rail Link will mean that such services will run entirely on their own infrastructure, and it will be possible to remove the third-rail capability altogether from these trains. *John Glover*

Eurotunnel PLC

Below: A Channel Tunnel freight shuttle vehicle sees an HGV being loaded; the minimal nature of the wagon sides will be noted. The dimensions of the vehicle far exceed anything which can be carried on Britain's main line network due to infrastructure limitations, but this gives a good indication of the clearances which will be needed if a true roll-on roll-off road freight operation were to be offered. *Ian Allan Library*

Eurotunnel PLC

Owner of the Channel Tunnel and operator of Shuttle services between its terminals at Cheriton and Calais. Separate services cater for motor cars (whose passengers ride in their own vehicles) and HGVs (whose occupants are provided with a lounge). The international passenger services of Eurostar and international freight operators EWS International and SNCF have long-term usage rights for the Channel Tunnel.

Heathrow Express

A BAA-owned operating company which provides electric passenger services under the names of Heathrow Express and Heathrow Connect between London Paddington and Heathrow Airport.

Heathrow Express
Above: The 279yd-long (255m) Wharncliffe Viaduct spans the River Brent to the west of Hanwell station, seen here being crossed by a Heathrow train en route for the airport. These are the only electric National Railways services to serve Paddington, although all lines are electrified to Heathrow Airport Junction. The date is 26 March 2005. *John Glover*

Nexus
Right: For the greater part of its length, the Tyne & Wear Metro uses parts of the former railway network. This is the case at South Gosforth seen here on 13 February 2004. The nearer 'Metrocar' forms a South Shields service, the one beyond is bound for the coast (Whitley Bay and Tynemouth) before heading back to St James in the city centre. Of note is the distinctive style of the North Eastern Railway footbridge. *John Glover*

Hull Trains
An open access passenger operation between London King's Cross and Hull, operated by First Group.

Nexus
Owner and operator of Tyne & Wear Metro, which runs on Network Rail tracks between Pelaw and South Hylton. See Tyne & Wear PTE.

Venice Simplon-Orient-Express (VSOE)
A private company offering high-quality services on special trains aimed at up-market leisure users. This may include steam haulage.

West Coast Railway Co
A private company providing seasonal steam-hauled trains between Fort William and Mallaig.

Wensleydale Railway
Part of the former North Eastern Railway branch from Northallerton to Hawes and the Midland Railway branch thence to Garsdale, the 22-mile section from Northallerton to Redmire remains *in situ* for use by passenger and freight services. Wensleydale Railway has a 99-year lease of the line from Network Rail and a full set of operating licences issued by ORR. It is also the first company to be charged with the local management of part of the national rail network and it operates the first of what may become a new designation of community railway.

Freight Operating Companies (FOCs)
The (currently) five freight train service providers are licensed by the Office of Rail Regulation (ORR) for moving goods by rail. They are open access operators.

They can provide locomotives, wagons, staff and planning services, as required by customers. International freight trains are licensed by the International Rail Regulator (IRR).

Direct Rail Services (DRS)
The rail freight operating company arm of British Nuclear Fuels Ltd, whose principal traffic is the movement of spent fuel from British nuclear power stations to Sellafield, Cumbria. DRS has expanded into the general freight market and operates intermodal trains in collaboration with W. H. Malcolm, the logistics company.

English, Welsh & Scottish Railway Ltd (EWS)
The largest UK rail freight haulier, which acquired British Rail's Rail Express Systems, Loadhaul, Transrail Freight, Mainline Freight, Railfreight Distribution and National Power's Rail Unit. The company has invested in 250 3,200hp Class 66 freight locomotives from General Motors and 30 Class 67s. The latter have a 125mph speed capability instead of 87mph (Class 66), for higher speed work. A fleet of 2,500 new wagons has been built for EWS by US wagon builder Thrall, part of a fleet total of over 14,000 vehicles. EWS operations include services through the Channel Tunnel. The company employs around 6,000 staff and has a turnover of £500 million pa.

Freightliner Ltd
Freightliner is the largest intermodal rail operator in Great Britain, concerned primarily with the movement of deep sea containers between ports and inland terminals. Around 100 trains a day serve 19 terminals. The company also operates in the domestic bulk market through **Freightliner Heavy Haul,** typically with demountable tank containers carrying chemicals and bulk foodstuffs. The company is owned by venture capitalists 3i and Electra.

GB Railfreight Ltd
A rail freight operator, which operates a fleet of 17 Class 66 diesel locomotives. The company is owned by First Group and operates intermodal, petrochemical, heavy haul and Royal Mail trains.

Jarvis
Coal operations, infrastructure work and plant movement.

Other operators

London Underground Ltd (LUL)
LUL, a subsidiary of Transport *for* London, is the operator of London Underground services, some of which run on parts of Network Rail infrastructure and serve stations operated by a TOC. The most extensive example of this is the Bakerloo Line between Queen's Park and Harrow & Wealdstone, on which services are also provided by Silverlink.

Conversely, some sections of line and some stations operated by LUL are used also by trains on the national rail network. Notably, this includes operation by Chiltern Railways over the Metropolitan Line between Harrow-on-the-Hill and Amersham.

Access to London Underground's track and stations is not subject to the regime set up at rail privatisation. In these circumstances, a good guide as to who operates the station is the appearance or otherwise of the trademark LU roundel.

Freightliner Ltd
Left: Container handling at Felixstowe docks. This picture gives a good idea of the size of even an 8ft x 8ft (2.44m) container, and the scale of the cranage needed to lift it. *Ian Allan Library*

London Underground Ltd (LUL)
Above: Besides sharing the usage of some tracks with National Railways, which may be owned by either party, London Underground also receives ballast trains hauled by EWS locomotives. Here, No 59202 is seen at Ruislip depot on 18 May 2004 with a London Underground battery locomotive in the background. *John Glover*

Absolute block system
The traditional mechanical signal cabin, with the signalman about to demonstrate what is sometimes a considerable effort needed to pull a lever. Signal levers are colour coded, red for stop signals, yellow for distants, black for points, blue for point locks and white for spare. Other than spares, each displays a prominent notice of its function, and this lever frame contains 80 or so separate levers. The location is Ferryhill No 2 on 10 June 1967. The block instruments can be seen on the shelf above the levers, and the plan of the area covered is suspended from the ceiling.
John E. Hoggarth

Ability to stop
'Never start anything you can't stop.' The dynamics of train operation are covered in a series of practical rules concerning their construction, regulation and use. A 500-tonne train travelling at 125mph takes time and distance to bring to a stand, and these will vary according to weather and track conditions. However, the rules which have evolved over many years, correctly applied, will result in a safely operated railway.

Absolute block system
The long established signalling system principle of never having more than one train in any one section of line, on the same track, at any one time. Each of those sections is known as a block, or fixed block, which in a traditional system consists of the distance between successive fixed signals, plus a safety overlap allowance to mitigate the effects of a minor misjudgement by the train driver when stopping at a signal at danger.

Acceptance
The permission of the signaller in the signalbox in advance is needed for a train to enter the section of line he controls. Such acceptance is needed before the signals can be cleared by the signaller in the rear and the train can proceed into the next block section.

Access agreements
Agreements, which may or may not be regulated, that set out the terms and conditions under which train operators obtain permission to use a relevant railway facility such as the track, a station or depot, from the owner or principal operator of that facility.

Accessible stations
Stations which provide ready access to all, and do not have physical barriers which prohibit and/or restrict access by individuals with disabilities, including those who use wheelchairs. Such considerations need to take into account the access to the station from the street and, often a problem, the means of moving between platforms (if required) if there are no lifts. Consequently, many stations may be only partially accessible (or not accessible at all).

Accessible vehicles
Passenger vehicles which allow access to those with disabilities, including wheelchairs, and in accordance with the Rail Vehicle Accessibility Requirements (RVAR). Vehicles must provide places where wheelchairs can be carried, and toilet accommodation (if any) must likewise be accessible.

Accident classification
There are four types of railway accident, defined as follows:
- Train Accident. What is often thought of popularly as a railway accident, this includes collisions and derailments, fires and trains running into obstructions.
- Movement Accident. These are the accidents in which a train is involved, such as boarding and alighting incidents or passengers falling out of train doors, staff being caught between vehicles while coupling or uncoupling them, persons struck by a train at a level crossing or staff working on the track.
- Non-Movement Accident. These accidents have no real railway connotation other than they took place on railway premises. Included in this group are slips, trips and falls, especially on stairs or escalators, being struck by a platform trolley, or staff injured when using tools.
- Failures of rolling stock, track and structures of a type which can in turn cause train accidents, such as broken rails.

Accidents vary in severity, and their incidence is different between passengers (and those meeting them), railway staff (including contractors), and third parties such as the customers and staff of station trading outlets. All have business to be where they are on railway premises; another category of accident is that to trespassers and suicides.

Broadly, deaths are most numerous in movement accidents, but both major and minor injuries are found most often in the non-movement accidents. The chance of a passenger being killed or seriously injured in a train accident is very low, but the rate rises with movement accidents and again with non-movement accidents.

Accident, definition
An unexpected and unplanned occurrence which results in physical harm (injury or death) to an individual, damage to property, a near miss, a loss, or any combination.

Accident, train
About half the total of train accidents are caused by running into obstructions. Here, malicious acts by the public are the most numerous cause, followed by animals on the line. Fires on trains account for a further quarter of incidents, again with nearly half of them caused maliciously but with almost as many caused by technical defects.

The remaining headings of collisions and derailments see staff taking the blame for about one third in each case.

Accommodation bridge, accommodation crossing
A bridge or crossing connecting two areas of land which were under common ownership before the construction of the railway, but which were severed when it was built.

Act of God
A rare, catastrophic and probably uninsurable event, which cannot reasonably be foreseen as a potential hazard.

Active suspension
Use of microprocessor control to detect changes in track formation or direction and to signal changes in the suspension configuration. The object is to improve the quality of ride.

Adhesion
The frictional grip of the wheel on the rail, thus determining the ability to start and stop a train without slipping. The adhesive weight is the total weight carried on the driving axles, to which the maximum tractive effort can be applied until the wheels start to slip according to the coefficient of friction. When this happens will vary in relation to the condition of the surface of the rail, which is notably poor during the leaf fall season.

Adjustment switch
A device which allows longitudinal rail movement to dissipate thermal forces of expansion and contraction as a result of weather conditions, and associated particularly with the ends of continuously welded rail sections. Such switches take the form of each pair of rail ends being over length, but tapered by being machined away on opposite sides and allowed to slide against each other. This action relieves stresses, but maintains a continuous supporting rail for the passing trains.

Advanced Passenger Ticket Issuing System (APTIS)
A system introduced by British Rail from 1984 onwards, and subsequently installed in nearly all staffed ticket offices throughout the system.

Adjustment switch
An adjustment switch in continuous welded rail, which allows some movement for expansion and contraction of the rails, but with the distance between the sleepers secured firmly. *BR*

Accommodation bridge
The remains of an accommodation bridge at Shrewley, near Warwick on Sunday, 16 November 1980. It had been decided that the bridge was too costly to maintain and it had been demolished by explosives earlier in the day. While this is a relatively deep cutting and the volume of materials correspondingly large, the need to use two trains to remove the rubble indicates the size of the job undertaken. *G. O. Swain*

A

Airless spraying
A travelling spray booth used for painting locomotives and rolling stock.
The Aerograph-DeBilbiss Co Ltd

The credit card-sized tickets contain details of class of travel, ticket type, adult or child, date, ticket number, National Location Code (of issuing office), machine number, journey from, journey to, route, period of validity, price paid, method of payment (cash, card or warrant), and time of issue. A magnetic strip is included on the back of the ticket to activate London Underground and Network Rail station gates where applicable. Return tickets consist of separate outward and return portions. Season ticket issues vary, notably by having a prominent expiry date and a space for entering the photocard number.

APTIS is now being replaced, but its general features as described above remain.

Advanced Passenger Train (APT)
The concept of the tilting Advanced Passenger Train was first made public in 1967, initially gas turbine powered with mechanical transmission and for which a prototype was built. Later, electric traction was adopted for WCML use, with a pre-production series introduced to (very) limited passenger usage in 1981. Mounting problems resulted in a decision to abandon the project in 1985.

Air brake
See Brakes, air.

Air suspension
The car body rests on a set of hollow rubber cushions or air bags. These are fed by compressed air which is under the control of a levelling valve, thus ensuring that the correct pressure is maintained to keep the vehicle body level.

Airless spraying
The process of atomisation of paint by forcing it hydraulically through an orifice at high pressure, and much used for rolling stock painting.

Airtrack
The proposed linking of Heathrow Terminal 5 to the South Western lines via new construction joining the Windsor & Eton Riverside branch, with a new station at Staines High Street and the addition of a reinstated curve west of Staines station to allow trains to run direct towards Reading and Guildford as well as London Waterloo.

ALARP
See As low as reasonably practicable.

Alive
Charged with electricity at an electric pressure above or below earth potential.

Approach control
This may be found at locations such as the approach to a junction with restricted speeds on one or more of the possible routes, or a terminal platform. The signalling is arranged so that the controlled signal does not clear until a specified track circuit close to the signal is occupied. This ensures that the driver prepares to stop at the signal, which in the event is not necessary, but it does mean that the train's speed is reduced significantly.

Approach locking
A signaller can change the route which a train is to follow, but there comes a point when to do so would be dangerous. Approach locking ensures that the route, once set up and confirmed, cannot be changed under normal circumstances.

Approach release
Electrical locking which prevents proceed aspects being given by a signal until the train has approached within a predetermined distance. By then, the driver has reduced his speed accordingly, preparing to stop at the signal. This is, in effect, a means of enforcing a reduction in speed, and may be found at junctions where the diverging route, if set, commands significantly lower speed requirements.

Apron
A paved or concrete area of hardstanding in depots, for purposes such as vehicle washing, fuelling or having toilets flushed out.

APT
See Advanced Passenger Train.

APTIS

See Advanced Passenger Ticket Issuing System.

Articulated vehicles

The mounting of the ends of two vehicles on a single bogie, which saves weight and capital costs, albeit at some loss of operational flexibility. Articulation also reduces the distance between adjoining vehicles, important where overall lengths are constrained as in Freightliner sets of wagons which have to fit beneath gantry crane installations with a predetermined length of travel.

The Eurostar trains, which also use this technique, are made up of two identical nine-car sets of trailers marshalled back-to-back, each of which has 10 bogies for the nine vehicles. The two end power cars rest on their own bogies and are thus completely separate.

As low as reasonably practicable (ALARP)

Assessment of the residual risk on the grounds that good practice means it should be 'as low as reasonably practicable', but that complete safety is not an achievable goal.

Aspect

The visual indication of a colour light signal as displayed to the driver. Normal aspects shown in order of most restrictive to least restrictive in a multi-aspect colour light area are red, single yellow, double yellow (in four aspect installations only), and green. Infrequently, flashing double yellow aspects may be encountered on the approach to high speed junctions. The red aspect is always positioned at the bottom of the display, in a position calculated to be the nearest to the driver's eye level. Somewhat incongruously, the same term is used to describe the position of a semaphore signal.

Asset

The term 'asset' covers whole systems, sub-systems and components. Thus 'Infrastructure assets' encompass fixed track, signalling, electrification, plant, telecommunications equipment and structures. 'Mobile assets' cover trains and other powered rail vehicles.

Assets, electrification

These comprise:
Overhead line equipment, including structures, wiring, support and registration arms.
Conductor rail equipment, including third/fourth rail, ramps, insulation and trackside cables.
Electrical distribution equipment, including High Voltage (HV) switchgear, HV cables, transformers, rectifiers and dc switchgear.
Grid supply points, connection to dedicated distribution network operator (DNO) and National Grid Transco (NGT) supply points.
Supervisory control and data acquisition (SCADA) systems to control and monitor the status of the electrification equipment.

Atomic power

'The use of atomic power in relation to railways seems likely to be indirect, namely through the use of nuclear energy at electric power stations, rather than through the use of atomic-powered locomotives.' *Modernisation and Re-equipment of British Railways, British Transport Commission, 1954.*

ATP

See Automatic Train Protection.

Autofare

A free-standing, passenger-operated ticket-issuing machine, accepting coin and notes and giving change, and able to offer tickets of a variety of types to a range of predetermined destinations.

Articulated vehicles
This articulated bogie is on the Advanced Passenger Train which may be found in the National Railway Museum at York. The result is one rather than two bogies per coach, plus an extra one for the end vehicle of the set. Vehicles may also be joined more closely, thus economising in length, but the body length of each vehicle will need to be shorter. *John Glover*

Autofare
A passenger-operated ticket machine which, at its most extensive as shown here, can issue tickets to 92 different destinations from a total of 18 different ticket types. Notes are accepted and change is given. This example is installed at Braintree and was photographed on 16 November 2001. *John Glover*

A

Automatic barriers etc
See Level crossings.

Automatic Route Setting
Where the route set in a signalling centre for an approaching train is activated by the description of the train within the system. This 'tells' the system the route which the train is required to take, which is then set accordingly and without human intervention. Such systems have to cope with the problems caused by out of course running such as platform availability, and the relative priorities given to each train in the case of route conflicts at junctions. Provision for manual override is thus necessary, but by and large, the system can be left to look after itself. In general, the role of the signaller becomes supervisory.

Automatic Train Protection (ATP)
ATP describes systems which monitor the speed of a train against that allowed on that part of the railway. It intervenes automatically to apply the brakes if a train is detected as going too fast and the driver has taken no action. ATP ensures that trains comply with speed restrictions and prevents them from passing signals at danger, although it will not prevent incidents caused by defects in the train or the track, for example.

ATP is installed on the Great Western main line between Paddington and Bristol, the Heathrow Express, the Chiltern line from Marylebone to Aynho Junction (Banbury), and the Channel Tunnel Rail Link.

Automatic Train Recording
An electronic system for the reporting of train movements, based on the passage of train identities through a signal panel train describer.

Automatic Vehicle Identification (AVI)
A semi-automatic mechanism for reporting train movements based on the location of freight rolling stock and its subsequent translation to actual train identities or activities as reported to TOPS. It is limited to the transport of coal used for electricity generation.

Automatic Warning System (AWS)
A permanent magnet and an electromagnet are placed between the rails, 200yd on the approach side of a signal and linked to the signalling system. When the signal shows green, the electromagnet is energised

and the driver of the approaching train is given an 'all clear' indication by a bell in the cab, and the cab indicator displays black. If the signal displays a more restrictive or danger aspect, the electromagnet is not energised and the permanent magnet causes a horn to be sounded in the cab and a yellow/black display on the cab indicator. The driver must then acknowledge the warning by cancelling it, and then brake as appropriate. If the warning is not acknowledged, the brakes are applied automatically.

This is an example of the fail-safe approach to safety; should the electromagnet fail to work for any reason, the driver automatically receives the caution indication.

Automotive
A term related to the conveyance of new cars by rail on specialist wagons. It is also used for the movement of car components to manufacturing plants.

Auxiliary catenary
The middle conductor of the three wires in compound overhead line equipment. It is suspended from the catenary and from it the contact wire is suspended.

Auxiliary supply
A secondary supply of power on vehicles for non-traction purposes. Uses will include air conditioning, heating, lighting, door movements, on-board cooking and for emergency batteries. It may be derived from axle-driven generators, or via the main traction power system.

Avoiding line, or cut-off
The construction of a new more direct line between two points. Thus the Midland Railway constructed a new main line avoiding Worcester. This term cut-off is associated particularly with the Great Western, and its lines which nowadays avoid Westbury and also Frome.

Axle
The shaft which connects two wheels to form a wheelset.

Axleboxes
The housings attaching the ends of the axles to the bogie, or to mountings on the underframe for a four-wheeled vehicle. These contain the bearings, which allow the axles and hence the wheels to rotate. Some modern freight vehicles have inside bearings.

Axle counters
A modern alternative to track circuits, axle counters record the number of axles as a train enters a section, and a second set of equipment performs the same task at the exit from that section. Provided the numbers recorded by each axle counter are the same, the train is proved complete and clear of the section. The signalling is now able to permit the acceptance of another train.

Although the track circuit is to some extent being superseded by axle counters, a shortcoming of the latter is that they cannot detect a broken rail.

Automatic Warning System (AWS)
The magnet which gives an indication to the driver of the train passing over it, as to the aspect of the signal controlling it, and which will apply the brakes if a horn sounds in the cab and the driver does not respond. This is at Gidea Park, seen on 24 September 1998. *John Glover*

Axle-hung nose-suspended motor

One end of an EMU motor coach motor is attached to the axle it drives by two suspension bearings, while the other is formed with a 'nose' supported by an attachment which provides enough resilience for the motor to follow the axle movements.

Axle load

That which is exerted on the track by each wheelset of a vehicle, which is the gross weight of that vehicle divided by the number of axles, assuming that the load (if any) is evenly distributed. Maximum axle loads are specified by the Civil Engineer, based on track and structure considerations, particularly the strength of railway underbridges. The maximum allowed in Britain is 25 tonnes. See also Route Availability.

Backing up

See Buffering up.

Balise

Trackside transmitter for train control systems, such as ERTMS and TASS.

Ballast

Ballast is laid on a base formation and forms the bed of the railway track. It consists of crushed and graded limestone or granite, according to source, and its purpose is to support the track both laterally and vertically and to hold it firmly in place. Ballast absorbs the shock and weight of passing trains and provides drainage into the cess. Unlike slab track, it is easy to move.

Ballast cleaning

Allowing the ballast to become clogged with dust and dirt and thus to retain water will result in the formation becoming weaker. Keeping it clean is therefore a critical maintenance activity. This is done by the use of an on-track machine which excavates and grades the ballast. It returns good stone to the formation and discharges fine stone and waste to the lineside, for removal or disposal by rail.

Ballast shoulder

The graded edge of the ballast, either side of each track.

Bank

1. A continuous incline on a railway, the steeper ones of which might in the past have required assistance from a resident banking engine to provide extra power. Banks will always be a limitation on performance, especially for heavy freight.
2. Short term for embankment.

Ballast
Ballast being removed from Ribblehead Viaduct on the Settle & Carlisle line, using six JCBs on 15 October 1989. Even from this oblique angle, the extra strength built into every sixth pier of the viaduct is noticeable.
Dr L. A. Nixon

Banking
Left: The Lickey Incline was a formidable obstacle, to the extent that a number of banking locomotives were often called upon to assist. Here, a Class 47 and train are being banked by no fewer than three 'Hymek' Class 35 locomotives – Nos D7024/25/22 – as they start away from Bromsgrove in June 1969. The cost of maintaining such an operation round the clock must have been phenomenal. *John Glover*

Barrier wagon(s)
An early example of the company train; this one is conveying VIP oil traffic from West Thurrock to Tipton, West Midlands, with a Class 86 locomotive in charge. The location is not stated, but it is probably in the Willesden area. The wagons are of the four-wheel variety rather than bogie wagons. There is a barrier flat wagon placed between the locomotive and the train, with probably another at the rear. *BR/Author's collection*

Banking

To provide a temporary increase in power in the form of an additional locomotive or locomotives (the banking engine, or bankers) to propel a train up a steep incline, or bank. The best known instance of this was the Lickey Incline between Bromsgrove and Blackwell, just over two miles at 1 in 37¾ on the former Midland Railway route from Bristol to Birmingham. For many years, this was the preserve of a locomotive specially built for the job at Derby, nicknamed 'Big Bertha'.

Bar coupling
See Coupling, bar.

Bardic lamp
A robust battery-powered lamp which can display red, yellow or green aspects as well as clear, and issued to railway staff. A bracket on the back enables it to be used also as a tail lamp for a train. The name Bardic is that of the manufacturers.

Barrier
That which restricts the movement of road vehicles at level crossings. Barriers may be in the positions up or down, across the railway, or across the road.

Barrier wagon(s)
Used to create a gap between the locomotive and the train's wagons, and again at the rear of the train, this is a safety precaution used when the contents of the wagons are considered hazardous. Certain petroleum products are one example. The barrier wagons may be of any available type, as long as their running characteristics are compatible with the rest of the wagons in the train.

Barrow crossing
Wooden surfaced crossings at the end of station platform ramps for the use of rail staff, or others under staff supervision. There may or may not be some element of train protection for users. With the withdrawal of most platform staff and the lack of need for barrows on today's railway, many if not most barrow crossings have now been removed. This has in turn created problems, notably in respect of disabled access, as footbridges or subways are frequently the only alternative. The latter are usually inside but occasionally outside the platform area, or both have access.

Baseplate
The metal support for a flat-bottomed rail on a sleeper, to which it is attached by clips.

Basic railway
A minor railway which is being run with the maximum economy. Typically, this has meant reduction to single track and one-train working, station buildings demolished and replaced by passenger shelters, ticket issue on train only, level crossings converted to AOCL or similar, and train service limited to what can be achieved with one train and its staff. Verdict: cheap, yes, but often rather nasty.

Bay platform
Some through stations will have one or more terminal platforms, usually for trains of perhaps four coaches or so, and often located at (relatively speaking) the outer ends of the through station. Examples are Lancaster and Manningtree where the bay platforms are used for the secondary services starting from (or possibly reversing) there.

Binliners
The former London Brick Co terminal at Stewartby, Bedfordshire, was used for the sending of bricks by rail, but it now forms part of the Shanks & McEwan waste disposal terminal and is the destination for trainloads of household waste. Containers of refuse are transferred to road vehicles and taken to landfill sites for disposal. *Ian Allan Library*

Bearer
A transverse sleeper, of timber or concrete, supporting the rails in switches or crossings.

Berne Gauge
The standard railway loading gauge used generally in mainland Europe, allowing more generous vehicle dimensions than those applicable in Britain.

Berth
1. Term sometimes used for a track circuit, at which the train 'berths' when it occupies it.
2. The standard bunk-type bed in a Sleeping Car.

BH
See Rail, bull-head and flat-bottomed.

Bi-directional line, bi-directional signalling
Lines that are fully signalled to take trains running in either direction with equal facility, and also known as a reversible line. A more limited (and less costly) arrangement designed to ease engineering works is an alternative. This is simplified bi-directional signalling (SIMBIDS), on which 'wrong line' operation has headway and speed restrictions imposed. It does avoid, however, the use of pilotmen.

Bi-modal trailers
These are semi-trailers that can be hauled by a conventional road tractor unit or mounted on a rail bogie. The system is operated in the United States and has been tried in Britain but with little success.

Bicycles, carriage of
The franchise agreements contain a provision that requires the TOC to provide facilities for the carriage of bicycles on trains, but only so far as it is practicable to do so and subject to the availability of space. The operator may require a reservation and can charge for the facility, provided that the charge is not unreasonable. (This expression has a long history in the transport industry; note that there is a distinct difference from saying that the charge has to be reasonable).

(The) Big Railway
Slang term used on preserved railways to refer to the National Rail system.

Binliners
Trains of specialist sealed containers conveying domestic waste from concentration centres to disposal sites.

Blade, point blade
The moving part of the running rails of a point or turnout, which enable trains to take alternative routes.

Blanketing
Providing a layer of stone dust (or similar) over clay track formations, to prevent contamination of the ballast when that is laid subsequently over the formation.

Block bells
The method used to communicate between mechanical signalboxes and allow the passage of trains. Using a single-stroke tapper, messages are sent by means of bell codes. They are answered by the other box repeating the message; not to do so may constitute a refusal. The resulting status of the section of the line in between the boxes is confirmed by the block instruments mounted on the operating shelf of each, above the levers.

B

Block instruments, block indicators

Normally three position instruments, which show the status of each running line between each pair of signalboxes in an Absolute Block System. Thus there would be four instruments on the operating shelf in a typical double-line setting. Those positions are 'line blocked' (normal position), 'line clear', and 'train on line'. It will be noted that the line is normally blocked and made available only when a specific request is made, rather than being available unless proved otherwise.

Block points

1. The limits of an engineering possession, between which a line is blocked as unfit for traffic for the duration of that possession.
2. Manned block points may be set up to keep traffic moving and to provide protection during the failure of signalling equipment.

Block system

See Absolute block system.

Block to Electric Traction

Instruction to block lines to electric traction by turning off the power (and the consequential use of diesel trains only).

Block train

A freight train in which all the wagons are of a similar specification. The train then moves as a block from one origin to one destination, without intermediate remarshalling. Often, the entire train will carry the same commodity as for instance in aggregates from quarry to the end user, but block trains may also consist of container carrying wagons. In this case, what is in each container is a matter for the consignor and consignee concerned, subject to any limitations such as the total weights of each.

Block train
This block train, headed by EWS No 66122, is passing Filton Abbey Wood station on its way to the Severn Tunnel and South Wales on 8 March 2005. *John Glover*

Blocking back

1. Blocking back occurs if it is necessary to cause an obstruction with a shunting or similar movement which comes to a stand on the running line. The blocking back protection procedure must first be initiated by the signaller authorising the movement. The requirements vary according to whether it is inside or outside the home signal.
2. Blocking back also refers to the situation when some kind of problem arises which halts a train at (say) a junction, with the result that subsequent trains behind it and approaching that junction will come progressively to a halt. Thus every (signalling) block is occupied, and the effects can be felt a long way back. The ideal is for the line controller to anticipate the developing situation at the earliest opportunity, and to take avoiding action such as diversions, to minimise delays wherever possible.

Blockade

A telegraphic code term which has recently seen a revival for the execution of major engineering works which require all lines in an area to be blocked, sometimes for quite extended periods. The original railway telegraphic use related to train accidents.

Board

Railway slang for a signal, more appropriately a semaphore signal, but used indiscriminately.

Boarding cards

See Regulation tickets.

Boat train

A train provided primarily (but not necessarily exclusively) for the conveyance of rail passengers to or from a port or harbour to connect with certain sailings.

Bobby

Slang for a railway signalman; the original signalmen were Police Officers.

Bogie

A frame containing suspension, axles and wheels on which a railway vehicle is mounted, supporting its weight and its load (four-wheeled 'Pacer' passenger units, some freight vehicles and rigid wheelbase diesel shunters excepted). Each has a pivotal centre plate to enable the train to negotiate bends and fluctuations in the track. Bogies usually consist of four wheels and two axles, although six wheels and three axles may be found occasionally. See also Articulated vehicles.

Bolster

1. The transverse member of a bogie frame or vehicle underframe through which the bogie pivot passes or to which it is connected.
2. Used on vehicles to support a load; a bolster wagon.

Bond

1. An electrical connection in the negative return circuit.

2. A financial transaction where the contractor deposits a defined sum of money with a third party (usually a bank) that is held in bond until the defined tasks have been completed satisfactorily.

Booked service
One which is timetabled and built into locomotive, carriage and crew diagrams, as opposed to a short-notice requirement which has arisen and is dealt with as expeditiously as possible.

Booked time
The time at which a train is scheduled to perform a certain task, eg booked arrival time, booked passing time, etc. Booked time implies that shown in the Working Timetable book (WTT), which may vary from that in the public timetable. (Such variations are due to the use of half-minutes in the WTT, and perhaps some judicious adjustments to help ensure on-time departures and arrivals.)

Booking office
The office on staffed stations where passengers may purchase tickets from a booking clerk, rather than from a machine. Other names are nowadays more prevalent, ranging from travel centre to ticket office. The term booking office comes from the earliest days, when travelling by rail meant having your name entered in a book to secure your place on the train and, of course, paying the appropriate fee for a ticket.

Bottleneck
See Pinch point.

Box
Railway shorthand for signalbox.

Brake horse power (bhp)
The power available at the crankshaft of a diesel engine (ie the indicated horsepower developed in the cylinders less the power absorbed in overcoming the friction of the moving parts of the engine).

Brakes
1. Principles
A fundamental component of safety on the railway is ensuring that trains reduce speed upon the driver sighting a restrictive signal showing a yellow (or double yellow then yellow) aspect, and being able to stop at a signal showing a red aspect.

Failure to achieve this will result in a Signal Passed at Danger with the potential for collisions and derailments. In order to ensure that a driver can stop at a red aspect (or attain a safe speed at a yellow aspect) requires that the signal is adequately sighted and that the train is capable of being slowed sufficiently within the sighting distance.

Normally, signalling is designed around passenger trains so that the sighting distances and speed limits are those applicable to the passenger trains that use the route and normal braking characteristics.

The situation for freight trains is significantly more

complicated, due to the more variable braking characteristics that are affected by the length of the train, whether or not the train is loaded, the nature of the wagons and the characteristics of the hauling locomotive. As a direct consequence of these factors it is sometimes necessary to fit devices that enable the brake force application to be changed to ensure that stopping distances are not exceeded.

Additionally, freight train speeds may be further restricted, leading to circumstances in which certain types of passenger train may be allowed higher speeds.

In all cases, braking characteristics will vary according to weather conditions affecting the surface of the rail, track curvature and gradients, wind direction and force and, in a different sense, the ability of the driver to see, and the time taken to react to, restrictive signal indications.

2. Evolution
The individual wagons on early railways had hand brakes only, which severely limited train speeds due to the difficulty in stopping. The only extra help available to the driver was that from the guard in his van, and the time consuming 'pinning down' of wagon brakes before descending heavy gradients. Gradually, the automatic vacuum brake began to be fitted in the 20th century, but progress was very slow. Even in the 1950s, vast fleets of new wagons were being constructed with no automatic brakes. Progress was temporarily halted when the decision to change from vacuum to air brake was made, since the two systems are incompatible, but air braking is now standard for freight and passenger trains alike.

On passenger trains the continuous brake was made compulsory by the 1889 Regulation of Railways Act, but although most companies opted for vacuum, some used the Westinghouse air brake system. In both cases the application of the brake by the driver results in air being either let into the system (vacuum) or let out (air). Likewise, any event such as the train becoming divided will result in a full brake application on both sections of the train.

3 Air brake

The standard automatic brake used in Britain, in which compressed air from the locomotive acts on a piston to hold the brakes off. The brakes are applied by the driver through the controlled release of that pressure. The decision to replace vacuum brakes with air brakes was taken in 1964. Compared with vacuum, the air brake offered safer operation of faster and heavier trains with existing signalling, but also made it possible to use compressed air in a range of ancillary equipments such as power-operated doors and air-sprung bogies. During a very long changeover period, much rolling stock was dual fitted. Today, only a small and diminishing number of dual-braked coaching vehicles remain.

4 Vacuum brake

The automatic but now effectively obsolete brake adopted by British Railways until the change to air brake. The essential difference is that the vacuum brake works by letting air into the system in which a vacuum has been created by the locomotive, whereas the air brake relies on the locomotive to produce a higher pressure than atmospheric in the system, which application of the brake controls releases. In effect, each system is the direct opposite of the other.

5 Braking distance

The distance that a train of given characteristics needs to stop when travelling at a given speed on level track, assuming normal rail and environmental conditions.

6 Operation

The air brake system has two pipes: the brake pipe and the main reservoir pipe. Passenger, parcels and empty coaching stock services normally operate with both pipes in use throughout the train. Freight services operate under the single-pipe system. The normal working pressure of the brake pipe is 72.5psi (5 BAR), and the main reservoir pipe is usually maintained between 85 and 105psi (5.9 and 7.3 BAR). The brake pipe coupling heads on the flexible hoses on the vehicle ends are coloured red, while the main reservoir pipes are coloured yellow (except for a few vehicles in international traffic, which are coloured white). The brake is applied by exhausting air from the brake pipe.

During normal running, a reservoir on each vehicle is kept charged via the brake pipe by a compressor on the locomotive. To apply the brake, the driver releases air from the brake pipe. As the pressure falls, a distributor valve releases air from the reservoirs into the brake cylinders. Here it acts on the pistons connected to the brake blocks through a system of cranks and levers (the brake rigging). The brake blocks clasp the running surfaces of the wheels, and the train comes to a stand.

The brake is termed automatic because a fault allowing air to escape causes the brakes to be applied. The fault could be anything from a break in the connections to a rupture caused by the train becoming divided. Either way, the train will come to a stand, in the same way as if the brake had been applied by the driver.

7 Continuity test

A test carried out to ensure that the brake pipe is coupled continuously throughout the train and that the required brake pipe pressure can be maintained.

Branch line

A secondary route from a terminus which acts as a feeder to the main trunk line, terms based on the likening of railway infrastructure to that of a tree.

Bridge bash, or strike

An incident in which a road vehicle or its load hits the deck of a railway underbridge or parapet for an overbridge. Any damage has to be checked by a person certified as competent to inspect the structure and authorise the reopening of the line, or not, as the case may be (Bridge Strike Nominee). Exceptionally, a bridge strike could be caused by shipping on inland waters.

Bridge, construction

Approximately half of the spans in Network Rail's bridges are masonry structures, and these account for nearly all the oldest bridges. Typically 150 years old, their prime period of construction extended to 1920. Bridge spans made of metal account for about 42% of the total, the majority of which are wrought iron or early steel structures dating from 1880 to 1920. Earlier cast iron structures still exist, predominantly on overbridges.

From the 1920s, the construction programme was much reduced, and this era also saw the introduction of concrete bridges. From then on, the proportions built using the three types of material were more equal, with concrete gradually becoming dominant. Post-1930 metallic bridges are usually steel fabrications.

Higher levels of activity were again reached between 1960 and 1980; this is the era from which most of the concrete structures date. Concrete construction accounts for around 8% of the total bridge stock.

The average age of railway bridges is around 100 years.

Bridge, type

In any discussion of railway bridging, the line of the railway itself is taken as the datum point. Bridges will always be defined in such terms; thus a railway bridge over a road is a railway underbridge, and a road crossing the railway above the tracks is a railway overbridge. This is an important distinction, especially in discussions with others, as misunderstandings can easily arise.

A variation is an intersection bridge, where one railway crosses another, at a different level. There may be no physical railway connection between the two lines.

Bridges for which the railway is responsible may also be at the side of the operational railway. These might date from the time of construction, when such provision was necessary to maintain existing access rights, as for instance in the case of an associated footbridge.

The total number of railway bridges in 2005, by type, is:

Underbridges	10,918
Overbridges	4,311
Side bridges	83
Total	**15,312**

Broken rail

A broken rail is one which, before removal from the track, has a fracture through the full cross-section of the rail, or a piece broken out of it, rendering it unserviceable. This includes broken welds. Broken rails have the potential to cause serious train incidents, such as derailments.

Budget

The amount set aside to achieve defined ends, with running costs set against the relevant income, within a defined timescale such as the company's financial year. This can be for the whole of the company or each of the various activities undertaken within it. Income and expenditure budgets for individual tasks may be treated separately.

The capital budget is that for expenditure on the acquisition of capital assets.

Builder's plate, Works' plate

A metal plate attached to an item of rolling stock giving details of where, when and by whom the vehicle was built, and the number (commercial builders). A Works' plate refers to those applied to railway company works-built vehicles, usually without a serial number.

Buffer

Mounted on the ends of railway vehicles, their purpose is to absorb shocks during shunting and when the train is in motion. Buffers consist of a plate on the end of a spring-loaded plunger, which compresses when in contact with another buffer.

Buffer beam

Transverse structural member at the ends of a rail vehicle underframe. It supports the buffers, and is also known as the headstock.

Buffer locking

This occurs where heads of the buffers of one wagon cease to meet those of the buffers of the adjoining wagon (or locomotive etc) and are displaced sideways to the extent that the head of one buffer passes the head of the one adjacent to it. Each head thus becomes aligned with some part of the buffer shank. This is most likely to happen on very sharp curves in sidings or other track irregularities, but to the buffers on the inner side of the curve only. All is well until the track straightens out, with a derailment the likely outcome. The larger the buffer heads, the less likely buffer locking is to occur.

Bridge, type

Above left: The railway underbridge on the Quarry line near Coulsdon South, where it spans the A23 London to Brighton road. Despite having a clearance for road vehicles of up to 15ft 3in (4.6m) and clearly marked to that effect, it was still thought prudent to apply conspicuous black and yellow diagonal stripes since this is less than present standards. The date is 2 August 2003. *John Glover*

Left: The Forth Bridge could be described as a Scottish icon; no other railway bridge has appeared on a coin of the realm in Britain. It is seen here from the North Queensferry side on 19 June 2004. Close inspection will reveal considerable signs of the maintenance work currently under way. *John Glover*

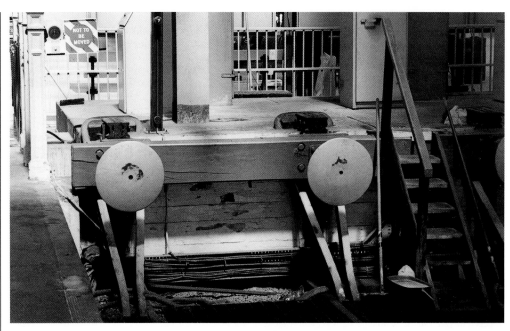

Buffer overriding
Similar to buffer locking, except that a vertical displacement occurs as the consequence perhaps of a rough shunt, with the result that both buffers on a wagon rise up and collide with the body of the adjacent vehicle.

Buffer stop
See Stop block.

Buffering up
When a locomotive backs (gently!) onto a train, the buffers touch, the couplings are engaged and the brake hoses connected.

Buffet car
A coach which offers a counter service of refreshments which probably includes hot food, often on a 'take away' basis and thus with minimal seating.

Bus substitution service
Defined in the Railways Act 2005 as 'a service for the carriage of passengers by road that is provided as an alternative to the whole or a part of a railway passenger service that has been discontinued, reduced or modified (whether temporarily or permanently)'. Note that the definition does not provide any indication of the permanence or otherwise of such a replacement. Also known in popular parlance as bustitution.

Rail services suspended temporarily as a result of engineering possessions are not normally considered in the same light as permanent replacements.

Bye-law
Rules made by railway companies and enforceable by law under delegated powers, concerning matters such as the conduct of passengers, and the associated penalties for transgression.

C

C&W
See Carriage & Wagon.

Cab
The driver's accommodation, containing the necessary equipment and controls.

Cab Secure Radio (CSR)
This is associated with driver-only operated trains and provides a speech link between drivers and signallers (only). CSR is an analogue system which extracts real time data on the location of trains from the computer within the signalling system, to ensure the correct identification of both the train driver and the signalling centre concerned. This avoids the possibility of the signaller giving instructions (such as permission to pass a signal at danger because of an equipment failure) to the wrong driver in error. CSR offers 100% coverage in areas where it is deployed, these being London and the South East, Merseyside and Strathclyde.

Cab signal
A signal installed in the cab of a train, repeating the indication of a lineside signal, or instead of a lineside signal.

Cable trough
Covered ducting containing electric cables, usually running alongside the rails in the cess, but sometimes found in the six foot.

Cant, also known as super elevation
The amount by which the outer rail on a curve is raised above the inner rail to counter centrifugal forces, so that the vehicle rounding the curve stays

level, or in equilibrium. However, the cant required has to be calculated in respect of an assumed train speed, which may not always be achieved. In any event, note must be taken of the requirements of slower trains and the fact that any train may come to a stand at any point on the network. See also Throw.

Cant deficiency
If trains travel faster than the speed assumed in determining the degree of cant on a curve, equilibrium will not be obtained. Cant deficiency is the further amount that the outer rail would need to be raised to restore that equilibrium.

Cant excess
If trains travel slower than the speed assumed in determining the degree of cant on a curve, equilibrium will not be obtained. Cant excess is the amount that the outer rail would need to be lowered to restore that equilibrium.

Cantrail
The metal frame member running lengthways along the vehicle at the junction of the side and the roof of a coach or van. Indicated on a modern vehicle without guttering by an orange line (for staff safety reasons).

Capacity Utilisation Index (CUI)
Measures the intensity of usage of the rail network as a percentage of the available capacity.

Capacity Utilisation Policy (CUP)
Developed by the SRA as a response to its obligation to promote a more reliable and punctual railway, since more rail traffic means a more heavily utilised network with less spare capacity. The Capacity Utilisation Policy seeks to find the best use that can be made of the existing network, balancing service provision, maintenance access and performance levels. This includes the formulation of strategies for growth, development and route utilisation, the identification of where enhancement investment in the network is needed, and the determination of how funds for capacity improvements can best be used.

Capital projects
Projects which results in the production of new fixed assets (equipment and works), which are sufficiently durable to be charged to capital as opposed to the revenue (or operating) account.

CAPE
A term still in common use and derived from the former telegraphic code, which read: 'Undermentioned train will not run. Advise all concerned.' In other words, train cancelled.

Capstan
A barrel-like vertical device at ground level, for winding ropes or cables and powered by electricity. Used for moving rail vehicles short distances in restricted areas such as workshops; others may still be used in some private sidings for similar purposes.

Car
An American term introduced into Britain at the end of the 19th century for passenger vehicles, via what is now London Underground. Now used on National Railways in preference to 'coach' or 'carriage' for all multiple-unit stock, diesel or electric, and sometimes for locomotive hauled stock too.

Car transporter wagon (CARTIC)
A four section articulated wagon set with five bogies, designed for the double-deck loading of cars and their carriage within the British loading gauge. The low central section on the lower deck between the bogies allows the maximum use to be made of the upper deck, but this is restricted at the ends. Used nowadays for trade cars only, most such wagons are enclosed to prevent damage and pilferage.

Cargosprinter
See Freight Multiple Unit (FMU).

Carriage
Largely superseded term for individual passenger-carrying vehicles which are not part of a multiple-unit.

Carriage & Wagon (C&W)
Usually short for Carriage & Wagon Examiner(s); those involved in the inspection and maintenance of such vehicles, usually as in 'this vehicle needs C&W attention to deal with (specified defect)'.

Carriage dock
A short platform with a ramped road approach at the end of a siding, which can be used to load railway coaching vehicles with end doors, or flat wagons. Used for the loading and unloading of road or military vehicles.

Car carrying wagon (CARTIC)
The limitations of the basic British loading gauge are such that it is well-nigh impossible to carry both an upper deck and a lower deck of cars within it over the bogies. One solution was a four-vehicle articulated set, on which the section between the bogies is lowered to just above rail level. This allows the upper level to carry cars in its centre section. Also, the articulated layout enables cars to be driven through with ease when loading or unloading. All these features can be seen in this picture, taken at the Ford Motor Co's works, Dagenham.
Ian Allan Library

Carriage key
Carried and used by staff for locking and unlocking the external slam doors (and sometimes for activating the internal lighting). At one time this was a universal fitting, but no longer.

Carriage label
Paper labels to be attached to coach windows, with gummed or self-adhesive strips, which denote the calling points of the train and sometimes its individual description eg 14.49 Leeds to Carlisle. This latter is however for the benefit also of the staff concerned, as stopping points may vary between different trains on the same route, and it would be easy to affix the wrong label. Now often replaced by electronic indicators.

Carriage line, carriage siding
A section of track which is used only to move empty passenger rolling stock, as in the approach to stabling sidings for carriages or a maintenance depot.

Carriage washing machine
Depot machine for the external washing of coaching stock. Placement where all trains entering the depot can pass through it is probably the most satisfactory, but all windows need to be closed first. Difficulties may be encountered in times of water shortages, or supplies becoming frozen. In general, vehicle ends including the driver's windows still have to be washed manually.

Carriage washing machine
Ideally, carriage washing machines are installed so that trains arriving at the depot pass through them on arrival, although this is not always practicable. A train of MkI stock is being taken through a typical facility. One continuing problem is the inability to use such washers in freezing conditions. *BR/Author's collection*

CARTIC
See Car transporter wagon.

Cascade
The transfer of passenger rolling stock from one service category to another as a result of introducing new trains on one of those routes — the 'hand-me-down' approach. In that way, the route which is less able to make a business case for stock replacement still receives 'new' stock. Alternatively, the rolling stock will be returned to the leasing company, but the same process is likely to take place, indirectly.

A similar approach may be used for other types of asset.

Catastrophic risks
Events with a potential for multiple casualties.

Catch points
A pair of sprung trailing points (ie normally encountered only in the trailing direction) and usually installed where track gradients are steeper than 1 in 260. Their purpose is to derail any train or part of a train which runs backwards out of control, derailment being judged a preferable option to possibly colliding head-on with a following train. Catch points were a formal requirement before all vehicles were fitted with continuous (and thus automatic) brakes. They are found less frequently today, and certainly not on single lines or those signalled for bi-directional working. They may also be used where a heritage line connects with the national network.

Catenary
A bare stranded copper conductor, being the uppermost of the wires forming the overhead line equipment, derived from the name of the curve assumed by a wire supported only at its two ends. Sometimes used to mean the whole of the overhead line equipment.

Cat's eyes
Railway slang term for position light shunting or subsidiary signal.

Caution
The single yellow signal aspect (or semaphore distant signal horizontal position) which advises the driver that the next signal is at red and to control the speed of the train to be able to stop at it.

Cautioning
An oral warning to a train driver of maintenance operations on or near the line ahead, or something untoward such as the presence of escaped cattle or trespassers (say). The driver should proceed with caution, but the actual speed will depend on circumstances and will not necessarily be very slow.

Central door locking
The installation of a secondary door locking system to slam door rolling stock in which the guard releases the doors at a station when it is safe to do so,

then allowing the passengers to unlock and open them in the usual way. The doors are relocked before the train departs. Little slam door rolling stock in general use is not now so fitted. See also Doors, slam.

Centre siding
A siding constructed between the pair of running rails on a double track line beyond a station, used to reverse trains which terminate there. Any movement to or from this siding thus block only one track, whereas movements to or from a location outside the running lines would sometimes block both. See also Reversing siding.

Cess, cess path
The space between the outside edge of the ballast and the edge of the lineside or bankside. This usually provides a safe area for track workers to stand or to walk along when trains approach.

Cess drain
The drainage system installed along each side of the track, immediately clear of the ballast shoulder, to make sure that the ballast doesn't become waterlogged in wet weather.

CD
See Close doors platform indicator.

Chair
See Rail, bull-head.

Channel Tunnel
The 51km rail link between Cheriton (Folkestone) and Coquelles (Calais) owned and operated by the Anglo-French company Eurotunnel. It was opened formally by HM The Queen and President Mitterrand on 6 May 1994.

Channel Tunnel Rail Link (CTRL)
The new high-speed link between Cheriton and London St Pancras, due to be completed in 2007. There are intermediate stations at Ashford International, Ebbsfleet and Stratford International and the route will be suitable for the carriage of international and domestic passenger services, as well as freight.

Charter train, excursion train
A train, normally hired by a group for their exclusive use but perhaps promoted by a TOC or independent excursion train operators and coaching stock owners. The train will run between points specified by the promoters on a pre-arranged itinerary with timings suitable for the purpose of the outing, train path and resource availability permitting. Such private hire arrangements can also specify class of travel and catering (if any) to be provided. Ticket pricing and sales are matters solely for the promoters, and the operating company takes no revenue risk. Hirings may be for any purpose, including business, leisure, religious, cultural and sporting events, for instance race trains to Newbury. (An early excursion train from Leicester to Loughborough for the temperance movement was hired by a certain Thomas Cook in 1841.)

Check rails
Additional rails installed parallel to, within the running rails and close to them (the flangeway gap) in the vicinity of a crossing on the other rail. They are designed to provide positive guidance for the wheel flanges of a train, if required, when the continuous path of the wheels on the other rail is broken for a short distance. These rails thus 'check' the movement, to ensure that there are no untoward results.

Check rails are also used on level crossings to keep the flangeway gap to the minimum for vehicles and pedestrians using the crossing, but also to ensure that material from the road or pathway between the running rails does not encroach into the flangeway.

Another location in which check rails are frequently found is on sharp curves, where fitting is mandatory on passenger lines with curves of 200m radius or less. The flangeway gap also needs to be increased. See also Track gauge widening.

Check rails may also be found on viaducts, for instance, as a precaution in the event of a derailment. Should this occur, the check rails would help keep the train's wheels close to the running rails.

Chord
Short section of line of 1/4 mile or less connecting two other lines, sometimes forming the only rail connection between them.

Circuit
An arrangement of conductors and electrical apparatus connected to a source of electricity supply.

Circuit breaker
A heavy-duty switch in the electric traction power supply system, arranged to open automatically when a current above a predetermined level flows through it, including the result of a fault. Circuit breakers are located in feeder stations and intermediately in track sectioning cabins. They can be designed and made to suit high voltages and currents.

Circuit breakers can also be opened and closed locally or remotely to disconnect or reinstate the supply to a circuit. Thus they can be used to isolate sections of the line from the power supply to enable maintenance to take place.

Also found on electric trains.

CIS
See Customer Information System.

Clasp brake
Where cast iron brake blocks are activated to clasp the running surfaces of the wheels to slow their rate of rotation and hence bring the train to a stop.

C

Classes of trains

Trains are classified according to their purpose and operating characteristics; the numbers 0-9 appear as the first figure in the Train Reporting Numbers in the Working Timetables (WTTs). The numbers are:

1	express passenger, emergency trains
2	stopping passenger
3	parcels, priority empty stock
4	express freight, 75mph maximum
5	empty coaching stock
6	express freight, 60mph maximum
7	freight, 45mph maximum
8	freight, 35mph maximum, engineers' trains
9	Eurostar trains
0	light engines

The rest of the WTT identifications refer to destination area (second entry, and a letter) and individual train or group of trains (third and fourth figures).

Clearance

The space which is free from infringement by any passing rail vehicle, thus denoting the minimum distance at which a fixed structure may be placed.

Clearance, electrical

Divided into static and passing clearances. The static clearance is defined as the minimum distance required between the live parts and any earthed parts of the overhead equipment, when not subject to uplift from a pantograph. Passing clearance is defined as the minimum distance between the overhead equipment or pantograph and any earthed material, rail vehicle or overhead equipment.

Clipping (of points)

The use of a heavy-duty clamp, provided for the purpose, to secure a point blade against the stock rail to retain a given position, aided by a wooden scotch in the open blade/stock rail gap and (possibly) by a padlock. Often used in the case of point machine failure. Points so secured are impervious to any attempts at movement by point motors or from mechanical frames.

Clockface timetable

A timetable for passenger trains which repeats itself on (usually) an hourly pattern. Thus trains leave from a certain point at 05, 20, 35 and 50 minutes past each hour over a specified period of (or all) the day. Sometimes, peak extras can be added by running them at, for instance, 07.25, 07.39, 07.45, 07.53, 08.01 and 08.13, without disturbing the basic service pattern. See also Regular interval timetable.

Close doors platform indicator (CD)

Panel on the platform which is illuminated by the person in charge of the platform to indicate to the guard or driver as appropriate that it is time to close train doors to enable punctual departure. Usually provided in conjunction with a right away (RA) indicator displayed to the driver on the relevant signal post that the doors have been proved closed and the train is ready to depart.

Closed circuit television (CCTV)

There are various railway uses, the main ones being the monitoring of station premises for security or crowd control reasons, and for enabling remote control of level crossings.

Coach

Passenger-carrying vehicle.

Coaching stock, coaching vehicles

All vehicles used for the carriage of passengers, although it originally referred to locomotive-hauled vehicles as opposed to the multiple-unit vehicles which are now commonplace. The term coaching stock includes those vehicles used to carry what was known as passenger rated (ie premium rate) traffic such as parcels vans or Post Office vehicles, which may form part of a passenger train and are thus equipped to travel at passenger train speeds and fitted with automatic brakes.

Coaching stock types:

Compartment

Coaches which consist of separate blocks of seats which face each other, with dividing walls and a door to the corridor. This latter forms a link to the other compartments, the exit doors from the coach, and lavatories. Connections in the coach ends give access to other vehicles on the train. Nowadays, the diminishing quantity of compartment stock is first class, with three-a-side seating giving six seats in each compartment.

The same term is applied to older vehicles without any side corridor (and in which up to 12 people might be accommodated per compartment with six-a-side seating), but these now exist only on preserved railways. In these cases, doors will be found on each side of each compartment.

Compo

Short for composite, a term applied to a coaching stock vehicle with both first and standard class accommodation.

Coaching stock types:
Compo
The MkI composite vehicle had an unusual window arrangement on the corridor side, as seen here with No M16235, one of the last to be built, at Derby in 1963. The purpose was to line up the external doors precisely with one first class and one second class compartment. Each of these was equipped with a top-hinged window on the other side of the vehicle, and internal supports were designed to carry stretchers when needed. This gave the ability to load and unload a stretcher from either side. Why two compartments? One for officers, the other for lower ranks. *John Glover*

Coaching stock, MkI, MkII, MkIII, MkIV

Left: The MkII coaching stock of British Rail in standard class featured 2+2 seating each side of a central gangway, ample luggage space between seats and on racks, shaped seats each with their own cushions and windows arranged so that everybody had a good view. This is the MkIIc version, the last non air-conditioned variety, distinguishable by the lowered ceiling which would have enabled the later fitting of air conditioning, but this never happened. These 66ft (20m) vehicles had 62 seats and a lavatory at each end. *BR*

Below: The MkIId stock were the first quantity produced coaches to feature air conditioning. This open first (FO) demonstrates the 2+1 seating pattern and the wider window (and hence seat) spacing. As a result, the first class coach contains 42 seats in seven bays, as opposed to the 62 seats in eight bays for the equivalent standard class vehicle. Thus, was the traditional 50% loading applied to first class fares justified. *BR*

Open

Coaching stock with an open and essentially unobstructed interior and a gangway down the middle. Designs vary considerably according to the type of use, and need to take account also of the door arrangements plus ancillaries such as lavatories. Seating may be face-to-face or airline style, or a mixture. With end doors only for longer distance travel, the main body of the interior may be divided by draught screens and, perhaps, luggage rack(s).

Saloon

Part or perhaps the whole of the interior of a passenger vehicle with separate seating bays and fewer doors than compartment stock, arranged so that passengers can move around within them. An end gangway to an adjoining vehicle may or may not be provided. The saloon arrangement was adopted for longer distance journeys in earlier days to afford passengers access to toilets within the vehicle.

Coaching stock, MkI, MkII, MkIII, MkIV

The first postwar coaching stock to British Railways designs appeared in 1951, the numbers of which were hugely expanded over the next decade. Later known as MkI, the vast majority of the fleet was thus formed by the mid-1960s, and this included suburban coaches and parcels vans. Most were built on the standard 64ft 6in (19.7m) underframe, although some used the shorter 57ft (17.4m) version. Few remain in service on the national network today.

Production versions of the MkII appeared in 1964. These were of semi-integral construction and were pressure ventilated. The completely redesigned bodies

had new style interiors. Later versions (MkIId onwards) had full air conditioning. Notably, no MkII catering vehicles were built (although some conversions were undertaken much later), so for many years the otherwise air-conditioned sets relegated customers to old MkI vehicles if they wanted a meal.

The MkIII was a step change to full integral construction, first appearing *en masse* in 1974. Large production runs of this 75ft (23m) vehicle over the next 15 years included the trailer cars for all the HST fleet; the various MkIII versions included sleeping cars. Still present were slam doors, other than on the last to be produced, the Class 442 'Wessex Electric' units built for the Bournemouth services, and track discharging toilets. In the view of many, the MkIII coach was an outstandingly successful design. Amongst its many positive attributes was the quality of ride on the BT10 bogies, in which air suspension replaced coil springing for the first time.

The 1989 23.4m MkIV was a relatively small build for the ECML electrification, with body sides designed to allow the train to tilt. Speeds of up to 140mph were envisaged, but tilting never came about and maximum speeds remained at 125mph.

Coasting
Shutting off power from the traction motors and allowing a train to run under the force of gravity on a downhill stretch and its own momentum.

Coasting board
In the event of a minor fault in the OLE (overhead line equipment), such as the contact wire being displaced, the display of a coasting board instructs the driver to lower the pantograph for a short distance so that it doesn't cause any more damage to the overhead equipment, and enables services to be maintained.

Collar
See Reminder appliance.

Combined transport
The use of road and rail for the movement of goods in a single journey.

Commencement board
That erected on the trackside at the start of a temporary speed restriction, displaying a number signifying the maximum speed at which a train should travel over the succeeding section of line. This continues until the Terminating board is reached, signified by a letter T.

Commuter, commuting
Over two centuries ago, Robert Burns was wishing that some Power 'the giftie gie us, to see oursels as others see us'. The Long Island Rail Road, New York, captures the sprit of commuting admirably in this cartoon, which was displayed on the outside of its coaching stock in 1970. Somehow, 'The Route of the Dashing Commuter' doesn't quite have the ring of 'The Route of the Flying Scotsman'. *John Glover*

Community Rail Services
Trains that operate on Community Rail lines and may also operate over the conventional network to other stations. Community Rail Services are supported by a Community Rail Partnership or a Railway Development Company.

Community Railways
The name was coined to describe the most marginal parts of the passenger railway system. As a group, Community Railways cover only one quarter of their attributable costs through fares revenue, so their existence has to be justified through the non-financial benefits they bring to the community. Community Railways are lines formally designated as such. Typically, they are local or rural routes, single or double track with normally one operator or a single passenger operator plus small freight flows. They usually serve the areas covered by just one or two local authorities with transport planning responsibilities. They have a line speed of 75mph or less, and are not intensively used lines which form part of a radial commuting network to principal cities. Greater local involvement is being sought, through various measures.

Commuter, commuting
Originally an American term for the holder of a 'commutation ticket', allowing him or her to make daily journeys between home and place of work for a given period of time, and for which the appropriate multiple of the single fare was reduced, or 'commuted'. Often, a single journey per day each way was all that was permitted. In Britain, the equivalent facility was known as a season ticket.

The term commuter was later adopted in Britain and extended progressively to mean any railway season ticket holder, any person travelling daily to work by train irrespective of the ticket type held, any travel to work by public transport, and then all travel to work by any means. Rather confusingly, it is also now used occasionally to refer to all journeys by public transport generally.

Company train
A train, the whole of which is chartered (or owned) by a single company, and used exclusively for the carriage of its own goods. See also Block train.

Compressor
An air pump, usually driven electrically, supplying air under pressure for use on trains for brakes, doors, suspension, horns, etc.

Computer Analysis of Passenger Revenue Information (CAPRI)
A suite of computer programmes used by the Rail Settlement Plan to collect and process passenger revenue and other settlements for Train Operating Companies and third parties.

Conditions of carriage
See National Conditions of Carriage.

Conditions, abnormal

Extreme loading on a part of the railway system. For example, this may be the result of extended delays on one part of the service impinging on another.

Conditions, degraded

The state of any part of the railway system when it continues to operate in a restricted manner due to the failure of one or more components.

Conditions, normal

The conditions which a part of the railway is designed to accommodate. This would include the peaks (eg the rush hours) and troughs in demand experienced during the day.

Conductor

1. A body or substance which offers a low resistance to the flow of an electric current.
2. Term for a railway guard whose duties include ticket issuing and revenue protection responsibilities,

Conductor rail

Source of electric current for the train in a third-rail electrification system. These are steel rails with high electrical conductivity, but with low carbon content and thus soft and of low tensile strength. The top of the conductor rail is mounted 76mm above the top of the running rail, with the centre of the conductor rail 406mm from the running rail's inside edge. It is supported by an insulator on every eighth sleeper, or more frequently on curves. Each insulator consists of a porcelain pot, into which is cemented an iron cap. The cap is designed to hold the conductor rail in place, without affecting its ability to expand or contract longitudinally according to the ambient temperature.

A composite conductor rail with a stainless steel contact layer and an aluminium supporting section is being tried.

See also Gap and Gapping.

Conflicting movements

A clash of operational actions where one train may be delayed while another moves across its path, as at a junction for instance.

Connections

When, to complete a journey, the passenger needs to make a change of train (or, perhaps, between a train and a bus or ship). The ability to do this depends on the time margin available between the arrival of the first train and the departure of the next. Some connections will be shown in the timetable; otherwise, connectional time between arrival and departure is normally taken as a minimum of five minutes (although can vary upwards or downwards in special circumstances). Such connections between trains are not guaranteed, but efforts are made to maintain them with infrequent services and for the last train services of the day.

Consignment note

A printed document stating the details as may be specified of the goods to be conveyed and between the places concerned to be completed by the sender, to the satisfaction of the carrier or his agents.

Consist

A computer print-out from TOPS carried by the driver of a freight train giving a list of the wagons, in order, and their contents to the extent that he needs to know, eg hazardous goods and how to deal with them if necessary.

Contact wire

The lowermost of the wires forming the overhead line equipment. The pantographs of electric trains press against the underside of this wire and collect the electric current required for propulsion.

Container

The International Standards Organisation (ISO) stackable container forms the principal type of intermodal traffic and was developed originally for the deep-sea shipping industry. It is also used for the inland distribution of non-bulk traffic by rail.

Container dimensions

Twenty Foot Equivalent (TEU) is a term for container lengths, based on the original 10ft, 20ft, 30ft and (later) 40ft lengths of ISO containers which were produced early on in the container revolution. The standard cross sectional dimensions were 8ft x 8ft. Early Freightliner trains were limited to a container length of 27ft (8.23m), as this was at the time the maximum length which could be carried on British roads. Today, 45ft (13.55m) 'Euro boxes' are common on intra-EU movements, while many containers are 9ft 6in (2.69m) high.

Container flat wagons

From the earliest days of containers, there was a need to reduce the floor height of rail wagons (later a skeletal construction) as much as possible, in order to maximise the height of the containers which could be carried and thus their own payloads. The result has been the development of smaller diameter wheels and the possibilities of placing containers on a lower level platform between the bogies. The latter however results in fewer containers being carried in a given length of train.

Containers are secured to the wagon from the underside by the use of twist locks, which are simply applied and are secure.

Container handling

The earliest form of transfer between road and rail for the new ISO containers in the new Freightliner terminals was an overhead crane supported by legs at both ends of the crane beam, and running on its own rails. This is the **gantry crane**, used to straddle rail tracks and roadways for the transfer of containers. Some such cranes are able to turn containers end-to-

Container handling

reach stacker

Right: This reach stacker carries a container towards the Freightliner train on which it will be placed at Southampton Maritime terminal on 23 October 2004. One of the two gantry cranes can be seen in the background, straddling four tracks. Besides the loading and unloading of trains, the containers also have to be moved to or from the shipping berths and on to and off the ships themselves. *John Glover*

straddle carrier

Below: The sheer size of this straddle carrier seen at Southampton Maritime Freightliner terminal on 23 October 2004 is an indication of how far matters have moved from the earlier days of rail freight transport. *John Glover*

end, as well as lift them and move them longitudinally.

Also of general use is the **lift truck**, a piece of mobile equipment which uses a **spreader** to lift containers or swap-bodies. It can offer limited horizontal movement. The spreader is the rigid beam used to hold a container or swap-body when being lifted by such devices.

A **reach stacker** is a heavy-duty lift truck which can reach over containers and swap-bodies and lift the containers beyond them, using a spreader. It can then place them on a rail wagon or a road vehicle/trailer. It may be equipped with a rotating spreader, which allows more flexibility in the accurate positioning of the load on the vehicle to which it is moved.

A **straddle carrier** is a different form of large lift truck, which is of sufficient size to straddle a container (or swap-body) and lift it from above with the use of a spreader.

Contenary

A special type of overhead wire used when clearances are tight. The term is a contraction of contact wire and catenary.

Contingency plans (for various possible events)

Made so that when things go wrong, every member of staff knows what to do and what they should be telling the public.

Continuity bond

An electrical bond across the gap in the running rails at points or crossings.

Continuous rating

See Traction motor rating.

Continuous welded rail (CWR)

See Rail, continuously welded.

Contribution

Contribution is measured by subtracting from the total revenue received the identifiable direct costs (train working and terminal costs) of the train services concerned. What is left is the contribution available towards covering the indirect joint and common costs.

Contributory revenue

Revenue earned on other services as the result of travel on a given service or group of services. For example, those passengers who transfer from a feeder or a branch line to a main line in the course of their journey contribute revenue to the rest of the network as a result of their travel on the branch. This principle remains valid even when the TOC operating the branch is different from the main line TOC.

Control period
The period in advance, normally five years, for which the Office of Rail Regulation determines the basis of the access charges to be paid by Train Operating Companies, and thus in effect the commercial income which will be received by Network Rail.

Control room
See Electrical control room.

Controlled emission toilets
On-train toilets where effluent is retained in tanks within the vehicle, rather than being discharged direct to the track (which was the standard system until the 1980s). This brings with it a need for a means of tank emptying in depots, and for it to be used on a regular basis.

Convention Internationale Concernant le Transport des Marchandises par Chemins de Fer (CIM)
International convention on the movement of goods by rail.

Conventional network
The majority of the railway network, which is not designated as either:
a part of the Trans-European Network (TEN routes) or a part of the Trans-European Freight Network (TERFN), or as a Community Railway.

Conventional signalling
The use of lineside signals, whether colour light or semaphore, operated from any kind of signalbox or signalling control centre.

Converging junction
A term to describe a junction, from the direction of travel relevant to the context, at which two separate lines each conveying trains which run in the same direction, join into one line.

Corporate manslaughter
A criminal offence with which the directors of a company may be charged, following accidental death resulting from their negligence.

Cost centre
The summation of costs incurred for a specific activity over a given period and under the control of an individual department, so that they can be compared with budget.

Counting passengers
The two main locations are on trains or at stations. For the former, train conductors may have some ability to undertake counts, but it will usually be necessary to staff trains specially to obtain comprehensive figures. The task is more difficult with heavily used commuter services, and an alternative is to conduct counts at stations.

Physical counts at stations can take various forms, ranging from a head count of those entering

Controlled emission toilets
The space needed for fully accessible toilets takes space away from other uses, notably seats. This shows the internal arrangements of Class 170 unit No 170203 of Anglia Railways on 25 June 1999, which are in the generous category compared with such facilities on earlier DMUs.
John Glover

and/or leaving the premises, those joining or alighting from specific trains, those interchanging between trains or between trains and buses, taxis etc (if applicable), or those with business at the station but not travelling. The practicalities become far more complex at large busy locations. Determining how many join or alight from each train can be much more difficult; the reader is invited to consider the problems of conducting an accurate count at a location such as Stratford, where the Central Line trains of London Underground have a cross-platform interchange with One's suburban services. Further journey information, such as method of station access, ultimate journey destination and reasons for making the journey can only be obtained by interview or perhaps reply paid cards.

By its very nature, such research can be a very costly exercise in terms of the time spent organising it, plus that of enumerators and interviewers, but also that taken in analysing the results. Yet it is an essential component of understanding and planning the business and trying to satisfy the customers to the best ability of the operator(s).

Country end (of station)
Quick and easy way of distinguishing one end of a (probably) suburban station from the other, which might be termed the London end (or Manchester end etc).

Coupling
Joining railway vehicles together securely, sufficiently to withstand traction shocks and the weights involved, together with brake, control and heating connections as required.

1. Three link
A basic, manual coupling between rail vehicles in which the elongated links are suspended from the coupling hook attached to the headstock at the end of each

Coupling
This diesel shunter has an Instanter coupler fitted, but carries a screw coupling for use when required. As can be seen, the latter is a rather more sophisticated piece of equipment, but the Instanter or three-link couplings cannot be beaten for simplicity. *John Glover*

vehicle. A shunter then has to use a shunting pole to lift one of the sets of links and place the bottom link on the coupling hook of the other vehicle. Brake hoses, if fitted, need to be connected separately.

2. Instanter
A variant on the three link, in which the middle of the three links is of a triangular shape. This allows the distance between the vehicles to be shortened and the side buffers of each to engage, thus reducing the slack.

3. Screw
The most advanced variant on the three link type, in which the middle of the links is replaced by a screw mechanism. This allows the distance between the vehicles to be lessened with a considerable degree of control.

4. Buckeye
A cast steel knuckle coupling used on coaching stock, which engages firmly and automatically when brought into close contact with that of another vehicle. It is then secured in position with a locking pin. Lifting the locking pin releases the jaws of the coupler, allowing it to separate from its partner. Brake pipes and heating connections still have to be connected manually.

5. Fully automatic
Coupling (and uncoupling) which can be undertaken entirely from within a vehicle cab, including the connection or parting of control and systems cables, and air brake pipes. For instance, Dellner, Scharfenberg or Tightlock couplers.

6. Bar
Where vehicles are uncoupled only occasionally in depots or workshops, a semi-permanent coupling can be effected between the vehicles making up (for instance) a multiple-unit or a set of container carrying wagons. This consists of a rigid bar together with semi-permanently coupled hoses, with the result that separation becomes a relatively complex job.

However, while there is a considerable saving on capital and maintenance costs, the price is a much reduced flexibility. This is caused by the inability to separate vehicles easily, and thus replace one of them if it becomes defective. Maintenance regimes too may favour vehicle separation, since different vehicles, for instance those with traction motors, may need to spend longer out of service than plain trailers.

Sets of vehicles in blocks will have conventional couplings and brake hose connections at the outer ends. In normal traffic, each will be treated as a single unit.

Cripple
Universal term, albeit a little unfortunate, for a defective railway vehicle. For wagons, categories range between:
- Needs repair, but safe to travel forward to destination, whether loaded or empty (wagon carries green card).
- Authorised for empty movement to nominated repair point at reduced speed (wagon carries green card).
- Not to go, confined to existing location until repaired or at least further inspected (wagon carries red card).
- Condemned, one journey only for breaking up, or to be broken up on site.

Cripple siding
A siding set aside in a yard for housing defective vehicles. (A similar feature for trolleys would be useful in many supermarkets!)

Critical rail temperature
The temperature to which continuously welded rail may be allowed to rise during, for instance, very hot weather, before there is serious risk of track deformation and measures to protect trains need to be undertaken. The critical temperature will depend on the stress free temperature of the rail and the quantity and degree of consolidation of the ballast.

Cross
Trains travelling in opposite directions are said to cross each other at, for instance, somewhere around the halfway point between two cities. If this is a station, it can be an opportunity for the exchange of crews so that they end up back at their home depot.

CrossCountry (XC), formerly NE/NW–S/SW
The core of CrossCountry is the route of the former Midland Railway from Leeds/York to Bristol via Sheffield, Derby, Birmingham New Street and Gloucester. In service terms, the extensions at both ends to Edinburgh and Penzance respectively can be included, also north from Birmingham via the WCML and south to Reading,

C

Southampton and Bournemouth. Only a few sections of the core as described above are electrified.

Cross dock

The transfer of freight from one vehicle or mode to another, for onward distribution, with little or no dwell time.

Cross span

A wire carried on insulators stretched across tracks holding the contact wires in the desired position.

Crossing

1. The V-shaped component of a turnout which enables a train's wheels to complete the movement from one line to another.
2. A track formation in which one line crosses another at grade, usually at a relatively shallow angle and forming a diamond shape in the centre, hence the name 'diamond crossing'. However, the lines may sometimes cross at right angles, or nearly so. There is no means for trains to move between the two lines concerned.

Crossing loop

The additional track installed on an otherwise single-track railway, usually at a station, to allow trains to pass each other.

Crossover

A pair of points or turnouts laid face to face, which allows trains to pass between one line and another. On running lines, the direction may be classified as either 'facing' (in which case the move can be made directly) or 'trailing' (which will require reversal).

Crossrail 1

The core centre portion of Crossrail 1 is intended to have deep level underground stations at Paddington, Bond Street, Tottenham Court Road, Farringdon and Liverpool Street. The Hybrid Bill presently before Parliament shows services to Heathrow and to Maidenhead in the west, and in the east to Whitechapel. From here, there will be two branches. One is to join the existing railway to Stratford and Shenfield, the other is to the Isle of Dogs and beyond to Abbey Wood. London Rail and the SRA set up a joint company (Cross London Rail Links Ltd) to progress Crossrail 1 (and also Crossrail 2). The aim is to relieve the Central Line of London Underground and also to provide a high-quality service giving access to the key financial nodes of the City and Canary Wharf, and also to Heathrow Airport.

Crossrail 2

Formerly known as the Chelsea-Hackney line, the core section remains unchanged as being between King's Cross St Pancras and Victoria with a single intermediate station at Tottenham Court Road.

CRS

See Customer Reservation System.

CSR

See Cab Secure Radio.

CTRL

See Channel Tunnel Rail Link.

CUI

See Capacity Utilisation Index.

CUP

See Capacity Utilisation Policy.

Culvert

A small bridge or pipe crossing under the railway, carrying a watercourse.

Cushions, on the cushions

Term to describe drivers and firemen travelling on duty, but not in charge of a train. At one time, a passenger compartment might be set aside for their use, because of the assumed state (probably correctly) of their overalls. Later, the use was widened to refer to any railway staff on duty who were using the train merely to get from place to place.

Crossover
A trailing crossover in welded track in a mechanically signalled area complete with point rodding from the box in the background. Facing point locks are not required. *BR*

C

Customer Information System (CIS)
The ability to find out from where and when your train will depart is a basic requirement of all passengers, fulfilled with various degrees of success by different TOCs at different locations. The electronic version of the flap-type indicator as seen here at London Victoria in March 2005 appears to be one of the more successful installations. A prime need is to be able to see the display in anything from bright sunlight to pre-dawn gloom. *John Glover*

Customer Information System (CIS)
The provision of both audible and visual forms of information, which may be operated automatically or manually.

Customer Reservation System (CRS)
The national system by which reservations on trains are made. This gives a passenger the right to occupy a specified seat (or space in a sleeping car) on a nominated train and date between two given points, subject also to the holding of a valid travel ticket for the journey to be undertaken. Group reservations will normally be for a block of seats of the required number.

Cut and cover construction
Where a railway is built by excavating the ground from above (the cut) and then subsequently covered over, hence the name. Strictly, the result is a covered way, rather than a tunnel. All but one of the 'tunnels' on the first phase of the Channel Tunnel Rail Link were built by this method, as was most of what forms the present day Circle Line of London Underground.

'Cut and run'
An operating policy approach to ailing or non-functioning engines such as one of the pair of HST power cars not working. The aim is to run non-stop to the terminus, omitting intermediate stops because of the resulting poor acceleration performance, which loses more time and can delay other services. Whether or not 'cut and run' is in the best interests of customers (as opposed to operators) is debatable.

Cut-off
See Avoiding line.

Cutting
Location where it is necessary for the railway to be constructed below the prevailing ground level. Its nature depends upon the geology of the ground, as it is important that the cutting sides are stable, to prevent slippage. Rock cuttings such as at Edge Hill, Liverpool, can have near vertical sides, but the cost of excavation is high. At the other end of the scale, slopes in clay or wet ground may need to be as shallow as 20% to prevent the sides from sliding onto the track. This may or may not be practicable in terms of the amount of land consumed, while the volumes of spoil to be disposed of are correspondingly greater. An interim solution is the use of retaining walls of stone or concrete to keep the cutting sides in place. In any cutting, care must be taken to ensure that drainage is adequate.

CWR
See Rail, continuously welded.

Cutting
The cutting sides here at the southern portal of Summit Tunnel, Littleborough, are decidedly steep, perfectly acceptable in areas of solid rock. It does however exact its own price, in terms of the physical effort needed to bore the tunnel and create the railway trackbed. *H. Weston*

D

Dangerous goods

There are nine classifications ranging from Class 1 Explosives, through Class 3 Liquids, Class 7 Radioactive to Class 9 Miscellaneous. The range of substances which are accepted for conveyance by rail is strictly controlled and each is allocated a United Nations substance identification number, dangerous goods class and TOPS commodity code. Special provision is made for the marshalling, movement and loading of substances and contingency plans exist for dealing with any incident involving such products.

Dated train

One which does not run for the full period covered by the timetable, eg Summer Saturdays only 18 June to 17 September, in a table which covers the period through to Saturday, 10 October.

DBHP

See Drawbar horsepower.

Dead

Electrical equipment is said to be dead when it is disconnected from a supply.

'Dead' locomotives or multiple-units

Those incapable of operating under their own power for whatever reason, or from the external power source if electric, and for which special instructions apply in relation to their movement on running lines.

Dedicated fare, or ticket

A fare and the associated ticket which applies to the services of one train operating company only, and to whose services the ticket holder is restricted. Revenue thus derived is not shared between all TOCs providing relevant services over that route.

Defensive driving

Driving a train in a conservative manner, with the objective of ensuring that the risk of overrunning a red signal and causing it to be passed at danger (SPAD), and thus being blamed for it, is very low indeed. Such an approach is likely to result in journey times being extended, and some argue that this is taking risk avoidance too far.

Delays

Delays to trains attributable to Network Rail (as opposed to the train operators) are measured in terms of delay minutes per 100 track km. In 2004/05, the most important of these, measured across the entire network for all traffic were, in descending order of importance: track circuit failures, points failures and broken rails or other track faults.

Demurrage

A charge made to a trader by a wagon's owner in respect of its detention beyond the period of time agreed for the purposes of unloading, loading, or both.

Departmental vehicle

A slightly anachronistic term nowadays, which refers to the often specialist fleet which belongs to (or is leased by) the various railway engineering functions, eg ballast wagons. They are used for internal railway purposes.

Departure board, indicator

A CCTV screen or maybe a much larger display in station ticket halls and similar for the benefit of passengers, showing the trains due to depart shortly, their platform numbers, destinations and stopping places and time expected (if not at a terminus). Separate versions applicable to each platform are likely to be displayed there. Similar arrangements may be made for arrivals.

Depot

Place where trains are stabled, serviced and maintained, notably overnight.

Derailment

An incident which results in a locomotive or any other railway vehicle leaving the track, but not involving a collision. In minimal form this might amount to the wheels of a single axle, or it could mean an entire train. Strictly, a derailment occurs if a wheel flange leaves the rail alignment and the wheel tyre is lifted above rail level.

Derailments may be caused by infrastructure faults, vehicle faults, excessive speed or severe braking by the driver, staff error, vandalism, or some combination.

Note that while a collision between two trains might *cause* a derailment, in accident classification terms this would be a collision and the consequential derailment is deemed to be a secondary effect.

Derailment
On the morning of 23 November 1983, the 'Night Riviera' sleeper from the West of England was derailed as it approached London Paddington. The locomotive turned over on its side. Both trackwork and signalling were severely damaged, and recovery needed the help of the breakdown cranes from Old Oak Common (nearer) and Willesden Junction (in the distance). Three passengers were slightly hurt. In those days, there were no complications as the result of overhead electrification.
Mick Roberts

Detection
Confirms that things are as they should be by either mechanical or electrical means. In signalling, specifically that the presence of a train and its location is confirmed by track circuit occupation, or that the interlocking of points and/or signals has operated correctly.

Detonator
A device of about 40mm diameter with lead straps attached, designed to be placed quickly on a running rail and secured there. If run over by a train, it will explode, the noise alerting the driver that something is wrong. Its purpose is for protection and emergency purposes.

Dewirement
When the pantograph and the contact wire are sufficiently out of synchronisation in position that the pantograph is no longer constrained and rises above the contact wire. The risk of this increases in high winds, when such instances are known colloquially as 'blow-offs'. These can cause extensive damage to both the pantograph and the overhead system, while the train itself also loses power. Dewirement can also result from damage to the OLE, from any cause.

Diagram
Sequence of train working to be undertaken by one unit of resource, for instance one driver's shift of duty, or an item of rolling stock for a period of perhaps up to a week. The diagrams show when and where each will be working. This is done with the objectives of ensuring that:
● All train services will be covered.
● The right type of train, of sufficient length, is used in each case.
● There is some judicious slack, but not too much, to recover from minor incidents.
● Train crews do not exceed their hours and that their meal breaks are honoured.
● Diesel locomotives or units reach a refuelling point before they run out.
● Train toilets are emptied and water tanks replenished when needed.
● All vehicles are presented for light maintenance when required.
● The whole is achieved with the maximum of economy.

Diamond crossing
Track formation where two tracks cross at an angle without any connection being made between them; name derived from the shape of the track within the crossing point.

Diesel-electric transmission
Power is provided by a diesel engine to drive a generator, the electric current from which is then used to drive the traction motors, which provide the movement. An auxiliary generator may be used to provide power for lighting, electric train heating (ETH) and air conditioning in passenger vehicles. Such a locomotive is said to be ETH fitted.

Diesel engine
The diesel engine works on the principle that air forced into the cylinders by the turbochargers is compressed by the rising pistons and reaches a temperature of some 960°C. A fine spray of oil is pumped into the cylinder as the piston reaches the top of its stroke. The heat ignites the fuel and the expanding gases drive the piston down on its power stroke.

Diesel-hydraulic transmission
Where power is provided by a diesel engine and the coupling between it and the wheels is achieved by pumping high-pressure oil to drive motors on the wheel assembly.

Diesel multiple-unit (DMU)
Term for a self-contained diesel-powered train where the traction system is usually located beneath the vehicles themselves. Units may comprise a single vehicle, or two or more passenger vehicles coupled together, with a driving cab at the outer ends of the set. There is thus no separate locomotive. The multiple-unit description refers to the ability for two or more such sets of vehicles to be coupled together and controlled by one driver from a single cab. This requires all the units to be thus operated to have mutually compatible coupling and control systems.

Dipped joint
On jointed track, a loosening of the bolts holding the fishplate in place can result in local movement, allowing the end of one rail to 'dip' below the other unless it is fully supported. This has consequential results for rail wear.

Direct costs
Those costs which are related directly to an activity as opposed to those which are not. Indirect costs are 'overheads'.

Directions and Guidance
Formal instructions which were issued to the SRA by central Government, the Scottish Executive or the Mayor of London.

Disabled Persons Protection Policy (DPPP)
It is a requirement of the SRA/DfT that all licensed train operating companies publish such a document, describing the facilities available and their policies for passengers with disabilities.

Disabled Persons' Reporting System
This allows passengers who are disabled, elderly or infirm, to pre-arrange assistance for their journey via dedicated telephone numbers.

Disc brake
A braking mechanism using friction pads applied by calliper action to a disc secured to the vehicle axle or wheel centre.

Disconnector
See Isolator.

Distant signal
See Signals.

Distributed power
In order to reduce the strain on couplings on heavy freight trains, especially on steeply graded routes, 'helper' locomotives may be cut into the consist at intervals. These are controlled by radio from the leading locomotive. This is an alternative to concentrating the traction at the head of the train. Although not presently in use in Britain, the idea has been considered.

Diverging junction
A term to describe a junction, from the direction of travel relevant to the context, at which one line splits into two separate lines, each conveying trains in the forward direction.

Diveunders
See Flyovers and Diveunders.

DMU
See Diesel multiple-unit.

Dolly
See Signals.

DOO
See Driver-only operation.

Doors, folding
External pairs of doors, each in two sections which, when opened, fold inwards on themselves. Thus they do not project onto the platform. They are used on the Class 14x 'Pacer' units of the mid-1980s.

Doors, power operated
Doors on a train where the opening and closing are controlled by the guard, or driver with DOO operation. Sometimes the guard merely releases the door controls, and it is up to passengers to press a button to open individual pairs of doors. Similarly, passengers may have the option of closing a set of doors by pressing another button, when movement there has ceased. An overriding control by the guard will shut all doors remaining open before the train departs. The benefit to passengers of a degree of control is to keep the train warm in winter, and to be able to enjoy air conditioning (where relevant) in summer. It can also be helpful in wet and windy conditions, or when it is snowing. From the operator's point of view, it gives control without having to attend to individual door locking at platforms, and hence increases safety. It also benefits punctuality.

Doors, slam
Passenger rolling stock built up to the mid-1980s, unless of the sliding or folding door types, used individually hinged external doors. Each door was 600mm wide, although wider doors were fitted from late MkII stock onwards. These were unlocked by the passenger and subsequently slammed shut, hence the name. In some cases, opening the door required use of the out-

Doors, power operated
Above: The door opening controls on a Virgin 'Pendolino'. *John Glover*

Doors, slam
Left: The last design of slam doors was that used in the MkIIb coach of 1968, and later builds. These had the wrap round ends with a substantial handrail to guide passengers. The door was thus made wider as was the entrance vestibule to match. Of necessity, these doors could be fitted at the ends of coaches only, and those at the other end of the vehicle opened from left to right, the opposite of that seen here on a MkIIc coach. *BR*

side handle, and thus first dropping the window if inside the train. While the first catch and second catch protection ensured that a door not properly closed would not fly open in transit, their correct use and operation was a matter for individual passengers. Any slam door could be locked out of use by the staff, using a carriage key. See also Central door locking.

Doors, sliding pocket
External doors which, when opened, move sideways into a pocket between the outer and inner surfaces of the body side. Such doors are usually top hung only. This is the traditional approach and in general use until relatively recently.

D

Double-sided platform
The double-sided platform, allowing as it does passengers to board and alight from both sides of a train, is relatively rare. This is Yeovil Pen Mill, Somerset, seen in March 1989. Today, it is unusual to find the train doors released on both sides of a train in such locations, which wasn't a problem with traditional slam doors. It is thus not impossible for a passenger to wait on a platform for the doors to be released, only to watch the train depart without being given a chance to board. *John Glover*

Doors, swing plug
External vehicle doors which, on opening, 'pop' outward from the bodyside. They then swing longitudinally from a fulcrum and parallel to the car body until fully open. On closing, the movement is reversed. Rubber edging strips around the doors form a seal when in the closed position.

Double-deck trains
As with buses, the double-deck train provides seating capacity on an upper as well as a lower level. However, the limitations of the British loading gauge have generally prevented such usage, albeit that the Southern Region of British Railways ran a pair of experimental electric units of compartment stock from 1949 until 1971 (the 4-DD stock in Southern parlance). Another problem to be overcome is the time taken at stations for egress and access, unless the number of door openings is increased proportionately.

Double heading
The use of two locomotives, for whatever reason, to haul a train. Such locomotives may be coupled in multiple, where there is full through control by one driver. The locomotives concerned must have compatible control systems. Alternatively, they may be in tandem. Here, the locomotives are coupled with through control of the brake only, and are separately manned.

Double line
Situation where there are two running lines, normally one for each direction, but either or both may be signalled bi-directionally.

Double-sided platform
Occasionally the situation will be found where a single track is served by a platform on each side. Examples of this layout will be found at Finsbury Park and Yeovil Pen Mill.

Doubling
The conversion of a single track railway to double track, with all the consequential civil, permanent way and signalling works. Similarly quadrupling, for conversion from (probably) double to four tracks.

Down line
See Line designation, direction

DPPP
See Disabled Persons Protection Policy.

Drain cock
Used to discharge compressed air from reservoirs.

Drainage, track
Of increasing importance as the speed and weight of trains increased, early track drainage systems proved inadequate for the task. Good drainage needs to collect and disperse water from the ballast, avoiding the creation of ponds.

Drawbar horsepower (DBHP)
The locomotive power developed at the drawbar, that is the power developed in the cylinders less the power required to overcome the friction of the engine and that needed to move the locomotive itself.

Driver-only operation (DOO)
DOO applies to multiple-unit passenger trains with sliding doors only, where there is no guard. The driver has full control of the operation of the train. To assist the driver, platform mirrors or CCTV, or some combination, is provided at all calling points. The driver also has radio contact with the signalling centre. Door opening and closing is under the driver's control, and a public address system is available to him. See also Single manning.

Driver training simulator

A static device of a driver's cab mock up, with all controls, and a video-type view through the cab windows. The Instructor can add hazards such as equipment faults and obstructions on the line, as well as changing the signal aspects. (The author's exit from Paris Nord on the Eurostar simulator was decidedly slow, but he didn't actually do anything wrong …)

Driver's reminder appliance

A device in the cab which enables the driver to set a reminder that the next signal ahead is at danger.

Driver's Safety Device (DSD)

Device which will stop the train if the driver becomes incapacitated and ceases to keep sufficient pressure of a foot on a pedal, hand on a control, or activates a device at given intervals. Also known as the Dead man's handle or plain Dead man.

Driving van trailer (DVT)

An unpowered coaching vehicle with a driver's cab, used at the other end of a train from the locomotive, so that the whole can operate in a push-pull manner. The van may be used as accommodation for a conductor or parcels, but not for passengers if the train is to operate at speeds of 100mph or more.

Dropper

An arrangement of copper wires or strips and clips by which one wire of the overhead line equipment is suspended from another, which is used to keep the contact wire at the correct height.

DSD

See Driver's Safety Device.

Dual electrification

A section of line which is electrified both at 750V dc third rail and also 25kV ac overhead. Trains equipped with either can work on such a line, or change from one to the other if fitted with both. A notable installation is to be found on the North London line, the western end of which is equipped with an additional conductor rail for the benefit of London Underground's District Line services.

Dual voltage

Locomotives or electric multiple-units which can run off either 25kV ac overhead or 750V dc third rail as may be required, or maybe other systems in the case of trains running through the Channel Tunnel. A second group is that which makes passive provision for dual voltage, or which can be configured for either. This gives more flexibility for future deployment. However, dual voltage vehicles inevitably carry weight and cost penalties for the additional equipment, which also needs to be maintained.

DVT

See Driving van trailer.

Driver
Left: The driver's desk controls on a Class 67 locomotive.
Ian Allan Library

Driving Van Trailer
Below left: The cab of a MkIII Driving Van Trailer, as used on services from London Euston until the coming of the 'Pendolinos'. Push-pull operation, which the DVT allowed, reduces the locomotive movements needed at the termini, and makes very quick turnrounds possible if necessary. *BR*

Dual voltage
Below: The Euston-Watford Junction dc electric services can be worked perfectly well by dc-only units, apart from their need to visit Bletchley for servicing. Nevertheless Silverlink decided that it required more units, and dc-only No 508303 was one of three acquired from Merseyside for the purpose. This one is seen arriving at Euston on 7 March 2005. It was built, originally, for South Western suburban services from Waterloo. *John Glover*

D

Dwell time

The time for which a train stands at an intermediate station, during which the wheels are not turning. The doors then have to be released, opened as necessary for passengers to alight and join, shut and then be proved shut before the train can restart. On a slick urban operation such as London Underground, dwell times may range from as little as 15sec off-peak at more lightly used stations to 40sec at peak at key locations. Dwell times for long distance rail services, where the coaches have fewer doors and many passengers have luggage, can extend to several minutes.

Dynamic track stabiliser

A self-propelled on-track machine which consolidates track ballast by inducing high-frequency vibration into it.

Dynamic vehicle profile

See Gauge, structures and vehicles.

Early, late and night

Turns of duty on a 24hr railway, normally 06.00-14.00, 14.00-22.00 and 22.00-06.00 for regular jobs such as signallers.

Earth

The potential of the general mass of the earth and of any conductor which is in direct connection with it. For the purpose of overhead line equipment, this includes the track return circuit and the structures supporting the overhead line equipment, provided these are solidly connected to the rails by a structure bond or earth wire.

Earthed

Connected to earth by means of an appropriate device. This may be a circuit breaker that has had it tripping device rendered inoperative, an isolator at a fixed earthing point or a portable earthing device.

Earth wire

A bare overhead wire electrically connecting the steelwork of two or more structures together and connected to earth.

Earthing connection

A metallic conductor for connecting electrical equipment to earth or to the track return.

Earthwork failures

Cutting sides of embankments which become unstable are classified as having failed, irrespective of whether or not they cause the derailment of a train. The term also includes drainage failures.

East Coast Main Line (ECML)

The main line from London King's Cross to York, Newcastle and Edinburgh.

East London Line Extension

This scheme dates from 1985, and became the responsibility of Transport *for* London for funding and construction in November 2004. It is intended to use the existing East London Line of the Underground as the in-town section, extended in the north via the old Broad Street-Dalston Junction formation, and to the south over former Southern Railway tracks. The inclusion of Whitechapel in Crossrail 1 would increase its importance as an interchange station.

Indicative route and potential route options are shown as Highbury & Islington in the north, with fur-

East London Line Extension
The East London Line has many of the attributes of the main line railways as can be seen in this view of Whitechapel station taken from the southbound platform in 2003. As with most of the other stations, it is relatively cramped, particularly the platform entrances and exits. There is also the problem with platform lengths; while Whitechapel has some disused platform at the northern end which can be revitalised, many of the others can accommodate no more than the four-car trains of Underground A stock which presently serve the line.
John Glover

ther extension possible, and branches to Clapham Junction (with a new station at Brixton) and West Croydon in the south. There would be a short stub from the latter to Crystal Palace. The existing line to New Cross remains.

Phase 1 will comprise the Dalston Junction to West Croydon section, with the branch to Crystal Palace; the rest will constitute Phase 2. Phase 1 is to be funded from new prudential borrowing arrangements and is due to be completed by 2010; there are no dates set for Phase 2. The completed line would become part of National Railways and be operated as such.

ECML
See East Coast Main Line.

ECS
See Empty coaching stock.

Electric Control Station
A building containing apparatus for the control of the substations and track sectioning cabins on electrified lines.

Electric multiple-unit (EMU)
Term for a self-contained electrically powered train where the traction motors are located beneath the vehicles themselves. Each unit consists of two or more passenger vehicles coupled together, with a driving cab at the outer ends. There is thus no separate locomotive. The multiple-unit description refers to the ability for two or more such sets of vehicles to be coupled together and controlled by one driver from a single cab. This requires all the units to be thus operated to have mutually compatible coupling and control systems.

Electric Token Block
This is one of the many ways of controlling single line sections of railway, on which there is potential for very destructive collisions to take place.

The objective of Electric Token Block signalling is to prevent more than one train being in a block section between two token block stations at the same time, and when no train is in that section, to be able to admit a train into the section from either end.

This is accomplished by the driver of every train carrying a token. This is issued from an electric token machine, one being situated in each of the signalboxes at the two ends of the single line section. These two machines are interlocked electrically, so that one token only is obtainable at any one time. By its nature, two successive trains in the same direction can each carry a token.

When he leaves a token station, a train driver must carry the token for the section of line over which the train is about to run; failure to do so renders him liable to disciplinary action.

Electric traction systems
The electrical equipment and conductors necessary to power trains on the railway. It includes the incoming supply feeders, switchgear and transformers which control and provide the electric current at the tractions system's line voltage, the distribution network and overhead line or conductor rail equipment. It does not include the current collection equipment of the train or other on-board equipment, except for the provision of electrical clearances between such equipment and the infrastructure.

Electric multiple-unit (emu)
Left: The front end of Southern's dc-only outer suburban 'Electrostar' unit shows how the front end arrangements have been tidied up over the years, as befits new trains delivered in the present century.
John Glover

Electric Token Block
Below: The handing of a token to the driver by the signaller, signifying his exclusive right to occupy the single line, is a relatively basic method. However, it works, and has done so very well. Here, the driver has just received the token, and the steel loop of which it is part can be seen on his shoulder. An apparatus to perform the same task appears to be out of use. The location is Worgret Junction on 25 March 1967, with an enthusiasts' train for the Swanage branch headed by Ivatt Class 2 2-6-2T No 41320. Through passenger trains to Swanage may one day return.
John H. Bird

E

Electrical Control Operator

The Electrical Control Operator is the person in charge of the Electrical Control Room who has control of the power supply to the electric traction system, and is responsible for all switching operations and isolation of electrical current thereon. There were 14 Electrical Control Rooms on Network Rail in 2004.

The Electrical Control Operator on the railway is known as the Control Engineer on the national networks, ie Grid Control Engineer, Area Control Engineer and Power Station Control Engineer.

Electrical control room

A room from which instruction can be received and issued for the control of equipment within its area. It may also house apparatus for the control of circuit breakers and isolators.

Electrical equipment

Any apparatus which is used for the generation, transmission, distribution, control or utilisation of electricity.

Electrification systems: 25kV ac overhead

The 25kV ac electrification system derives power from the high-voltage national electricity transmission and distribution networks owned and operated by National Grid Transco and the distribution network operators. At each supply point located along the railway, the overhead line equipment is used to distribute that energy along the track.

The electrification system is divided into sub-sections by trackside switching stations, which comprise a number of 25kV circuit breakers. Additional electrical sectioning is provided by means of section isolators, insulated overlaps and neutral sections.

Electric trains collect current by means of the roof-mounted pantographs. These make sliding contact with the contact wire, which itself is suspended from the catenary wire.

The security of the electricity supply is an essential feature, and duplicate circuits, each capable of supplying the traction load, are provided in most cases.

Electrical units

These are the Système International (SI) metric units, based upon the metre (m) for length, kilogram (k) for mass and second (s) for time:

A	Amp(ere)	unit of current
F	Farad	unit of capacitance
H	Henry	unit of inductance
W	Ohm	unit of resistance
V	Volt	unit of potential difference, or force
W	Watt	unit of power.

Electrification systems:

1 1,500V dc overhead

Although heralded as the new British standard in 1932, only a handful of systems were to use it and all were converted to ac (or closed) by the mid-1980s. However, 1,500V dc was used for the Tyne & Wear Metro, the first stage of which opened in 1980. The dc overhead was extended over Network Rail lines from Pelaw to Sunderland and beyond to South Hylton when that section of the Metro was opened in 2002.

2 660/750V dc third rail

2 660/750V dc third rail

An additional rail, (the positive rail) is laid beside the two running rails and is used to carry dc power to electric trains (see also Conductor rail.). One or both the running rails are used to return the (negative) traction current to the substation. The conductor rail positioning is influenced by the incidence of junctions; nowadays it will normally be laid on the opposite side to the cess side to create a safe walkway alongside the track, and on the opposite side from the platform face at stations.

Power is derived from the high-voltage national electricity distribution network. This is distributed to substations via a high-voltage cable network, usually contained in a concrete trough route alongside the running lines.

At each substation, the voltage is transformed down, converted to 660/750V dc using rectifiers, and distributed along the track via the conductor rail. It is picked up by the train using shoes, which slide along the conductor rail and make top surface contact.

After passing through the motors, the current flows back through the running rails until it is returned to the rectifiers in the traction substation.

Today, third rail electrification may be found extensively on what was once part of the Southern Railway, as well as parts of the North London Line and the dc lines to Watford Junction, and the whole of the Merseyrail Electrics operation.

Electrified line
That which is so equipped, regardless of system.

Electrified track capability
This measures the length of electrified and energised running track on Network Rail, including loops but excluding sidings and depots. The type of electrification is shown as at March 2005.

System	km	%
25kV ac overhead	7,748	24.6
3rd rail 600/750v dc	4,497	14.3
dual ac overhead/3rd rail dc	35	0.1
1,500v dc overhead	39	0.1
Total, electrified	12,319	39.1
Non-electrified	19,163	60.9
Total	31,482	100

Approximately 60% of all rail traffic is electrically powered, on approximately 40% of the network.

ELU
See Standard Length Unit.

ELR
See Engineers' Line Reference.

Embankment
The converse of a cutting, where it is necessary for the railway to run above ground level. The ideal situation during construction is to use the material from cuttings to construct embankments, with the two volumes balancing as nearly as possible. The intention is to provide a gently graded route for the railway throughout.

Quality of construction is important and some settlement will take place over a period of time. Any serious movement in an embankment needs to be detected before this becomes a landslide. The first signs may be as innocuous as the movement of fence posts.

Emergency situation
A current unforeseen or unplanned event which has life threatening or extreme loss implications and requires immediate attention, eg a fire.

Emergency speed restrictions
See Speed restrictions, temporary (TSRs) or emergency (ESRs).

Empty coaching stock (ECS), Empty stock
Movement of passenger trains, parts of trains, or maybe a miscellaneous selection of hauled stock which is not at the time available for carrying passengers. This includes, for instance, journeys to and from depots, or positioning journeys at the beginning or the end of the day. By definition, such trains do not directly earn revenue for the operator, but most are likely to be an intrinsic part of the train plan.

Engineers' Line Reference (ELR)
System dividing the whole of the network into discrete units.

'Enterprise'
The title given to EWS's national wagonload service of trunk services between hubs, and supporting trip workings for collection/distribution.

Engineer's train
That for which the sole purpose is use on civil engineering or similar works.

Embankment
Lineside vegetation needs clearing from time to time, not least to ensure that visibility for drivers is not impaired. A road-rail vehicle sets about scrub removal.
Ian Allan Library

E

Environmental Impact Statement
Trains of nuclear flasks containing irradiated fuel from nuclear power stations are taken by rail to the UK Atomic Energy Authority's chemical reprocessing plant at Sellafield, Cumbria. This January 1966 view shows such a train headed by one of the short-lived 'D57xx' Metrovick Co-Bo diesels. The environmental credentials of this particular locomotive would seem to be somewhat suspect! *UKAEA*

Environmental Impact Statement
The identification of environmental aspects to determine the past, present and future impact of an organisation's activities on the environment. Such activities may have a positive or negative effect. The Environmental Impact Statement is prepared to support an application for future development and sets out the results of that investigation.

Environmental noise
The noise of rail operations comes under a number of headings, not all of which are applicable in any one case:

Locomotive or power cars
- power unit, roof exhaust, cooling fans, compressors
- bogies, brakes, couplings
- warning horns

Rolling stock
- air-conditioning systems
- bogies, brakes, couplings
- bodywork flexing
- slamming of doors

Wheel/rail interface
- running contact of wheel and rail
- passing over switch and crossing work, track joints, curves (squeal)

Structures
- radiated noise from bridges and tunnels

Level crossings
- warning horns or bells, also from the approaching trains

Terminals
- public address announcements
- general hubbub of maybe large numbers of people
- warning horns of motorised trolleys or similar
- vehicle movements, both road and rail
- machinery

Infrastructure
- construction
- maintenance

The perceived importance or otherwise of each source will relate to its intrusiveness, the frequency of occurrence, the time it happens during the day (and/or night), and the cumulative effect of several causes. Densely populated residential areas are likely to be the most sensitive.

e.o.h.p. (Except as otherwise herein provided)
An expression dating back many years, when railway goods rates were regulated by law to the extent that the companies were not allowed to give undue preference to any trader. Thus rates were laid down for each type of traffic, in great detail, eg bricks, by type. But there was always the possibility that another type of brick would be presented for carriage. This was overcome by specifying a rate for 'bricks, e.o.h.p.' and thus covering all eventualities. Just occasionally, e.o.h.p. is still found in use to mean something non-standard.

Equivalent fatalities
A means of measuring the scale of the human effects of accidents, in which both fatalities and injuries are expressed in terms of fatalities. In this, 10 major injuries are equated to one fatality and 200 minor injuries are also equated to one fatality.

ERTMS
See European Rail Traffic Management System.

ETH, also ETS
See Train heating, electric train supply index.

Escalator
A staircase consisting of an endless chain of steps, driven by an electric motor and continuously ascending or descending.

ESR
See Speed restrictions, temporary (TSRs) or emergency (ESRs).

European Rail Traffic Management System (ERTMS)
ERTMS is being developed to provide a new generation of train control and signalling, including Advanced Train Protection, by supervising train speed and braking. Trains use data (eg gradients, signal aspects, braking performance) to calculate a safe speed envelope. The system will intervene if the train overspeeds, to bring it back into the envelope. The system stops a train safely if a signal is at danger.

As the name suggests, one aim is to enable one common signalling system across Europe, bringing with it greater operational efficiency as well as safety benefits and interoperability. The ERTMS technology has different levels offering different capacity and performance.

Examination of the line
Procedure as prescribed in regulations for using a locomotive, or in some instances a train, to run slowly through a section of line to check for obstruction, damage, animals on the line, etc.

Exceptional load, also out of gauge load (OGLO)
A load will become exceptional either because of its bulk or because it imposes a heavier axle loading than the norm for that route. If this is established either physically or by calculation, special arrangements have to be made.

Such arrangements can apply to a single journey or to a regular movement. Instructions are sent out to signallers by Operations Control. In some circumstances, adjoining lines have to be blocked, or the train may not be allowed to move where this involves passing trains carrying passengers. Nearby sidings may have to be cleared, specific routes observed and speed restrictions imposed. Alternatively, another route might be available with fewer or no restrictions.

Excursion
A day return railway journey undertaken for pleasure purposes, with the inference of using a modestly priced ticket.

Excursion train
See Charter train.

Expansion joint
See Rail, stress.

Fail-safe
A design philosophy in which any form of equipment failure results in a safe outcome. Thus the AWS system requires current to be flowing in the track magnet if the result is to be a sounding of a bell in the driver's cab confirming that the next signal is green. No current as a result of equipment failure, and the warning horn sounds, irrespective of the signal aspect.

Fare
The amount paid by a passenger in consideration of being given the right to be carried on a journey as specified, and represented by the issue of a ticket.

Fares basket
Means of fares regulation by the SRA. A limit, or cap, is applied to a weighted average of the relevant fares on each train operator. The fares policy was reviewed in 2003, and the cap on each operator's Commuter Fares basket and Protected Fares basket is now set at the 2002/03 value of each basket, increased by RPI+1% in January 2004 and cumulatively each year after that. (RPI = Retail Price Index.)

Operators have a degree of flexibility to adjust individual fares, as long as the value of the fares basket as a whole does not exceed that cap, and no individual fare rises by more than 6% above RPI.

Fares Incentive Adjustment Payment (FIAP)
A modification to the fares cap to take into account the punctuality and reliability of the TOCs in their franchise payments to, or from, the SRA.

Fares regulation
The Railways Act 1993 and the Transport Act 2000 gave the SRA the power to regulate fares through its franchise agreements with the train operators, where the SRA considered it necessary to ensure that fares were reasonable. Essentially, this covers commuter fares where rail travel has a degree of market power, and elsewhere if necessary to protect the interests of rail users. Thus long-distance Saver leisure fares are regulated.

Just over 40% of passenger fares revenue comes from fares that are regulated by the SRA. Those that are not regulated include all first class fares, off-peak cheap day returns, long-distance open and advance purchase fares, promotional fares and fares which did not exist in February 2003.

Fault Reporting and Monitoring Equipment (FRAME)
A system which records signals and telecommunications faults.

FB
See Rail, bull-head and flat-bottomed.

Exceptional loads
Left:
Carriage of exceptional loads can require a great amount of planning. These examples originated in Cologne and were transported by train ferry from Zeebrugge to Harwich on *Suffolk Ferry*. They then needed to be moved to North Western Gas Board's premises at Warrington. The two ensembles were each 16.94m long, 2.59m wide, and weighed 116 tonnes.
BR/Author's collection

Feasibility study

A structured process that identifies the engineering options and their implications, including economic and environmental issues. It culminates in a feasibility report and a design development (and sometimes an implementation proposal).

Feeder

A transmission line or cable in the power distribution system for bringing a supply of electricity to a substation, connecting a substation or track sectioning cabin to a feeding point, or connecting the running rails to a substation.

Feeder station

A building containing electrical switchgear and equipment for receiving main supplies from the electricity supplier, transforming them and distributing electricity to the overhead line equipment.

Fettling, fettling up

The small scale but regular attention which is needed to keep track formations in full working order. This includes localised lifting, greasing or oiling of joints, keeping nuts tight and clips and pads in place, repacking of ballast and the replacement of any missing components. Such tasks, if not carried out, will only lead to greater problems later.

FFG

See Freight Facilities Grant.

FIAP

See Fares Incentive Adjustment Payment.

Financial period

The railway financial year is divided into 13 four-weekly (28-day) periods running from Sundays to Saturdays, 1 April to 31 March. Minor adjustments are made to period lengths in P1 and/or P13 to fit the calendar precisely. Fares adjustments, timetable changes and statistical results are all tied into the period dates.

Statistical references to Period 5 and so on refer to these periods. The standardised lengths and days of the week makes them more directly comparable one with another than more variable monthly accounting.

First class

Travel in a superior class of accommodation which, as a minimum, offers more legroom and wider seats than that in standard class. Traditionally, first class fares were 50% above ordinary fares for standard class and rarely discounted (as in cheap day tickets), but this is no longer applied anything like so rigorously. On long distance journeys, principal stations may offer first class lounges, while on trains there may be (for instance) meals served at seats or some complementary refreshments. Only trains specifically identified in the timetable offer first class accommodation; previously, it was assumed that all trains did so unless shown as second (now standard) class only.

Passengers travelling standard class may be offered first class travel upgrades at nominal cost outside business times, particularly at weekends.

First filament failure

Lamps in colour light signals have more than one filament, for safety. When the first filament fails, the bulb needs replacing, but the signal still works normally and there is no need to caution trains.

Fishplates

Steel plates, each with four holes, which are used to secure the ends of two rails together in jointed track and form a continuous running surface. Four fishbolts are passed through one fishplate, then through two holes cut in each of the rails to be joined, then another fishplate. The whole is then tightened using special nuts. Fishplates need to be greased regularly to allow for expansion and contraction in hot or cold conditions. The use of long welded rail reduces substantially the need for fishplates.

Fitted

A wagon fitted with the automatic brake, which is controlled from the locomotive, as opposed to brakes on each wagon only, operated by hand. The latter are now virtually extinct. Freight trains may still be referred to as 'fitted', or 'fully fitted'.

Fixed assets

Land, buildings, plant and machinery, rolling stock and other assets that cannot be turned into cash (in contrast to current assets).

Fixed distant

See Signals.

Flange

The extended part of a railway wheel which projects below and inside the running surface of the rail, which enables it to provide the main vehicle guidance system by keeping the wheels on the rails.

Flange lubricator

A device to reduce wear on wheels and rail alike, placed adjacent to the railhead in an area of sharp curves. It is designed to deliver an application of grease in response to the passage of the wheels. However, over-application can cause the train to skid and produce wheel flats.

Flat

See Wheel flat.

Fleet size

The number of passenger vehicles in a fleet is normally divided into type, seating capacity, toilet provision, etc, and may be expressed in terms of the number of units (if applicable) rather than individual vehicles. A distinction needs to be drawn between:
● The number needed to operate the timetabled service plus a judicious spares coverage.

Flyovers and diveunders
The judicious construction of flyovers can much aid rail traffic bottlenecks, in this case at Bishton to carry the up relief across the up and down South Wales main line to the east of Newport. *BR*

- Those which would be available if they were not undergoing scheduled cleaning and light maintenance.
- Those undergoing heavy maintenance or overhaul and hence out of traffic for an extended period.
- Those stopped long term for reasons such as accident damage.

Similar calculations may be made for fleets of locomotives and freight vehicles.

Flighting of trains

The practice of grouping together trains in the timetable which have similar operational characteristics and stopping patterns. This avoids the situation where a faster train tends to catch up the slower one in front and thus itself gets delayed, and leaves a widening gap behind it and the succeeding slower train. Flighting makes the best possible use of available track capacity, but may not be in accord with customer needs.

Floor, on the floor

Railway euphemism for the position of an item of rolling stock which has 'become derailed', an expression which carefully avoids any reference to cause or attribution of blame. It usually refers to a minor incident in a depot or siding.

Flyovers and diveunders

Devices used where one running line needs to cross another and where substantial delays can be avoided by grade separation. Flyovers achieve this by lifting one track and its approaches sufficiently above the level of the other to cross it on a bridge. A variation is the diveunder, where the emphasis is on lowering one track to pass below the other in a short tunnel. The result from the operational point of view is the same. The earliest example is at the south end of Rugby, where the lines via Northampton merge with those direct from Euston.

Footplate staff

Drivers, drivers' assistants and traction trainees, and at one time, firemen.

Formation

1. The levelled and graded bed onto which the track is to be laid, the material between the ballast and the subgrade to either increase or reduce the stiffness of the subgrade, or prevent overstressing.

2. The different types of vehicles from which a train is made up, the order in which they are assembled and which way round they are, or similarly for electric and diesel units. Short formations, where a train has fewer vehicles than it should have, is often expressed as '4 vice 8', if one four-car unit is deputising for two four-car units, and so on.

Foul

Positioned in such a way as to impede normal movement, causing an obstruction.

Fouling point

The point beyond which, on converging lines, rolling stock on one road could foul other stock moving on the converging road, and the clearance for staff is less than the safe minimum.

Four foot

See Track gauge.

FRAME

See Fault Reporting and Monitoring Equipment.

Franchise agreement

An agreement between the SRA or now the DfT and the holder of a franchise, under which the private sector provides specified rail services at agreed quality standards for a defined period of time, and the DfT either makes support payments or receives premiums as a result.

F

The franchise agreements entered into at privatisation were divided into six principal parts, as follows.

Part I Definitions in the agreement and the commencement of the franchise.

Part II Operational requirements during the franchise term.

Part III Financial arrangements between the SRA and the franchise operator.

Part IV Term of the agreement and how it may be terminated early.

Part V A series of obligations which are concerned with the preservation of the franchise business and the protection of successor operators and the SRA.

Part VI General provisions.

Currently, in addition to continuing to list the services to be provided, the agreement relies on a financial model to deal with various changes.

Fraud squad

A colloquial term for groups of staff involved in protecting the railway from loss of revenue through travelling without a ticket. Such staff might descend *en masse* on a particular station, or on a train, and carry out a comprehensive ticket check on all passengers.

Freight

A term for goods which came to Britain relatively late for land transport, although long established for shipping and air. Nowadays in general use for movements by rail, especially for containers and other traffics where speed is seen as an important attribute. The term freight also refers to the charges made for its carriage.

Freight terminal loop
A quick and easy means of emptying the contents of a hopper wagon is to use gravity, as here at Hayes, Middlesex, in Tarmac's delightfully named 'unloading house'. *Ian Allan Library*

Freight grants

Introduced originally under the Railways Act 1974, Government grants are provided to reflect the benefits derived from society in general in transferring freight from road to more environmentally friendly modes such as rail. There are three grants applicable to rail:

● **Freight Facilities Grant (FFG)** This is awarded to the providers of terminals, wagons, material handling machinery or other equipment that is necessary to achieve modal shift to rail. Typically, the grant provides around 2/3 of the total cost of such facilities thereby levering in significant private investment.

● **Track Access Grant (TAG)** Awarded to freight operating companies (FOCs) to offset the cost of access to the network for unprofitable flows.

● **Company Neutral Revenue Support Grant (CNRS)** Designed to replace TAG for certain intermodal traffic flows, eg for containers to ports. It is paid retrospectively for each unit carried. Unlike TAG, it is paid retrospectively to the person who takes the risk on the flow concerned which may be the FOC, or it could be another operator.

Freight grants are presently suspended.

Freight multiple-unit (FMU), or Cargosprinter

The use of two power units (Multi-purpose vehicles or MPVs) to 'top-and-tail' freight-carrying vehicles in a fixed formation train. The MPVs are wired together through the train so that the whole can operate as a multiple-unit and thus reverse direction without a locomotive run round. A typical composition might be (say) eight wagons carrying (for instance) containers or timber. Another possible use is for engineering purposes such as weed control by spraying.

Freight terminal loop

The freight terminal loop enables a train to be completely turned while on the premises, so that it is able to return whence it came without intervention for remarshalling. This is a feature provided at most coal-fired power stations from the 1960s-era onwards, and saves both locomotive work and train crew time. The method is also used by Eurotunnel for its shuttle operations.

Freight traffic

Around 1,600 freight trains operate every day in Britain, of which approximately 10 travel through the Channel Tunnel to and from the Continent. Traffic consists of bulk products such as coal, iron ore, petroleum and aggregates, through to manufactured goods such as steel, mineral water and finished cars. Many deep sea shipping lines rely on rail for moving large volumes of containers to and from the ports. In Britain, there is a network of over 1,000 rail freight terminals.

Fringe box

The first signalbox beyond the boundary of a signalling control centre, which acts at the interface with the mechanical system.

Full Crew Diagrams

Staff diagrams where the driver and guard (or conductor etc) stay together throughout their respective shifts. This contains the problems if services are running out of course, such as one train being ready to leave, but no guard available, while another has no driver. While this doesn't solve the difficulty of the train with no staff, it does stop the effects spreading.

Fully allocated costs

The distribution of all costs incurred between the various parts of the business, for instance station operating costs between the train operating companies using it.

FURNO

Term retained from the former telegraphic code with an obvious derivation, meaning 'Until Further Notice'.

Gangway

The flexible structure at vehicle ends providing access between adjacent coaches, which is usually but not always open for public use and may be used when the train is in motion. Hence a gangwayed as opposed to a non-gangwayed vehicle. Vehicles can also be gangwayed at one end only, particularly multiple-units where there is a driving cab at the other end. These will be gangwayed within the unit only.

Gantry

See Signal gantry.

Gantry crane

See Container handling.

Gap

1. An interruption in the continuity of the conductor rail on third rail systems, caused by points or otherwise. The conductor rail will resume on the other side of the track, but there may be considerable gaps at complex junctions.
2. That between the train and a platform, a particular problem when the latter is curved and the distance can become that much greater. Hence 'Mind the gap'.

Gapping

On third rail systems only, the unfortunate albeit rare occurrence if all the pick-up shoes of a train become totally isolated from any conductor rail supply. This has the result of the train being devoid of power and unable to move, unless its own momentum can take it forward. This emphasises the importance of care in conductor rail placement.

Gardening activities

Railway slang for engineering works, especially major possessions.

Gate box

Usually a former signalbox, which is now responsible only for the control of the gates or barriers at a level crossing and the immediate protecting signals.

Gauge capability

A measurement of the length of route which is capable of accepting different freight vehicle types and loads by reference to size. There are five gauge bands on Network Rail lines and the route km cleared for each are as follows:

Band	Height	Width	Description	Route km	
W6A	3338mm	2600mm	standard freight vehicles	4,955	
W7	3531mm	2438mm	8ft container gauge	2,794	(also W6A)
W8	3618mm	2600mm	8ft 6in container gauge	5.648	
W9	3695mm	2600mm	swap body gauge	1,714	
W10	3900mm	2500mm	9ft 6in container gauge	6	(also W6A)
W10	3900mm	2500mm	9ft 6in container gauge	60	(also W8)
W10	3900mm	2500mm	9ft 6in container gauge	939	(also W9)
Total, Network Rail, March 2005				16,116	

Note that the dimensions associated with each band do not necessarily include bands lower down the scale. Thus while a W10 height is greater than W9, the width is less, hence the notes on the right of the column. There are no route km which accept W7 or W10 gauge only.

Gauge corner cracking

Gauge corner cracking of rails is a type of rolling contact fatigue, and was the cause of the Hatfield derailment. It is the result of excessive contact stresses at the wheel/rail interface, which in turn produces deformities in the structure of the rail near its surface. This interaction of forces is determined by the vehicle (wheelsets and their support), the track (rails and their support), and operators (who determine the speed, traffic density, and station stopping patterns). In turn, these are the responsibilities of ROSCOs (mostly), Network Rail, and the TOCs plus the freight companies. A total railway system approach is needed to overcome it, since the maintenance of a satisfactory wheel/rail interface is a fundamental requirement for any railway.

Gauge, structures and vehicles

1. Structure gauge

The structure gauge is the boundary enclosing the clearances required outside the swept envelope to enable the railway to be operated in safety. The structure gauge should include provision for staff safety, where staff are permitted on the railway while trains are running. It forms the 'envelope' between which train profiles must fit.

2. Static vehicle profile

The profile formed by the maximum permitted cross-sectional dimensions of vehicles and, where applicable, their loads when at rest on straight and level track. It should take into account allowances for tolerances in the manufacture of the vehicles and the effects of vehicle loading on the suspension. It thus defines the maximum profile to which railway vehicles can be built in terms of dimensions of height and width, and then loaded, without risk of striking a lineside structure. This includes tunnels, overbridges, retaining walls, station platforms, underbridge parapets and girders, and signal posts.

3. Dynamic vehicle profile

This is the static profile enlarged to allow for the maximum possible displacement of the vehicle at rest or in motion, with respect to the rails on straight track. It should take into account vehicle suspension characteristics including body tilting where provided, and allowances for tolerances in the maintenance of vehicles, including wear. The effects of end-throw and centre-throw of vehicles on curved track are not included and are disregarded in the development of the dynamic vehicle profile.

4. Kinematic envelope

The increasing speed of trains over the years has resulted in the need for a more advanced concept of the space which a train occupies. This is the kinematic envelope, defined as the volume of space swept by a train in motion. The dynamic vehicle profile is enlarged to allow for the permitted tolerances in track gauge, alignment, level and cross level and the dynamic and static effects of track wear. The effects of end-throw and centre-throw of vehicles on curved track are not included, and are disregarded in the development of the kinematic envelope.

5. Swept envelope

The swept envelope is the kinematic envelope enlarged to allow for the effects of vertical and horizontal curvature, including centre- and end-throw of vehicles, and the super-elevation applied to the track. The swept envelope may be defined separately for each structure or for sections of the route and should take account of all railway vehicles using the line.

Gauge, track

See Track gauge, Track gauge widening

Gauntleted, or interlaced, track

Gauntleted track is found where a double track railway encounters a width obstruction at track level, sufficient to require the inner rail of each track to cross that of the other for such distance as necessary, before recrossing and resuming its normal position. It is very rare in the UK, but an example can be seen on Croydon Tramlink, on the Wimbledon side of Mitcham tram stop. Interlacing here avoided the problems caused by the reinforcement of the cutting sides to shore up buildings, following a partial cutting collapse. The technique allows the lines to remain separate and without the moving parts associated with pointwork, but the signalling must still prevent more than one train (or tram) being on the interlaced section at any one time. Another reason is to provide corner clearance for wagons under a particularly restrictive overhead structure, such as a bridge arch.

GDP

See Gross Domestic Product.

GEOGraphic Information System (GEOGIS)

A major database of railway infrastructure assets owned by Network Rail, containing information on the physical locations, age, construction and ownership of track, buildings and structures.

GEMINI

A system linking the equivalent of PROMISE that had been a stand-alone system to the real time date in TRUST. It is used for resource control for multiple-unit trains. As GEMINI had twin data inputs, the zodiac sign for 'the twins' was adopted.

Georgemas Plunger

A device enabling the train driver to operate the points at Georgemas Junction, an isolated junction on the Far North line where the lines to Wick and Thurso divide.

Global System for Mobile communications – Railways (GSM-R)

This is the European standard for railway communications. It is designed to support all radio applications required for railway operations, including speech, data and control communications. Completion of implementation in Britain is anticipated for 2012. GSM-R offers:

- A fast set-up time of a few seconds for emergency calls.
- Functional addressing — a train can be called up by its running number.
- Location dependent addressing – the driver does not need to know the signaller's phone number; the system will forward the call to the right signaller.
- Group and broadcast calls – use of the driver's red emergency call button will mean other trains in the area will hear the call, and the signaller can address all trains in an area.
- GSM-R is also the bearer for the European Train Control System. GSM-R will be usable by all staff through portable and mobile units, and a terminal in every signalbox.

GLW

See Gross laden weight.

Golden assets

Railway infrastructure which has the greatest potential impact on train performance.

Goods

The traditional English term for commodities carried by train, implicitly at relatively slow speeds. Often subdivided by category, eg merchandise, coal, coke, steel, cement, cattle, chemicals, etc. Hence goods train, goods depot etc. Now mostly displaced by freight.

Goods brake van

A vehicle designed to allow a hand brake or (where applicable) the train brake to be operated by the guard.

Goods line
One which is signalled permissively as opposed to absolute block. Permissive working allows more than one train to occupy a section under defined circumstances, and goods lines are consequently not available for use by passenger trains.

Grade separation
See Flyovers and diveunders.

Gradient
The rate at which a railway track rises or falls in relation to the horizontal. 1 in 200 indicates a vertical change in the level of one unit of length along a stretch of line 200 units long. Expressed as a percentage, this is 0.5%. To eliminate the decimal point usually associated with railway gradients, this may be expressed as 'per thousand' rather than 'per cent'. Thus, 1 in 200 becomes 5‰.

Gradient post
Posts at the side of the track at points where gradients change. These show the gradient, expressed as 1 in 200 (or as appropriate) by means of arms attached to the post. These arms are inclined in the upward or downward direction as necessary. The other possible indication is Level, in which case the arm is horizontal.

Great Western Main Line (GWML)
The main line from London Paddington to Reading, Didcot and South Wales as far as Swansea, the line to Bath and Bristol and thence to Taunton, Exeter, Plymouth and Penzance, and the cut-off from Reading to Taunton via Westbury. It is electrified only between Paddington and Heathrow Airport Junction, a distance of 11 miles, for use by Heathrow Express and Heathrow Connect trains.

Green Card
1. The green defective wagon label, which is put on a wagon which needs attention but is considered fit to travel, with limitations such as maximum speed or to a workshop only. See also Red Card.
2. A Green Card employee who is deemed unfit for his or her previous duties and provided with lighter work.

Green to green time
Time which elapses between a train passing a signal at green until the signal again shows green for the next train.

Green Zone working
An area of protection for trackside workers, which separates work on the line from train movements (other than engineering trains or similar at slow speed). The simplest way of creating such a zone is to stop all trains on all lines at the location concerned.

Grid supply points
There were 112 grid supply points in 2004, where power from the National Grid and distribution network operator is made available.

Gross Domestic Product (GDP) deflator
This is a price index applied to the gross domestic product to eliminate the effects of inflation.

Gross laden weight (GLW)
The weight of a wagon (in tonnes) when loaded to the maximum permissible, including the weight of the wagon itself. This is important in terms of the need to cross load bearing structures en route and any restrictions thereto, and also in the ability of the locomotive to haul (and brake) the loaded train.

Ground frame
A small lever frame, sometimes open to the elements, which controls train movements not directly connected to or operated from a signalbox. The levers may be remotely locked and unlocked by the signaller or, on single lines where reversal is necessary, by a key attached to the train staff. There are examples of this at Bere Alston (Devon) and Bourne End (Bucks). More modern installations may have a miniature switch panel.

Ground disc
See Signals.

GSM-R
See Global System for Mobile communications – Railways.

Guard
Where provided, the guard is the staff member in charge of the train and responsible for the passengers. It is the guard who gives the driver the authority to start from a station.

Guard boards
Used on conductor rail systems and a nominal 175mm in height, these boards may be found wherever staff regularly have a need to be alongside the electrified line. Their purpose is to prevent inadvertent contact.

GWML
See Great Western Main Line.

GWR (Great Western Railway)
See Railways Act 1921.

Ground frame
A ground frame to change the points and a token machine at Bourne End station, the intermediate point on the Maidenhead-Marlow branch, where trains need to reverse. The track diagram, which shows the two station platforms, but from which only one train can proceed to Marlow (centre bottom) is just visible. It is photographed on 6 November 1998. *John Glover*

Half-life refurbishment
Opportunity for a rebuild or replacement of major vehicle sub-systems, also known as mid-life overhaul. This may include complete refits of the passenger accommodation. Rail vehicle life is generally assumed to be about 30 years, so half-life refurbishment will take place around 15 years from new. However, it does imply the extended absence of successive vehicles from the operational fleet until the work is complete, for which some form of cover will be required.

Halt
Term used for a station which has probably never been staffed, often with a short platform only, probably with minimal custom and with little potential for more. The word 'halt' has been expunged from station names over the years, but there remain a number of locations where such a term would be appropriate. Trains are likely to stop by request only, from a hand signal by a passenger waiting on the platform, or by the passenger advising the guard if he wishes to alight. A variation still sometimes found but not for public use is Staff Halt, at (for example) Hoo Junction and Durnsford Road, Wimbledon.

Hand signalling
If all else fails . . . Where necessary, resort must be made to this most basic means of signalling with flags, or lamps at night. This usually comes about as a result of extensive power signalling failures, or planned engineering occupations. However, this assumes that there are sufficient competent staff to be able to do this, let alone sufficient flags!

Handlamp
An electric or other approved hand-held lamp which, when alight or switched on, is capable of displaying a red, yellow or green aspect, in addition to a white light.

Hazard
A situation with the potential to cause harm including human injury, damage to property, plant or equipment, damage to the environment, or economic loss.

Hazardous substances
See Dangerous goods.

Head-span or cross-span wire
A wire stretched across the tracks between two support masts and holding the overhead line equipment in the desired position.

Headshunt
A length of track which allows shunting movements between sidings to be made without obstructing other lines, particularly the running lines.

Headstock
See Buffer beam.

Headway
The minimum interval permitted between successive trains on a particular section of track, measured in minutes (and fractions of minutes). The minimum headways are likely to be achieved when all trains have similar operational characteristics and the same stopping patterns. Limiting factors on the headway achievable include the signal spacing and train speed, but also a host of other factors including the time taken by passengers to board and alight at stations. Hence the use of whistles, to hurry them up!

Heavy rail
Rail mode with capacity for heavy volume of traffic, characterised by high speed and rapid acceleration, with a separate right of way from which all other vehicles are excluded. There is a sophisticated signalling system. The term heavy rail is used internationally to distinguish the main line railway systems from the more specialised and slightly lighter metro systems such as London Underground, and light rail as in Manchester Metrolink, Sheffield Supertram, Midland Metro and similar.

Heritage railways
Heritage railways are those which have retained or have assumed the character, appearance and operating practices of former times. It is a general term applied to preserved railways, but also and more loosely to some lines on the national system. They are likely to be minor lines of some historical or other note; perhaps their architecture has survived and is still in good condition.

Heritage trains
A relatively recent term which has grown up to describe locomotives and rolling stock old enough for

Halt
Unfortunately, the diminutive Durnsford Road halt for Wimbledon Train Care depot is situated on the up fast line; consequently the services it receives are somewhat limited. Early morning up local trains call there, subsequently weaving across the down fast to the up slow line. It was photographed on 19 March 2005. *John Glover*

somebody to want to preserve, largely irrespective it would seem of any intrinsic merit, other than longevity. Such trains may still be running on the national system, but are usually not so described until approaching the end of their days.

Hi-Vi
High visibility jackets, the wearing of which is mandatory at all times for those working on or about the track. Coloured orange, they include reflective strips front and back to aid the ability of train drivers and others to see the individual in the dark.

High hazard fault
One where the consequences are potentially very serious, specifically the loss of train detection by the signalling system so the train effectively ceases to exist, or obscured signals so that they cannot be seen properly by a train driver.

High Level Output Specification (HLOS)
This is the Government's statement of the required railway industry outputs and the amount of funding that is available to meet them. The first HLOS is to be published by the Department for Transport by June 2007. A similar document, covering Scotland, will be issued by the Scottish Executive.

Should the assessed costs of meeting the requirements fall short of the funding available, the Office of Rail Regulation will need to determine which part of the outputs should be achieved and, by implication, where any necessary economies will be made.

The present Control Period for Track Access Charges lasts until March 2009, the following period (CP4) being from April 2009 to March 2014.

High Speed Diesel Train (HSDT, HST IC125)
When the Advanced Passenger Train project seemed to be getting nowhere and the outlook for large scale electrification was bleak, the 125mph HST was the engineers' answer for a diesel train which made the most out of existing technology. Introduced in 1975, over the years the HST fleet of 99 complete trains provided the majority of InterCity services on the Great Western, the East Coast (pre-electrification), the Midland and CrossCountry main lines. The twin power cars of each set were partnered with the newly developed 23m MkIII coaches of fully integral construction, which performed equally impressively. The whole train, from concept to execution, was one of the British Railways Board's greatest achievements. Much of the fleet remains operational 30 years on.

Hose
A flexible pipe used to make compressed air connections between vehicles as part of the braking system, or similar for other purposes elsewhere.

Hot axlebox, hot box
Description of an axlebox on a railway vehicle which has become overheated and in extreme conditions may catch fire. This can be caused by lack of lubrication, the ingress of dirt, or overloading the vehicle. It may be necessary to remove the vehicle from the train at the earliest opportunity or, at best, to continue at reduced speed.

Hot axlebox detector
Lineside apparatus mounted on a sleeper which, by infra-red radiation, detects actual and incipient hot boxes, transmitting the information to a VDU in the controlling signalbox. The equipment, using lineside scanners, can differentiate between left and right journals of wheelsets, detect more than one box running warm on one wagon, count the number of axles on a train and identify the position of hot boxes.

Hot standby
Having a fully crewed train, which is not scheduled to perform any revenue-earning work, ready and available to respond to any service disruption by being slotted into an existing diagram.

HSDT, HST
See High Speed Diesel Train.

Hump shunting
Now obsolete in Britain, this was the method used in the large 1950s marshalling yards, where a shunting locomotive propelled uncoupled wagons over a (usually artificial) hump so that they ran down the other side under gravity into a number of sorting sidings. However, 'Not to be hump shunted' is an instruction still to be seen on some rolling stock deemed unsuitable for this treatment, snow ploughs being one such type.

Hunting
Continuous side-to-side oscillation of the wheels/bogies of a rail vehicle, caused by the forces acting between the wheels and rails. Such 'hunting' occurs only above critical speeds of somewhere around 30mph, below which the swaying and rolling movements are determined by track features. Four-wheeled freight vehicles were particularly prone to this problem, suffering a number of derailments in the 1960s. Following this, speed limits were lowered substantially. The solution was found in the complete redesign of suspension systems. With passenger stock, the problem was more the low quality of ride for the passenger.

Hypothecation
The collection of taxes from a particular source, which are then applied directly to a specified expenditure heading. UK Governments have always resisted such direct links, on the grounds that taxation is Government income, for the Government to spend as it so decides. However, road Congestion Charges introduced under the Greater London Authority Act 1999 and Transport Act 2000 are examples of hypothecated charges.

IC125
See High Speed Diesel Train.

IECC
See Integrated Electronic Control Centre.

Immunisation
The protection of the signalling and communication systems from interference by high voltage electric currents in the traction power systems.

Impedance bond
A track bond which allows traction currents to flow freely, while impeding track circuit currents. Effectively, this allows a return path for traction currents, while still allowing the track to be sectioned for track circuit protection of trains.

Implementation
The undertaking of physical works to deliver the detailed design.

In advance, in rear
These terms are used to describe the physical position of signals in relation to a given location of a train. 'In advance' means the next to be encountered by the train, 'in rear' means the last. In all cases, the normal direction of travel is assumed. May also be used in multiple as in 'three (signals) in advance' when referring, perhaps, to the location of a failed train.

In house
A term referring to the performance of work by the company itself, rather than the alternative of putting it out to a third party to perform.

In advance, in rear
(illustration of terms used in the entry) Network Rail

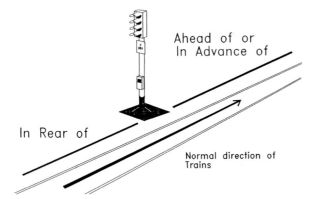

Ahead of or
In Advance of

In Rear of

Normal direction of
Trains

"AHEAD OF" or "IN ADVANCE OF" AND "IN REAR OF"

"Ahead of" or "In Advance of" and "In Rear of" must always be considered in relation to the normal direction in which trains run. (i.e. a location which a train has yet to pass is <u>Ahead of</u> or <u>in Advance of it</u> and a location which it has passed is <u>in Rear of it</u>. If you are looking at the front of a signal, you are <u>in Rear of it</u>. If you can only see the back of the signal you are <u>Ahead of</u> or <u>in Advance of it</u>.

Incident
An unplanned and uncontrolled event which, under different circumstances, could have resulted in an accident. The word 'incident' is also commonly used as a euphemism for an accident in public statements.

Indirect costs
Costs which cannot be directly related to an activity and which do not vary with output. Many infrastructure costs are of this nature, although they may not be charged in this way.

Inflation
A process of steadily rising prices which leads to a reduction in the purchasing power of a given amount of money.

Infrastructure
Works, plant and equipment used for the operation of a railway including its permanent way, and plant and equipment used for signalling or exclusively for supplying electricity for operational purposes to the railway, but it does not include a station. It refers to track, structures supporting it, signalling, and fixed electrical plant such as feeders, switchgear, substations and the like.

Infrastructure services
Services provided by FOCs for Network Rail to enable maintenance and renewals of the network to be undertaken. This includes the movement of ballast to and from engineering sites and the transport of specialist equipment for use in such operations.

Injury
Any physical damage or harm to a person reported at the time and place of occurrence, whether or not requiring medical treatment. For employees, an injury includes those resulting in time lost from duty.

Inland port
Rail freight interchange used as a destination for trunk flows from a port. This reduces exposure to port charges and congestion, while increasing speed of response by locating goods closer to their final destination. Some are inland clearance depots, from which containers for international traffic are despatched sealed without further examination, having been passed as such by Customs Officers. This covers also the import of sealed containers, which then undergo Customs examination at the inland location.

Inside (a signal)
A train standing beyond a signal, maybe only marginally so, but thus under its protection.

Insulated rail joints
Provided on track circuited lines so that while rails are joined physically, they remain electrically separate. Nowadays, jointless track circuits are also possible, although not achievable in all situations.

Insulator
Material which offers extremely high resistance to the passage of electricity. It is used for separating live equipment from dead or earthed equipment, or for separating live equipment from other live equipment.

Integrated Control Centre
The co-location of TOC control managers, those of track operator Network Rail, and their respective teams, with all being overseen by a single manager. The intention is that decisions can be made more or less instantaneously, including during major incidents, with the aim of reducing delays overall and providing a more efficient service to users.

Integrated Electronic Control Centre (IECC)
A power signalling centre where all data displays, safety interlockings, etc are computer controlled. Under normal circumstances, trains are signalled automatically in accordance with the timetable which has been incorporated into the database. This uses the TRUST system identities. Signallers only intervene by exception.

Integrated public transport
See public transport, integration.

Interchange
The act of changing between trains, or between a train and any other mode of transport. For this to be successful, various conditions are necessary. These include clear signing and information systems, sufficient time, distances to be covered not excessive, and some back-up to cover what happens when things go wrong such as late running. It is helpful if the passenger already holds the necessary tickets for the entire journey, where this is possible.

InterCity 125
See High Speed Diesel Train.

Interlaced track
See Gauntleted, or interlaced, track.

Interlocking
See Locking and interlocking.

Intermediate block section
This is a means of adding to the number of block sections (and hence line capacity) by the subdivision of an existing one. Additional signallers are not required.

A track-circuited section of line is provided between the section signal and the intermediate block home signal, both of which are worked from the same (absolute block) signalbox. The intermediate block home signal controls exit from the intermediate block section and also the entrance into the block section ahead.

Intermodal freight
The carriage of goods between origin and destination using two or more forms of transport, with interchange

managed to ensure the maximum advantage in time, cost, efficiency and environmental factors. An example is the use of rail transport in connection with a deep sea voyage.

Intermodal operations
Those in which the freight is placed in a load-carrying 'box', which itself is designed to be carried by more than one transport mode. Transfer between modes at terminals is undertaken typically by an overhead crane. The main types of unit are:

- Containers. Used primarily for deep sea shipment, they are lifted from their top corners ('top lift').
- Swap bodies. Used mainly for road, rail and barge shipment in Europe, most are fitted with pockets along their bottom edge ('bottom lift').
- Piggyback trailers. Road-going semi-trailers, capable of being lifted onto railway wagons as with swap bodies.
- Bimodal trailers. Specialist road trailers which can convert to railway wagons.

Interchange
Top: Interchange need not imply a large facility; this simple shelter with a marked bay for a bus is deemed adequate at Ellesmere Port, Cheshire, seen on 2 May 1999. *John Glover*

Above: National Rail and London Underground meet at London Victoria, but this is only the District/Circle and the Victoria lines. The bus station is immediately behind the camera, this being the busiest interchange of bus and rail of all the London termini. This view is dated 19 January 2001. *John Glover*

International passenger services
The Channel Tunnel Rail Link (CTRL) required much new construction or, as here, reconstruction. This is the resuscitated former branch from Southfleet Junction to Fawkham Junction, which will no longer be needed when the whole of the CTRL is open for traffic and international trains are diverted to St Pancras. The location is the railway bridge over the B260 road near Longfield station in January 2001. *John Glover*

International passenger services

International passenger trains are licensed by the International Rail Regulator (IRR). The duties and offices of the IRR are combined with the ORR but are legally distinct. The Chairman of the ORR holds both offices.

Interval

The actual difference in the times at which successive trains pass a fixed point. On systems where all trains have a similar performance and stopping pattern, the interval is often expressed in terms of 'x' trains per hour (tph).

Invitation to tender

A collection of documents issued to one or more potential suppliers (for instance, of franchised passenger rail services) to invite commercial bids to undertake specified tasks, under such conditions as the contracting body may determine.

Island platform

An island platform is one placed between the pair of running lines, with all passenger access being by footbridge or subway (or very occasionally by crossing the track).

Isolation

Electrical equipment is said to be isolated (and thus made safe) when it is disconnected from any source of electricity supply. However, when a section of line is isolated electrically, it is not blocked, since diesel trains can still run and electric trains can coast for considerable distances without power.

Isolator (or disconnector)

A piece of electrical equipment for disconnecting one section of equipment from another. May also be used to earth a piece of equipment.

Jarrah, Karri

Extremely hard-wearing Australian woods, used for wooden sleepers and nowadays particularly for switch and crossing work.

Joint line

A line which was vested in the ownership of two or more railway companies, giving them both rights of access. The principle extended to complete railway companies, such as the Midland & Great Northern Joint, and the Somerset & Dorset Joint, both now closed. Should the vertical integration of railways again be considered, the access arrangements of the early years of the 20th century would merit careful consideration.

Jointed track

Track which has not been continuously welded, and which retains the traditional lengths of 60ft rail as rolled, although these may on occasion be 45ft or 30ft.

Journal

The part of the axle which rests on the bearings inside the axlebox.

Juice, juice rail

Railway slang for traction current and conductor rail, respectively.

Jumper

1. An insulated flexible cable connecting the circuits of one vehicle to the circuits of another.
2. Slang expression (also jump squad) for travelling ticket inspectors, either singly or *en masse*, from their propensity to jump onto trains immediately before departure when there is no escape for those without tickets. See also Fraud squad.
3. Slang for suicides.

Junction

The place of convergence of two or more lines and named, as in Trent Valley Junction (Rugby) other than at locations within station limits or similar. The term junction is commonly (and variously) abbreviated to Jnc, Jcn or Jn. There are still several stations incorporating the word in their titles (eg Clapham Junction), although the practice is diminishing. Thus there is but one such station now in Scotland and three in Wales.

Junction indicators

Whereas a semaphore installation will display separate signals on a bracket for two diverging routes, with the height of each post indicating the principal and subsidiary one, only one colour light signal head is used. This is topped with a junction indicator, sometimes known as a 'feather', in which rows of five white lights are inclined to an angle of 45°, 90° or 135° to the left or the right as appropriate. This will indicate to the driver the route which has been set up by the signaller and is in addition to the normal signal indications.

Other commonly used indicators are those outside large stations, where the normal signal is supplemented by an illuminated number (a theatre-type indicator), showing the driver into which platform the train is being signalled. For departing trains, it might show FL for fast line, or as appropriate. For visibility reasons, these are used only in relatively low speed areas.

Junction margin
In timetable compilation, the amount of time to be allowed between conflicting moves to ensure that the second train is not delayed.

Karri
See Jarrah.

Key
The wedge made of wood or spring steel used to secure bull-head rail in place, in the chair in which it sits.

Key Performance Indicators (KPI)
These attempt to measure progress over time in matters deemed to be important and to meet business objectives. By such means, it is intended to focus the efforts of individuals or teams, and comparisons may be undertaken at local, regional, national or even wider levels. However, they do need to be used with caution. If a KPI is set to measure percentage improvement from one period to the next, those already performing very well will score badly on this index. A very different result will be achieved if the KPI is measured in physical terms, such as failures per track km.

Kinematic envelope
See Gauge, structures and vehicles.

Kiss-and-ride
Rather than leaving the car in a station car park (see Park-and-ride), the alternative is for somebody else to drive the passenger to the station, and then drive the car away. This has become known as kiss-and-ride. While there is no need to accommodate the vehicle during the passenger's absence by the provision of parking spaces, it can create quite severe problems of traffic congestion in the evening, when a number of cars are milling around the station forecourt and waiting for the trains with those to be collected on their return.

Kissing
The act of two railway vehicles being pushed together gently, so that their buffers just touch, or kiss.

Knitting
See Overhead line equipment.

Knocking out
Slang term for giving the 'Train out of Section' signal (2-1) on the signalling system block bells.

KPI
See Key Performance Indicators.

Ladder junction
A series of facing, or trailing, crossovers in a multiple track setting, by the use of which trains can cross the entire layout or such part of it as they need. Thus with a six-track layout (down/up branch, down/up slow, down/up main), it will take four crossovers to move from the down main to the down branch thus:
● down main to up slow
● up slow to down slow
● down slow to up branch and
● up branch to down branch.

Lamp iron
A bracket to be found on the ends of rail vehicles on which can be placed a battery electric lamp to provide a tail light. Used if the built-in tail light system fails due to loss of power, for whatever reason.

Land use planning
Local authority control of development which affects (for instance) rail freight through control over the location of ports, terminals, warehousing and distribution facilities. It can also promote the re-use of brownfield sites and protect greenfield sites. Land use policies can put a new station next to new and relatively high-density housing for the labour force. Development planning has considerable implications for the railway in constraining or promoting rail network capacity.

Last mile cost
Normally taken to mean the cost of the road journey between the origin of a freight cargo movement and the first intermodal terminal, plus the cost of road transfer between the destination intermodal terminal and the customer's premises, ie excluding the rail (or rail plus sea) transit. Confusingly, it is sometimes used to mean the cost of the transfer from the destination terminal to the customer's premises, plus that of the next movement away from those premises.

Lead time
The time between a decision being taken to proceed with a certain project, and that which must elapse (for perhaps a whole range of reasons) before that project comes to fruition.

Leading end
The front end of a train in the direction of travel.

L

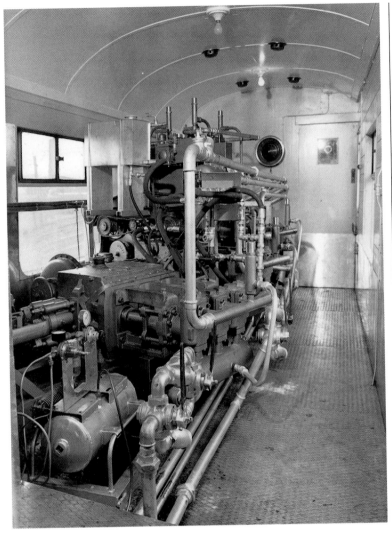

Leaf fall season

The period in the autumn of roundly five weeks when leaves fall, causing problems of low adhesion for trains. Train wheels crush the leaves into a sticky mulch, which seriously reduces the coefficient of friction. Various remedial measures, such as the application of Sandite, have proved only partially effective. High-pressure hoses are another solution. The main problem is that acceleration and, particularly, braking take much longer if wheel burn or wheel flats are to be avoided. Special timetables are sometimes put into force, especially where heavy gradients are also involved such as in the Chilterns. Leaf residues can also cause problems in the operation of track circuits.

Left-hand running

The system used for railways in Britain from the beginning, in which trains keep to the left-hand running track. It is also found in many overseas countries like France, where the early railways at least were built by British engineers. Left-hand running is also found in many Commonwealth countries.

Level crossings

The crossing of a railway and a road at the same level, ie not grade separated. Level crossings fall into a number of categories based on the provision of gates, lifting barriers, traffic lights or nothing at all, how these are worked and by whom, or automatically, the responsibilities of the various parties involved for safe use, the types of visual and audible warnings given to users, and the degree of protection provided.

● *Manually controlled gate (MCG)*
  (number = 264, line speed up to 125mph)
  Access is protected by the presence of gates. As the train approaches, a railway employee will close the gates across the road and clear protecting signals to

Leaf fall season
Above: Weedkilling trains have long been a feature of the network. This apparatus is installed in a former passenger vehicle, which patrols the railway and spray chemicals from on-board tanks to keep the vegetation under control. *Ian Allan Library*

Level Crossings
Right: The provision of tell-tale bells hung from a pair of stanchions is an inexpensive method of reinforcing the electrification message on the sign at the roadside that the height limit in this case is 16ft 3in. Overhead electrification is a less obvious obstruction than an overbridge. The location is East Gate Junction, Colchester. In this 1959 view, the signalbox name sign can just be seen from that part of the box which protrudes from behind the house. This provides a good observation point for the signaller when closing the gates to road traffic. *BR*

Left: The traditional hand operated gates are being opened here to road traffic at the end of the station platform at Wedgwood, Staffordshire, following departure of a train towards Stoke-on-Trent. As can be seen, gate closure does not prevent passenger access to the platform. *John Glover*

Below: Full lifting barriers are provided here, at Ferry Road, Rye, East Sussex, seen on 29 May 1999. The red lights are flashing and the second set of barriers is falling. The first set, on the left side of the road on which vehicles approach, falls first, followed by the second set immediately afterwards, but giving a short period of grace to allow any vehicle which has stopped on the crossing to drive clear. *John Glover*

allow the train to pass over the crossing. The gates will then be closed across the railway line to allow the free flow of road traffic to resume.

- *Manually controlled barrier (MCB)*
  (number = 242, line speed up to 125mph)
  Crossings protected by barriers, across both carriageways of the road, and operated by a railway employee. The operation of the barriers, road traffic light signals and audible warning devices is interlocked into the signalling system. Typically, the crossing operator would be situated within a 50m clear view distance of the crossing.

- *Manually controlled barrier protected by closed circuit television (MCB-CCTV)*
  (number = 358, line speed up to 125mph)
  Similar to the manually controlled barrier crossing. The only difference is that the railway employee uses the CCTV system to monitor and control the operation.

- *Automatic half-barrier (AHB)*
  (number = 470, line speed up to 100mph)
  Access prevented by means of two half-barriers that block the flow of road traffic, but not the exits. This leaves an escape route for trapped motorists. The primary protection is a combination of road traffic light signals, audible warning devices and the half-barriers. The operation of the lights and

Right: Not all level crossings carry road traffic. This is the scene at the CCTV controlled Poole High Street crossing to the east of the station from the adjacent footbridge, on 7 October 2000, shortly after the barriers had been raised. Road vehicles are now barred during shopping hours. Although the footbridge is always available, it is noticeable that few pedestrians can be bothered to use it, even though the barriers can be lowered for a considerable time if trains are passing in both directions. *John Glover*

L

sirens followed by the barriers is initiated automatically as the train approaches (a constant warning time for road users is a function of using predictor technology). The barriers are raised automatically when the train has passed, unless there is another train approaching that would arrive within the minimum road opening time of ten seconds. The crossing equipment is supervised from a manned location. Telephones are provided for public use and connected to the supervising point.

● *Automatic barrier crossing locally monitored (ABCL) (number = 45, line speed up to 55mph)* Similar to AHBs (ie half barriers, telephone), but monitored by the train driver.

● *Automatic open crossing, remotely monitored (AOCR) (number = 1, line speed up to 55mph)* No barrier protection. Warnings to road vehicles and pedestrians are by road traffic light signals and an audible signal. The warning sequence is initiated automatically by the approach of a train and stops when the train has passed clear of the crossing. The equipment is monitored remotely. Telephones connected to the monitoring point are available for the crossing user.

● *Automatic open crossing, locally monitored (AOCL) (number = 140, line speed up to 55mph)* Similar for road users as the AOCR type. The main difference is that there is no provision of a telephone for the crossing user, with monitoring of the crossing equipment left to the train driver. If another train is following, the lights will continue to flash after the passage of the first train, an additional signal will light up to show the approach of another train and the tone of the audible warning will change.

● *User-worked crossings.* All user-worked crossings with vehicular rights are private and only for authorised persons, but in some cases, there is public access by footpaths and/or bridleways.

● *User-worked crossing protected by miniature warning lights (UWC-MWL) (number = 155, line speed up to 125mph)* Gates or full lifting barriers and miniature warning lights warn the user of an approaching train. These lights may be either red and green or a pair of red lights, the operation of which is linked to the signalling system.

All the above crossing types are described as active because the level crossing user is made aware of the presence of a train. All types that follow are described as passive (total, excluding footpath crossings = 3,967) as the level crossing user is responsible for detecting the presence of an approaching train.

● *User-worked crossings (UWC) (number = 2,290, line speed up to 125mph)* Operated by the crossing user. In the default position, the crossing is protected by the use of barriers or gates across the 'road' enabling free access for train movements. The crossing users operate the barrier/gates manually to obtain access to the crossing. After crossing, users are required to

Right: Local monitoring of a level crossing in this case requires the driver of a train departing from Ardrossan Harbour to first start the lights and bells sequence by pressing this button, which is situated on the station platform. The crossing is about 200m distant. The date is 1 August 2004. *John Glover*

Below right: A gated user-worked crossing with full instructions, north of Arundel; 12 April 2004. *John Glover*

Footpath crossing on routes like the West Coast main line are highly undesirable, even if they are protected like this one near Grayrigg, with ladder stiles each side and copious notices. A double-headed Freightliner train is passing on the down line with Nos 86607 and 86614 in charge. The construction of a replacement at a nearby bridge was under way at the time this photograph was taken on 4 May 2000. *John Glover*

close the barriers or gates behind them. In order to successfully negotiate the crossing, by opening and closing the barrier/gates in the correct order, the user must traverse the railway lines five times (four times on foot, and once in the vehicle or with livestock). Some authorised users keep these crossings padlocked to prevent unauthorised use.

● *User-worked crossing with telephone (UWC-T) (number = 1,617, line speed up to 125mph)*
Similar to the standard UWC, but with the addition of telephones for the crossing user. Typically, provided in rural settings where a user may need to regularly move vehicles or livestock over the crossing. The user is required to use the telephone to call the signaller in order to obtain permission to cross and inform the signaller when the crossing is clear for rail use.

● *Open crossings (OC) (number = 60, line speed up to 10mph)*
As the name suggests, the interface between the railway and the road is open with no barriers or gates. The only protection provided is signage, warning road users that they must give way to any oncoming train. The crossings are such that there must be sufficient sighting for the road vehicle users to stop in time to allow the passage of the trains. In addition, the train speed is limited to 10mph or there is a requirement for a train to stop (at a stop board) before proceeding across the crossing.

● *Footpath crossings (number = 2,456)*
As the name suggests, footpath crossings are designed primarily for pedestrians. There may be stiles or wicket gates to restrict the access to the crossing point. There is no requirement for the user to call the signaller to obtain permission, although there is a requirement for a minimum sighting time

for the crossing user. In cases where sufficient sighting time is not available, there is a requirement on the railway to provide a whistle board to warn users of the presence of an oncoming train. A variant is the bridleway crossing, provided on routes used by horse riders. Rights over these crossings are generally public, although some are private and restricted to authorised users.

Data source: RSSB Special Topic Report, January 2004. Numbers of crossings correct at 31 March 2003.

Lever collar
See Reminder appliance.

Licensed operator
A company or organisation which has been granted a licence by the Office of Rail Regulation or the International Rail Regulator to operate rail services under terms and conditions enforceable by that Office.

Life-expired
In accounting terms, an asset with no book value once its original cost has been fully depreciated or amortised. In physical terms, it is an asset still in operational use which has reached or exceeded its normally accepted life span.

Lift
A means of vertical transport for passengers, but sometimes also for parcels, between (say) the platform and street level which may be either above or below. Many of the rather more basic parcels lifts, which were generally found more often, have in recent times been adapted for the carriage of wheelchairs or pushchairs, and perhaps for the more elderly in general. Staff attendance may or may not be required.

Lift truck
See Container handling.

Lifting
1. The raising of a vehicle off its wheels in a workshop, whether by jacks or a crane, to allow access to the underside so that maintenance and repairs can take place.
2. The permanent removal of track, whether from a siding, or a complete length of railway following closure.

Light engine, light diesel, light electric or light locomotive (LE)
A locomotive travelling on its own or 'running light', but sometimes more than one locomotive. If accompanied by a brake van, it becomes a Light Engine and Van.

Light maintenance depot
Location where the following services may be provided:
● The refuelling or the cleaning of the exterior of locomotives or other rolling stock.
● The carrying out on locomotives or other rolling stock of maintenance work of the kind which is normally undertaken at regular intervals of 12 months or less, preparing them for service. This includes the detection and rectification of faults.
There are 91 light maintenance depots leased by Network Rail to Train Operating Companies and which carry out train servicing functions.

Light Rail
A rail mode associated with urban operation, with a light volume traffic capacity compared with heavy rail. Typically, it uses articulated 750V dc electric vehicles of two or three sections, operating singly or as pairs, on fixed rails in an exclusive or sometimes shared right of way. Such sharing is generally with road and/or pedestrian traffic, with signalised priorities for the light rail system. Passengers board from either high or low level platforms. Vehicle power is drawn from the overhead by a pantograph, although the Docklands Light Railway uses a protected third rail.

Light running
1. Distance covered by trains which are not carrying revenue-generating passengers, freight or parcels, eg movements to and from fuelling and maintenance depots, or positioning the stock for its next use.
2. Movements undertaken by a light engine.

Like-for-like renewal
The removal and restoration or refurbishment of an original item where the work does not require any fundamental design change, or replacing it with an operationally equivalent new item.

Limit of shunt, limit of shunt indicator
When a driver is authorised by a subsidiary signal to draw ahead of a signal at danger in order to perform a shunting operation on a running line, a 'limit of shunt' indicator defines the furthest point to which he may proceed without further authorisation.

Limits of deviation
A lateral allowance contained in authorising Acts or Orders (under the T&W Act 1992) for new railways. This gives the builders the licence to choose the precise route to be followed within such limits, for instance to overcome unforeseen physical constraints. Generally, the excess land so acquired has to be resold after construction.

Line blocked

A signalling term that trains are stopped, with no traffic passing over the section of line in question. This refers only to the line or lines specified, in the case of double or multiple track lines. It does not imply that the line is unfit for use.

Line capacity

The maximum number of trains that can be accommodated on a given section of line, per direction, in a given time period of (usually) one hour. The result depends critically on the similarity or otherwise of the trains concerned, in technical capability and stopping patterns, but also on signal spacing. The maximum line capacity is likely to be attained when all trains are identical and have the same calling patterns, as on most of London Underground where 30 trains per hour (tph) or more is often achievable.

Line clear, train on line, line blocked

The indications of the three-position block instruments on the shelves of mechanical signalboxes with the absolute block system.

Line designation, direction

All running lines are designated up or down to distinguish them from each other. This minimises the chance of error when describing a situation in operating terms. Buildings such as signalboxes may also be specified as being on either the up side or the down side of the line.

The direction chosen was normally determined by the relative importance of the towns at each end. Thus it is usually up to London, and down to everywhere else. The expression 'up to London' later became part of the English language. However, there are variations, and of course, not all railways go to London. Thus, for the Lancashire & Yorkshire Railway, it was always up to Manchester, on the Midland Railway it was up to Derby, although the line from Derby to St Pancras became 'up' a couple of decades ago.

The only safe way to find out is to seek a source of reference such as a Working Timetable.

Line designation, type

The names of all lines are designated formally. Fast lines (also known as the main lines) are usually those on which the highest speeds are permitted in a multiple-track area, or the main running lines in a two-track area. Additional tracks as in a four-track area are known as the slow lines, or relief lines on the Great Western. Other commonly found names are goods lines, carriage lines (for empty stock), reception lines (as at a goods yard), through lines (which avoid platforms), and platform lines. The local variations, sometimes referring to places as in 'Up Fife' or 'Down Guildford' are endless.

Line light

An indicator on the driver's desk that current is being drawn from the overhead wires. When the light is lost (and cannot be reset), it is an indication that there may be a fault with the pantograph or overhead wires, which requires immediate attention to avoid serious damage.

Line speed

The maximum general speed permitted for a line, eg 75mph. This may be subject to localised speed restrictions. Other restrictions may be applied to the train itself and/or its load. A further differential may apply to certain train types, notably Sprinter diesel units, whose relatively low mass and light weight imposes minimal wear and tear on the infrastructure. See also Speed restrictions.

Line speed capability

This is a measurement of the length of running tracks, including loops but not sidings and depots, in each of four speed bands. As at March 2004, the situation was as follows:

Speed capability	km of track	%
Up to 35mph	5,570	17.6
40-75 mph	16,585	52.5
80-105mph	6,994	22.2
110-125mph	2,415	7.7
Total	31,564	100

Where differential speeds apply to a section of track, the highest line speed has been assessed for that section.

Lineside

A general term to encompass the railway land enclosed by the lineside fencing, including cutting sides etc. Huts used for storage, for instance, will be known as lineside huts.

Lineside discharge

The use of running lines to load or off-load freight, if the line is little used and track capacity can be made available. An example is the Far North line in Scotland, for timber loading. This approach is especially useful if the flow is short term only as, for instance, in many requirements for aggregates, eg road building. Another solution in such cases is to build a siding on which wagons can be left for discharge, to be removed again when the flow ceases.

Lineside fencing

The operational railway is a dangerous place and it is a requirement in Britain that the boundary should be fenced throughout. Other than on dockside lines and similar, there are no exceptions, even in the wildest and least frequented parts of the kingdom.

Fencing and its maintenance thus represents a considerable cost and it is the responsibility of the railway to maintain it in good condition. There are those who resent the restriction it places on their movements and are minded to destroy parts of it. New, stronger designs are replacing wire chain link fences and palisade steel security fences consisting of vertical members stabilised by horizontal struts are now often seen.

Nowadays, its main purposes are to prevent cattle straying on to the tracks and to discourage trespassers.

Lineside signals
Those located at the side of the line for observation by the driver of an approaching train, as opposed to cab signals.

Lining
Adjusting the alignment of track on the straight and maintaining accuracy of curvature.

Liquidated damages
Financial compensation at rates agreed in advance of the occurrence of the loss payable by a contractor for losses incurred as a result of his breach.

Listing (of buildings etc)
The legal protection applied to buildings and structures deemed to be of architectural heritage value, and applied by the Office of the Deputy Prime Minister (or local authorities). In England and Wales, subdivided into Grade I, II* or II; in Scotland Category A or B (in order of most restrictive to least restrictive). Such listing may have considerable implications for the owners in the way in which repairs and maintenance may be undertaken, or alterations may be carried out (if at all).

Live
Electrically charged.

Live rail
See Conductor rail.

LLPA
See Long line public address.

LMS (London, Midland & Scottish Railway)
See Railways Act 1921.

LNER (London & North Eastern Railway)
See Railways Act 1921.

Loaded train miles/km
Distance travelled by a train available to fare-paying passengers, or carrying revenue-earning freight, engineering materials or staff.

Loading bay, loading dock
A purpose-designed area for loading and unloading, often raised to the level of the wagon floor to ease access. The loading dock is more commonly associated with a similar facility with doors on the ends of certain rail vehicle types, and used for instance in the loading of motor vehicles.

Loading gauge
Strictly, the maximum physical dimensions of height and width to which an open rail wagon can be loaded or any rail vehicle constructed, but see Gauge, structures and vehicles for a detailed review.

Loading of trains
This topic is considered under a number of headings:

1. Load factor
The total number of passenger miles/km produced by a train (or group of trains) divided by the number of seat miles/km produced by that train (or

Listing (of buildings, etc.)
Above: Harlow Town station was built new in 1961 and is generally considered to be one of the best of its period. This view from the station entrance shows the three towers containing lifts (for parcels), an area which was kept entirely clear of passenger flows. The station has since been listed, and is seen here in October 2001. *John Glover*

Right: The railway lifting bridge over Deptford Creek was intended to give access to small ships, but it has long since been secured in the closed position as seen here. This is the route of the London & Greenwich Railway, one of the earliest in the capital. The bridge was photographed from a Docklands Light Railway train on 4 October 2003. *John Glover*

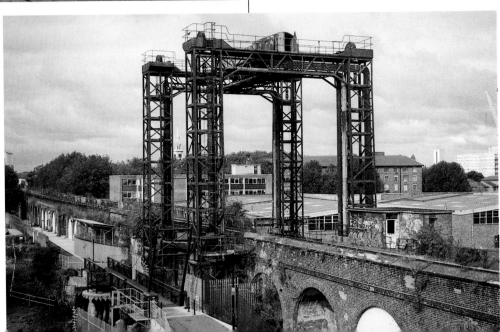

group of trains). This measure is that of seat occupancy and is expressed as a percentage, which may exceed 100%.

Alternatively, load factor may be measured at a point, for instance the terminal, or perhaps at a busy intermediate station (the Clapham Junctions of this world).

It should be noted that while the load factor for the train as a whole may be 100%, indicating that nobody has to stand, the situation in individual vehicles may be very different. Notably, passengers tend to congregate at points where they are likely to be near the platform exit, and at a terminal platform that means the front of the train. This tends to get overcrowded while the rear coach may be relatively empty but it does not stop those at the front complaining!

Another cause of uneven loading is the difference between first and standard class accommodation, where both are available.

The practical problems associated with measuring load factor reasonably accurately should not be underestimated.

2. Load factor standards
Maximum standards for passengers as a percentage of seats which are occupied on individual trains compared with the number of seats available. This may vary according to the type of rolling stock, the length of journey, at what point the measurement is made, and whether the journey is at peak or off-peak times. A standard of 100 would indicate all seats occupied, with no standing; 135 indicates that there may be up to 35 standing for every 100 seated.

3. Crowding
Crowding of trains brings its own operating problems in the additional time taken at each and every station for passengers to alight and board (preferably in that order). This is not to suggest that trains take the same time at each station since their passenger usage will vary; rather that the time taken on a crowded train will be that much longer than on one which is relatively lightly loaded.

Cumulatively, this reduces line capacity and the total number of trains which can be run in a given length of time, which can make the problems that much worse. This is a complex situation, which leads quickly into emotive arguments about seating density. See also Load factor and Passengers In Excess of Capacity, below.

4. Overcrowding
Overcrowding is made up of at least three elements, these being:
● The density of people (an objective measure).
● Perception (a subjective measure).
● The number of people for a given density.
Definitions of overcrowding also vary according to whether it is on a long distance or a commuter train or at a station, and the organisation or group making the comments.

Definitions of overcrowding by different groups of people:

	Rail industry	Passengers	RMT	HMRI	SRA
Intercity (long journeys)	Cannot shut the doors	No spare seats	Flow of people restricted	Potential for harm as a result of the number of people	No spare seats
Commuter (short journeys)		No handholds, or standing for more than 0-20min			Standing passengers having less than 0.55m² each
At stations Source: RSSB	Standing the wrong side of the yellow line	Being shoved and pushed			

5. Standing capacity
The number of standing passengers which can be accommodated in reasonable comfort, although there is clearly an element of subjectivity. It can be arrived at by calculating the free floor space and allowing x passengers per sq metre. A maximum crush capacity is calculated by manufacturers, on the basis that this will represent the highest load which the vehicle could carry, and is thus used for defining the braking performance needed.

6. Passengers in Excess of Capacity (PIXC)
All train operators have a general obligation to avoid excessive overcrowding. PIXC is a measure of passenger density on busy trains, specifically London commuter services at peak times and some other services such as those of First ScotRail services crossing the Forth Bridge. Elsewhere, the SRA may specify a minimum number of seats to be provided.

Where PIXC controls operate, each operator is required to conduct an annual passenger count at defined points. The results are compared with the contractual limit and the operator must agree a timetable and train plan with the SRA showing the proposed allocation of rolling stock to services, to keep peak crowding down below the limit set out in the franchise agreement

The contractual limit is expressed as a percentage. From the annual counts, the number of passengers in excess of capacity must be no more than 4.5% of the total number of passengers on the trains in either of the morning or evening peaks, and no more than 3% in the two peaks combined. Capacity is deemed to be the number of standard class seats on the train for journeys of over 20 minutes. For shorter journeys, an allowance for standing room is also made. That for trains with sliding or folding doors is based on 0.55m² per person. The standard allowance is therefore in the order of 35% above the number of seats. The calculations are done in aggregate for all the trains in the peak period, but unused seats or standing space are not used in the PIXC calculations as an offset.

Options to control demand include additional or longer trains and altered stopping patterns, and also through pricing. Some remedies may involve considerable investment as well as practical considerations, and can thus only be implemented in the longer term, if at all.

Locomotive
Few dc straight electric locomotives have been built in Britain. The most extensive fleet of 24 was constructed mainly for freight use as part of the Kent Coast electrification of 1959-61. Here, No E5017 heads a mixed freight east through Ashford, as then recently rebuilt. Notably, these locomotives were equipped with pantographs for use in a modest number of sidings which were wired to avoid having conductor rails in such locations.
Photobus/Author's collection

The SRA's primary objective is to ensure that TOCs plan to prevent excessive overcrowding, and to ensure that it is cured as soon as possible to the extent that existing resource levels allow. There are contractual financial penalties on operators that provide less than the agreed capacity, and as a last resort enforcement action can be taken under s55 of the Railways Act 1993.

Local Improvement Groups
Semi-formal regular meetings between staff and managers to exchange views and to consider suggestions as to how methods might be changed or equipment modified to produce a more effective or economical operation.

Local Transport Plan (LTP)
The Local Transport Plan system for local authorities is devised at local level in partnership with the community. The LTP is partly a bid for Government funds, but also a strategic planning document. The objectives need to be consistent with improving safety, promoting accessibility, contributing to an efficient economy, promoting integration and protection of the environment. Its content needs to include sections on an analysis of problems and opportunities, a long-term strategy to deal with these, a costed five-year implementation programme, and a series of targets and performance indicators.

'Lock and block'
The system of signalling by which a train does not enter a section of line (the block) until the preceding train has left, the signal controlling the entrance to that section being locked at danger and only released when the preceding train leaves the section.

Locking and interlocking
At its simplest, locking ensures not only that the points have been changed to the direction required, but that they stay in that position. Traditionally, this is carried out by a locking piece which is inserted by a lever in a slot cut in the bar connecting the two switch blades. To change the points, the bar has to be removed, the points changed with their own lever, and the bar reinserted in a second slot. Similarly, in a mechanical signalbox, point and signal levers can only be pulled in certain sequences, and then only when any necessary authorisations for that movement have been obtained.

Interlocking is the means whereby the various parts of the system are mechanically, electrically or otherwise locked, so that conflicting indications to train drivers cannot be given accidentally, or changes made to the settings when it is too late or otherwise unsafe so to do. An example of a contradictory situation would be the points set for one direction, but the signals cleared for another. Modern systems incorporate all the same functions, which are required by law as well as good practice. More formally, interlocking executes the safety logic to reduce the risk of error when controlling points and signals.

Interlocking may be defined as any device, mechanical, electro-mechanical or computerised, which prevents different parts of the system from giving contrary indications or allowing unsafe operational situations to be created.

Locomotive
A powered railway vehicle used for hauling trains, but which does not itself carry a revenue-earning load.

Locomotive wheel arrangements, main-line diesels and electrics
The notation used for the wheel arrangement distinguishes between bogies, the axles of which may either be motored or be used only to carry the locomotive's weight (and thus reduce axle load on the infrastructure). Additionally, there may be guiding wheels, though not on any current locomotives.

The number of axles on a bogie may be one, two or three, classified A, B or C respectively. The addition of an 'o' shows that each axle is powered individually; a non-powered axle is numbered. Thus while a Class 66 with three powered axles on each bogie is a Co-Co, a Class 31 with its central carrying axles is an A1A-A1A. The eight-wheeled bogies on the Class 40s, with their outside end carrying wheels were 1Co-Co1. Electric locomotives, being generally lighter as a result of not carrying their power source around with them, are mostly Bo-Bo.

Locomotive wheel arrangements, steam
The Whyte notation is still a useful guide to steam locomotives, some of which are regularly operated on National Railways. This referred to the number of wheels on the locomotive (both sides), divided into three groups:
- leading wheels, pony (two) or bogie (four)
- driving wheels, coupled by an outside rod
- trailing wheels

Thus a main line express locomotive with a four-wheeled bogie, six coupled wheels and two trailing wheels is a 4-6-2, and so on. Where there are no trailing wheels, for instance, a 0 is substituted, as in 2-6-0. Such locomotives have a tender to carry coal and water. Variations include the use of the suffix T for tank locomotives, which are self-contained.

The Whyte notation is still used for diesel shunting locomotives, nearly all of which nowadays are 0-6-0s (Classes 08 and 09).

Locomotives, haulage capability
For diesel locomotives, this is a function of three elements:
● The adhesive weight of the locomotive.
● The power of the engine, net of efficiency losses and those for train supply.
● The transmission to the main generator and hence the supply of electric traction current to the axles and wheels.
For electric locomotives, the power source is external and there are two elements only:
● The adhesive weight, as with a diesel.
● The characteristics of the electrical equipment.
Briefly, electric locomotives are able to receive higher levels of power supply for relatively short time periods, which has corresponding benefits for their rates of acceleration.

Logistics
The science of ensuring that the right products reach the right place in the right quantity at the right time at the right price to satisfy customer demand. It is concerned also with storage and warehousing.

London railway passenger service
A service which carries passengers between places in Greater London, or between places in Greater London and places outside Greater London. Interestingly, this 2005 Act definition appears to exclude most long distance services, which stop in Greater London only at the terminus concerned.

Long line public address (LLPA)
Station public address, sourced over a considerable distance from signalling centres or similar, and probably arranged so that announcements to a number of stations can be made simultaneously. The biggest problems are ensuring that it works reliably and that the information given is fully relevant to all the recipients, and appropriate to them at the time they get it.

Longitudinal timber
Large cross section baulks of timber, used on some bridges and positioned under each rail longitudinally. Here they can act as weigh-beams, balancing the weight of the rail and its rail traffic over a greater distance. They are also the securing point for rail baseplates. Such timber is also used to support rails along the edge of pits in depots.

Lookout
A competent person appointed to observe rail traffic, to give timely warning by the means provided of the approach of a train to those working on the track, to check that the correct action is taken as a result of such warnings and to repeat them if necessary. Further warnings must be given if a second train approaches, and horns sounded by train drivers must be acknowledged. The lookout wears a designatory armband.

Loop, dynamic
A section of double track of sufficient length to allow a higher speed train to overtake a slower speed train or, in a single-track area to allow trains in opposite directions to pass without either train having to stop to await passage of the other. Examples of the latter may be found on double track lines now mostly single, for instance between Saxmundham and Halesworth (Suffolk).

Loop, passing
On a single line, this device allows trains in opposite directions to pass each other. They are most frequently found in the vicinity of stations and their capability is related to the length of train which can be passed.

Passing loops may also be found on double-track lines as an extra infrastructure feature, again often at stations. The normal use is to allow a faster train to overtake a slower one, both of which are proceeding in the same direction.

Loop, terminal
A freight example is the discharge arrangements at power stations served by merry-go-round trains, as at Didcot and West Burton. These loops return the train to the main line in the reverse order in which it arrived, and thus ready to return whence it came.

Of a rather different nature is the arrangement at Newcastle Central, where a passenger train from London can arrive by one Tyne bridge, and then return to London via the other, without reversing.

Loose shunting (of wagons)
Shunting with limited control. A locomotive propels a wagon (or wagons) to which it is not coupled into a siding, and stops. The wagons continue. Ground staff then secure the wagon brakes, while the locomotive has already backed away. Alternatively, the locomotive can continue pushing as necessary until the whole comes to the intended stopping place. To be used with caution; yard gradients are a very relevant consideration!

Low level, high level
Descriptive appendages to station names, now discontinued other than for Heath (Cardiff Valleys). Upper and Lower can be found at Tyndrum, and Upper and Central at Helensburgh, both ScotRail. Others are still in existence but not recognised officially, such as Willesden Junction (Silverlink). That does not, however, prevent them from being recorded at separate stations by some sources.

LTP
See Local Transport Plan.

Margin

In timetabling, the time allowed between successive events. In a railway sense, the margin refers to operational events which need to be timed not to obstruct each other. For instance, the number of minutes earlier that a stopping train has to leave a certain point with reference to the following faster train, if the latter is not to be delayed. Hence 'the stopping train needs a 12-minute margin to reach A'. See also Junction margin.

Marginal costs

Those which would be saved if a specific operation did not take place, as opposed to those which could be properly allocated to that operation. Thus, if a train crew and train are available and have spare time, the marginal costs of an extra journey are little more than the power costs, plus some wear and tear on the train and the infrastructure. It thus takes very little revenue to make the journey worth while, and this is the reason that services on commuter lines between the peaks are often relatively frequent.

Marker board

Board erected at the side of the line to delineate the extent of a work site (of which there may be more than one) within a possession. Each double-sided yellow board has two vertical flashing lights on each side. These show yellow on the work site side and red on the possession side.

Market pricing

The price in terms of a fare or rate which it is normally accepted the market will pay for a service. The result is often prices per unit of production (eg per mile) which can vary considerably. Market pricing will result in charges which vary between different routes, or for the same journey at different times of the day. One objective might be to charge what the traffic will bear, or to even out the volumes of off-peak and peak travel. The conditions of travel may become more specific, such as to travel on a specific train and/or to purchase the ticket in advance.

Marshalling yard

Centralised facility where wagons are sorted for a variety of destinations, although the yards that remain are much smaller and more compact than the large yards of the 1950s and 1960s. These are now flat yards, ie those without a hump and hence with no assistance (or only incidental assistance) from gravity.

MAS

See Multiple-aspect signalling.

Master controller

A device operated by the driver which controls all the traction motors by means of control circuits.

Match wagons

Vehicle fitted with incompatible coupling connections, one at each end, so that a locomotive fitted with one type may be used to haul vehicles fitted with those of another type. The match wagons themselves have no other purpose; consequently the 'wagons' may consist of redundant coaching stock. Such vehicles can be especially useful in cases of train failure. Note also that brake hoses need to be connected.

MEAV

See Modern Equivalent Asset Value.

Mechanical signalling

The traditional signalling system from a mechanical box with levers (ie using muscle power), with rodding to operate the pointwork and wires to operate signals. Some points may be electrically worked, in which case the lever is shortened to warn the signaller that very little force will be needed to operate it.

Merry-go-round (MGR)

A system of operation in which the locomotive stays attached to its wagons, and the whole moves as one from loading to discharge point and back without remarshalling at any point, and possibly without stopping either. This requires rapid loading and unloading, both of which can be automatic, with the terminals laid out as loops. The system was designed around coal movements from colliery, or other bulk loading point, to power station.

Metro

A generic term for metropolitan railway systems, which might be defined as high-capacity and high-frequency self-contained networks which:
● Serve the central area and inner suburbs of a city.
● Carry traffic largely made up of intra-city journeys.
● Are signalled throughout or are controlled automatically.
● Have station platforms at car floor level.
● Are physically segregated from all other forms of transport.
Wherever desirable, metros have easy passenger interchange with outer-suburban railways and local bus or tramway services.

Merry-go-round (MGR)
The HAA (TOPS code) 32-tonne merry-go-round four-wheeled coal hopper, which has long been the mainstay of this operation. At the time of their introduction, these vehicles had twice the capacity of most of the huge fleet of wagons they set out to replace. *BR*

MGR
See Merry-go-round.

Microfranchises
Microfranchising involves the separate tendering of a self-contained line on a basis that might include responsibility for operation and maintenance of the infrastructure as well as the provision of the passenger service. It would only apply to certain limited categories of self-contained lines.

Midland Main Line (MML)
The main line from London St Pancras to Bedford (electrified), then to Leicester, Derby and Sheffield, with a branch to Nottingham (all non-electrified).

Milepost
A series of marked posts, normally on the down side of the track, recording the distance in whole miles from a given point. Intermediate quarter miles, half miles and three quarter miles are often marked as such only. The provision of mileposts is a statutory requirement.

Miles and chains
The imperial measurements used universally by the railways of Britain when they were constructed and which (apart from the Channel Tunnel Rail Link) are still in normal use. There are 80 chains to the mile, a measurement which divides easily into halves, quarters and eighths etc. 1 chain = 22 yards (which is also the length of a cricket pitch).

Miles per casualty (MPC)
This is a principal measure of the performance of rolling stock assets, particularly locomotives or multiple-units. It works on the premise that the greater the distance that an asset travels between being recorded as a failure, the better it is performing.

However, as with all such measures, a degree of caution is required. First, what is regarded as a failure? This is taken to be an incident due to the asset itself which causes a delay of five minutes or more. Thus, a signal failure might delay a train, but it isn't the train's fault. If the brakes fail to release, that is. Changing the definitions can make large differences.

Secondly, it is important to compare like with like. Is it meaningful to compare a 30-year-old electric unit with a brand-new freight locomotive? Freight locos don't get delayed through problems with sliding passenger doors. So, whatever the result, what does it prove? More practically, what action does it suggest management should take?

The third element is the relevance of distance between failures, compared with time in traffic. How does one make a valid comparison based on distance, between a passenger locomotive covering large distances at high average speeds, with a relatively short distance freight limited to 60mph?

Even so, miles per casualty is probably the best available measure, provided it is used with caution and a determination to limit usage to situations where it is both useful and valid. For all its faults, it is useful as a benchmark measure to prompt a management challenge in understanding why the same vehicles in different circumstances behave differently. This is one of the key means to enable managers to address poorer performing trains. It is also one of the few measures that can be used contractually to incentivise procurement contracts for new trains.

Mixed train
A train conveying both passenger and freight vehicles.

MML
See Midland Main Line.

Modal shift
Modal shift is the movement of any type of traffic, passenger or freight, from one form (mode) of transport to another. The term may also be generalised, in the sense that BAA Heathrow has an objective to increase the proportion of airport passengers arriving at Heathrow by public (as opposed to private) transport to 40% by the year 2007. Whether this be by rail, Underground, coach or bus is not specified.

Modern Equivalent Asset Value (MEAV)
The Modern Equivalent Asset concept was used at rail privatisation to establish the capital value of assets with a view to their replacement. A Modern Equivalent Asset is defined as one which provides the same service potential as the existing asset, but takes some account of technical updating.

Moira
A rail industry passenger demand forecasting tool which models the effects of timetable changes on demand patterns and revenue allocations. Moira is a name and not an acronym. The name of the model who launched British Rail's InterCity in 1966 was Monica. Subsequently, other passenger analysis models have had girls' names beginning with M.

Motor car, motor coach
A car in a multiple-unit train on which the traction motors are mounted, together with the associated switchgear. With electric units, this is often one vehicle only out of (perhaps) four, but on many diesel unit types all vehicles carry motors.

Motorail services
The carriage of private cars by trains which also carry passenger accommodation, usually in sleeping cars. From a once large network, only a summer Fridays-only service remains, that run by First Great Western between Paddington and Penzance.

MPC
See Miles per casualty.

M

Multi-modal studies
A programme of Government studies of transport options in key corridors across Britain.

Multi-purpose vehicle (MPV)
See Freight multiple-unit.

Multi-SPAD signal
A signal which has been passed at danger as a Category A SPAD more than once in 12 months, or three or more times in any three-year period.

Mulitfret
An intermodal wagon with a platform height of 945mm above rail level to carry swap-bodies or containers.

Multiple-aspect signalling (MAS)
System using colour lights, track circuit block and (usually) route setting.

Multiple-unit
See Diesel multiple-unit and Electric multiple-unit.

Multiple working
Multiple working is used to control more than one separate motive power entity (each, say, being a diesel or electric multiple-unit which has been designed for the purpose) from a single cab. This enables trains to be lengthened or shortened easily, according to the traffic requirements of the time. This is achieved by connection of the jumper cables between the two (or more) units involved; these may be integral with the couplings. Limitations are the variety of systems in use, which mean that only compatible types can be connected, and a maximum in the number of units which can be so joined into a single train.

Locomotives may also be coupled in multiple, or 'multipled'.

In an operational sense, it must always be remembered that joining two units produces a spare train crew, but separating two units doesn't automatically result in a second train crew materialising to take the 'other' half away!

National Conditions of Carriage
The legal terms of the contract between the passenger and the Train Operating Company(ies) concerned and other carriers as appropriate. Purchase of a travel ticket by the passenger is deemed to represent acceptance of those conditions. Where tickets are issued on the train rather than at stations, which may be unstaffed, the boarding of that train is taken as signifying the acceptance of the conditions.

A reference to the Conditions appears on each and every travel ticket issued. Copies of the National Conditions of Carriage are available free from Railway Ticket Offices.

National Radio Network (NRN)
A multi-function industry communications system. On this analogue system, trains communicate by radio with 550 sites, which are connected by land line to the radio control system. This acts as an exchange for routeing calls; drivers have to set their radios to the frequency channel of the area in which they are travelling, sometimes depicted by lineside signs. The NRN system covers most of the railway — but not tunnels or deep cuttings.

NRN communicates with a very limited number of control centres for emergency calls; it is to be replaced with direct train to signaller communications.

National Rail (All Systems) Timetable
This is the principal fully comprehensive public timetable book, from which other more limited publications and leaflets are derived. It is published twice a year, but there are usually supplements. This is the public face of the Working Timetables (WTTs). It contains only items of direct relevance to the passenger, and precise timings may vary. Fractions of minutes are not used; a WTT may show a train departing at $14.30^1/_2$, but the public timetable will show 14.30.

Arrival times are sometimes padded out to give additional recovery time. This can often be detected by comparing the time (for example) of the up 'Yorkshire Pullman' from Leeds to Wakefield Westgate at 12min, whereas the return evening service takes 17min for the same nominal journey.

Another point to watch is the use of the symbol s, as in 09s12 for a Euston-bound train at Watford Junction. This means 'stops to set down only', the implication being that if the train is early it need not wait until the time stated. Likewise, the u symbol means 'stops to pick up only'. This keeps short distance passengers off long-distance trains, thereby preventing overcrowding, and avoids having to show Watford Junction as a stopping point on the departure boards at Euston. People are less inclined to take the risk of using the train for such a short journey if the first advertised stop is Stafford!

National Rail Communication Centre
Deals with disruptions to the network; the Centre assimilates and processes the information, putting out bulletins to call centres, travel offices, live departure/arrival boards, the media and others.

National Rail Enquiry Service (NRES)
NRES employs 1,400 staff in five telephone call centres at Newcastle upon Tyne, Plymouth, Wath-on-Dearne, Bangalore and Mumbai to answer questions about the 18,000 or so services which run daily over the national rail network of 10,460 route miles. A little more than half of all the 105 million annual enquiries are made through the website. NRES is a function of ATOC, a service which is provided on behalf of all train operating companies who meet the £30m pa cost. The telephone number is 08457 48 49 50, website www.nationalrail.co.uk.

National Railways

A term coined by the Department for Transport to encompass the whole of the railway industry previously under the control of British Rail, in the post-privatisation era. It is often abbreviated to National Rail. Similarly, the 'double-arrow' BR symbol was acquired by the Department, for use at stations and for applications such as road signs to indicate a National Railways station.

National Task Force

A cross-industry forum of Network Rail operators, suppliers, the SRA and ORR, set up to provide direction and co-ordination of train performance and other issues.

National Timetable Conference

An annual event which takes place in February each year, in which all operators meet Network Rail to bid for the timetable they wish to provide. The time between then and the introduction of the timetable (December) is taken to refine the detail, resolve any conflicts and prepare the National Rail Timetable.

Network Code

A standard set of rules (previously known as the track access conditions) approved by the ORR which are incorporated in and underpin all individual Track Access Agreements. A separate set exists for freight access agreements.

Network concept

The basic objective of transport policy is to create or support an effective system with good facilities, and for the operators to adhere to the norms and regulations of the industry for their own benefit and that of consumers.

Consumers consider transport as a system with a well-connected network of services, which is convenient and easy to use. It is based on the philosophy that the whole is greater than the sum of the parts. The component parts of the system are interrelated, and any change in one part of the system will affect all others through a chain reaction. There is therefore the need for planning and co-ordination to ensure that the elements of the whole work together for the benefit of both operators and consumers.

Network Rail Asset Register

A register which records knowledge of the company's assets, their condition, capability and capacity, in a manner which best achieves:
● The maintenance of the network.
● The renewal and replacement of the network.
● The improvement, enhancement and development of the network.
● The operation (including timetabling) of the network.
This is a requirement of Network Rail's licence.

Neutral section

An arrangement of insulators in the OLE designed to ensure that two adjacent sections are kept electrically separate, even during the passage of a pantograph.

New trains, diesel

A number of new designs have been introduced since privatisation, including:

Class	Type name	Builder
168	'Clubman'	Adtranz/Bombardier
170	'Turbostar'	Adtranz/Bombardier
175	'Coradia'	Alstom
180	'Adelante'	Alstom
220	'Voyager'	Bombardier
221	'Super Voyager'	Bombardier
222	'Meridian'	Bombardier

New trains, electric

A number of new designs have been introduced since privatisation, including:

Classes	Type name	Builder
334/458/460	'Juniper'	Alstom
357/375/377	'Electrostar'	Adtranz/Bombardier
360/444/450	'Desiro'	Siemens
390	'Pendolino'	Alstom

No Signalman Key Token (NSKT)

In this system for single lines, the driver collects a conventional token from a token block instrument on the platform. The token is released by the signaller (who is at a central location) using a coded date transmission over dedicated telephone lines. There is no on-train equipment, but the cost of dedicated telephone lines and other equipment is high.

It is installed on the Central Wales and Castle Cary-Dorchester West lines, and the Whitby, Pembroke Dock and Newquay branches.

New trains, electric
The Class 377 'Electrostar' units of Southern have large open areas with handholds, within the sliding doors, to accommodate standing passengers. Yes, more standing space means fewer seats, but the acceptability of this is related to passenger journey length and between which points the numbers of passengers outstrip the number of seats available. Rolling stock design is full of compromises; who now can remember how uncomfortable it was to stand in straight-through compartments, with nothing to hold on to except the luggage rack — if you were tall enough to reach it? *John Glover*

Non-passenger-carrying coaching stock (NPCCS)

Mostly parcels vans; see also Parcels for a fuller discussion. Includes vehicles such as BGs (Brake Gangway) with no passenger accommodation, but not those where part of the vehicle is used for passengers.

Normal

The situation to which signals (and the signal levers controlling them in a mechanical signalbox) must revert when there is no traffic around. For stop signals this is the 'danger' indication, for distant signals 'caution'. Signal levers at normal will be at the back of the signal frame. See also Block indicators and Reverse.

Nose-suspended motor

See Axle-hung nose-suspended motor.

Not to Stop orders

See Cut and run.

Not transferable

Condition attached to virtually all travel tickets, which means that the ticket may be used by the purchaser, or the person for whom it was purchased, and no other person. This makes the transfer of the ticket to a third party illegal, as can happen for instance with tickets for unrestricted travel during a given time period (eg one-day Travelcards, etc), enabling a prosecution of touts or others to be mounted. At all times, tickets remain the property of the issuing company, and must be given up on demand. See also National Conditions of Carriage.

One train working
Even single track stub end branches with no pointwork are likely to display a fixed distant signal to the driver as the end of the line is approached. This example was to be found outside Whitby on 30 August 2004.
John Glover

NPCCS

See Non-passenger-carrying coaching stock.

NRES

See National Rail Enquiry Service.

NRN

See National Radio Network.

NSKT

See No Signalman Key Token.

Occupation bridge, Occupation crossing

A bridge or crossing used to carry a private road which pre-existed the railway to a farm or factory which was built at the time of railway construction, to maintain access. User rights are generally as for the road it carries.

Occupied

The presence of a train on a section of line, denoted in a power signalbox for instance by a row of red lights on the track diagram, signifiying its position.

Off

A signal showing a green (proceed) indication; a yellow or double yellow might be described as 'not fully off, yet'.

OGLO

See Exceptional load.

OLE, OHLE

See Overhead line equipment.

On

A signal showing a red (stop) indication or, in the case of a semaphore distant signal, prepare to stop at the home signal.

On-track machines (OTM)

Rail-mounted self-propelled machines used for track maintenance and similar tasks.

One-train working

Used for a section of single line, leading to a terminus. One train only is allowed to enter this section and, for as long as this situation remains, no signalling is necessary to protect the train other than at the entry/exit point. The driver may or may not be required to hold a single line token.

OOU

See Out of use.

Open access

A general term used for non-franchised services. Open access describes the legal process by which non-franchised operators can gain access to the railway infrastructure, and thus the ability to run services competing with or perhaps complementing those of other operators. All freight operations are open access. Operators must satisfy the specified safety and other standards required by licences and access agreements.

Open access operator
A railway operator providing railway services, which are not franchised or subject to international regulation.

Open access (or common user) terminals
Similar in some respects to private sidings, but with the important difference that they are open to many or all customers. They may be linked to warehousing provision and intermodal transfer facilities. Operation may be by a Freight Operating Company or a third party logistics provider.

Open crossing
A level crossing which is unprotected by barriers, gates or road traffic signals, relying entirely on signs and their correct observance by road users.

Operating expenditure
The key day-to-day expenditure of the company, chargeable to the operating account.

Operating ratio
The operating ratio of a service is the ratio of its direct costs (or those which would cease were the service not to exist) to the revenue taken.

Operational Research Computerised Allocation of Tickets to Services (ORCATS)
The suite of computer programmes which provides the CAPRI system (CAPRI = Computer Analysis of Passenger Revenue Information; now replaced by LENNON = Latest Earnings Nationally Networked Over Night) with a file of revenue allocation factors; a clearing system. The objective is to provide an apportionment of fares revenue to individual TOCs on passenger flows where there is more than one operator for any part or all of the journey. The approach is based on typical daily demand profiles as applied to a particular timetable.

ORCATS
See Operational Research Computerised Allocation of Tickets to Services.

OTM
See On-track machines.

Out of course running
When a train runs substantially outside its allocated timetable path.

Out of use (OOU)
A frequently used abbreviation to describe pointwork etc; OOU neither specifies nor implies whether the condition is temporary or permanent, unless specifically stated as in 'OOU awaiting removal', 'OOU awaiting commissioning', or 'OOU UFN' (until further notice).

Outside (a signal)
A train standing in front of a signal and therefore not under its protection.

Over run
1. Engineering works for which a possession was granted, but which were not completed within the allotted time.
2. A train which fails to stop at the prescribed stopping point, eg at the end of a platform for a passenger train, and stops a short distance beyond. There is no connotation of having passed a signal at danger. See also Overlap.

Overbridge
A bridge that crosses above the railway.

Overhead costs
Costs incurred by the business as a whole and not chargeable directly to any particular activity, but which nevertheless have to be apportioned out and recovered through those activities.

Overhead line equipment (OLE, sometimes OHLE)
An arrangement of wires suspended over each electrified track for the supply of electricity to the electric trains, together with their associated fittings, insulators and other attachments by means of which they are suspended or registered in position. Also known irreverently as 'the knitting'. (OLE may also refer collectively to the whole of the electric track equipment, together with its structures, foundations, etc.)

Overhead line equipment (OLE, sometimes OHLE)
The overhead line installation on the Clacton branch, which dates from 1959, north of Wivenhoe, seen on 29 May 2004.
John Glover

Overlap

In allowing a train entry to a section, the controlling (section) signal gives the driver formal permission to proceed to the next signal, which may be at danger. The overlap, where provided, is the distance beyond the signal in advance which is also clear (and kept clear) of obstructions, to guard against driver error in not bringing his train to a complete stand in time. Thus the overlap must be clear before a train can be allowed to approach the signal.

Overlaps may be up to 400m in length. Circumstances sometimes require overlap length to be reduced considerably, but in such locations running speeds are reduced to ensure that trains can stop within the overlap section. A driver whose train occupies an overlap by passing a signal at danger has performed a SPAD, which is dealt with accordingly.

Overlap spans

An overlap length of two overhead line equipments between the end of one equipment and the commencement of the next, arranged in such a manner that the pantograph may pass smoothly and without break of circuit from one contact wire to the next over the same track.

P Way

See Permanent way.

'Pacer'

The bus-bodied diesel units on rigid four-wheeled chassis of Classes 140-144, with folding doors. Built from 1984 to 1987, their short 15m or so bodies are based on that of the Leyland National bus (itself now quite rare outside preservation). Each is supported on a pair of single axles only. This gives a distinctive quality of ride, especially on jointed track. These were the bargain basement vehicles of the period.

Pacer
The 'Pacer' units dating from the mid-1980s were built with bus-style seats, as seen here in Cardiff Valleys unit No 143605, on 17 June 2000. They represent the economy-minded approach to rail investment of the period; whether they really were 'bargain basement' vehicles is perhaps another matter. The cheapest possible options do not always represent best value.
John Glover

PALADIN

See Performance and Loading Analysis Database of Information.

Paladin Data Extract and Reporting System (PEARS)

A versatile train performance measurement facility producing analysis reports focusing on train performance and delay attribution.

Panel

1. The operating console in a signalling centre, or panel box (as opposed to traditional lever frames).
2. See Track panel.

Pantograph

The current collector mounted on insulators on the roof of electric motor coaches or locomotives which bears against the contact wire. It is a collapsible frame, which follows variations in the height of the contact wire. When lowered, it disconnects the motor equipment from the overhead line equipment.

Parallel moves

Train movements over a junction or perhaps a series of junctions, the timetable for which is arranged so that more than one movement can be made at any one time. Generally, this can happen with face-to-face moves across a double junction. This makes the best use possible of available track capacity, as potentially conflicting moves between trains, with one delaying the other, are minimised. Clearly, the ideal is not always possible, so parallel moves are a timetable planner's aspiration rather than a requirement.

Parcels

Originally, a term for items carried by a train made up of coaching stock and other fully braked vehicles able to run at compatible speeds (thus including parcels vans), as compared with the much slower

Pantograph

Far left: North London Line local services between Richmond and North Woolwich need Class 313 dual-equipped trains which start their journey on fourth rail, then use the third rail on leaving Gunnersbury, changing to 25kV ac overhead at Acton Central, and then have to lower the pantograph again at Hackney Wick for the otherwise disconnected section of third rail to North Woolwich. This was the sign greeting the driver at Hackney Wick on 8 December 1998. *John Glover*

Left: The limited headroom in rail vehicles means that the pantograph needs to be recessed into the vehicle roof, as seen here with a Class 317 EMU at Cambridge. The internal roof height is similarly reduced. Passive provision is commonplace nowadays, even if the train is to be equipped with third rail pick-up only, since it increases its flexibility should there be a call for its use elsewhere. *John Glover*

Parcels

Left: Like other traffics, many associated problems are related to volumes and here the culprit is mail bags and the simultaneous sharing of the platform with passengers would clearly be undesirable. Note that the main stack has been placed almost entirely under the platform awning. This undated photograph is of Redhill (RH), a major point in the Post Office's distribution network. *Author's collection*

and less expensive transits expected with a goods train. Latterly, parcels traffic included Post Office mails, newspapers, mail order goods, fruit, fish and horse boxes. Red Star parcels were carried by nominated passenger trains on a station-to-station basis. Little of this traffic remains on rail nowadays, and most of such accommodation has been removed from passenger trains (or simply not incorporated in new builds). The main resultant problem has been lack of space for the carriage of bicycles.

Park-and-ride

The action of leaving a private car, motorcycle or bicycle at or in the vicinity of a station and then taking the train. The car park doesn't have to be railway owned, and the vehicle can be left on street if highway regulations so permit. Many station car parks were created from disused railway goods yards, which accounts for their long and narrow dimensions in many cases.

Parkway station concept

Below left: Many stations are provided with car parks, sometimes quite extensive. This is the up side of Preston station on 16 March 1999, where railway land used in the past for Lancashire & Yorkshire Railway services had been declared surplus. Clearly, a multi-storey car park would make better use of the land, but the solution adopted requires little more than surfacing, marking out and lighting. *John Glover*

Parkway station concept

A station built or developed with the specific intention of encouraging passengers to make car journeys to the station, which was provided with adequate car parking spaces. Good road or motorway access was thus an important consideration. Originally associated with long distance travel, the concept was later diluted.

P

Passenger demand
Passengers flock to join two-car 'Pacer' unit No 142051 at St Helens Central on a Wigan North Western to Liverpool Lime Street service. With three sets of folding doors only in an overall length of 31m, loading times on an urban service such as this will be relatively slow. *John Glover*

Parliamentary, or Parly, trains

Dating from the 1844 Act which required all railway companies to run at least one train a day on all lines calling at all stations, at minimal fares for the indigenous. Such Parliamentary trains could be inconveniently timed and as slow as only reluctant railway companies (but not all of them) knew how. The name stuck, and is today applied to trains deemed to have similar operating characteristics, although without offering cheap fares.

'The slowest times (in 1866) were those of the Parliamentary train, which left Bristol at 11.30am and pottered drearily through 118 miles of continual stops . . . to set down its privileged passengers at the London terminus at a quarter to six.'

Partnership stations

Local stations where the involvement of the community is sought, through station adoption, or the community use of station buildings, or through the support of a 'friends' group.

Passenger demand

Few people travel by train merely to experience the pleasure of the journey; the railway provides access which enables people to undertake other activities. Thus demand for travel is said to be derived (from that activity). Generally, passenger demand is derived from the levels of economic activity, employment, population, residential location, car ownership levels, fare levels, quality of service and competitive pressures, and how all of these are likely to change over time.

Passenger Demand Forecasting Handbook

A compilation of summaries of the many academic studies undertaken over the years on this general subject, compiled originally by the British Railways Board. It was designed to bring together evidence of the responsiveness of passenger demand to changes in external factors, prices, and aspects of quality of service. The aim was to assist managers in making decisions about investment or service planning, without further costly and time consuming research. See also Rail Industry Forecasting Framework.

Passenger journeys

The passenger journey and the number made is perhaps the most basic measurement which can be made of the business. It is easily derived directly from the number of single tickets sold, counting double for returns, and so on. Season tickets, rover tickets or similar are more problematic, as they require a view to be taken on the likely frequency of use. Often, passenger journey statistics will be compiled for a given section of line.

It may be observed that such computations will not include those who do not pay, for whatever reason. Staff travelling on duty are not passengers. The number of journeys made may also be estimated from physical counts.

Passenger line

A line used by passenger trains and signalled to the required standards on absolute block principles. See also Goods line.

Passenger miles/km

This statistic relates the number of journeys made times their length in miles or km. In many ways this is a more satisfactory measure than passenger journeys, as it differentiates between a journey from Euston to Watford Junction and one from Euston to Glasgow Central rather than treating them equally. However, both statistics have their uses, and the value of each depends very much on what information is required.

Passenger receipts

Crudely, the receipts from the sale of travel tickets at any particular station or group of stations, but which in practice have to be shared between operating companies according to the formulae devised under ORCATS and CAPRI/LENNON before that credited to any particular company can be calculated. There may also be miscellaneous receipts, for instance from car parking charges, the sale of timetables, or use of lavatories.

From the point of view of an individual TOC, it is the sum of all the fares allocations received by that company.

Passenger Service Requirement (PSR)

The minimum level of services which had to be provided by franchised passenger operators and so specified in the first round franchise agreements. The PSR for each TOC outlined the parameters within which it had to design a timetable and was set out route by route, specifying service characteristics. These included frequency of trains, stations to be served, maximum journey times, times of first and last trains, weekend services and through services.

PSRs could be changed only by a process of extensive stakeholder consultation, although derogations were available, for instance when engineering works prevented some services from operating. For franchises let since 2004, the PSR has been replaced by the Service Level Commitment.

Passengers' Charter

Franchised train operators are required to publish and adhere to a code of practice in dealing with passengers, which includes the payment of compensation for cancelled or delayed trains.

Passing loop

See Loop, passing.

Passing station

An intermediate station, usually a smaller station on a main line, at which the principal trains do not stop.

Path, pathing

The technical characteristics of the train, its stopping pattern and the time allowed for station stops (see Dwell time) at each station determine the time it will take to make a given journey between two timed points. These points are usually locations where a following train can pass the first train or where routes converge/diverge. In timetable terms, when drawn on a time/distance graph, the service will occupy a defined path. The art of constructing a timetable includes the assimilation of all such pathing requirements, including the resolution of junction conflicts, and producing a robust document as a result.

Pathing time

An additional time allowance made when timetabling services if unavoidable conflicts with another train or trains arise. The train which has to give way has pathing time added at the relevant point in its schedule, and shown as such in the Working Timetable.

Paved Concrete Track

See Slab track.

Pay train

A concept pursued energetically by British Rail, especially in Eastern England. Large numbers of stations were destaffed and tickets were issued on trains only for local journeys. Originally, single tickets were all that was available, with rebooking required if a change

of train took place. Later, a less oppressive regime took its place, with a greater range of tickets from a choice of outlets. 'Pay train' still indicates the acceptability (if not the need) of paying on the train, but it is a concept that fits ill with penalty fares schemes.

Peak hour

The peak hour itself, which is likely to vary according to location, is the busiest 60 minutes during the whole of the commuter peak period of about three hours.

Peak period

A period of maximum demand, usually associated with the twice daily commuter peaks. There are also business peaks, and those in connection with exhibitions, sporting events and entertainment generally. Such events are associated with the day concerned, but weekend travel has many differences from that on Mondays to Fridays. Other peaks such as holidays and tourism may occur on a seasonal basis, while travel to and from school is restricted to about 190 days per year.

Franchise agreements define the peak, that for Liverpool Street being trains arriving between 07.00 and 09.59, and departing 16.00-18.59. A less formal definition of peak periods is that they begin when the normal scheduled headways reduce (and more assets are used for service provision), and end when headways between trains return to normal.

Peak shoulder

The peak shoulder is the time of transition from or to the off peak, in the hour or so immediately before and after each peak period. During this time, when passenger numbers are rising (or falling), the transition in timetables has to be made. Ideally, both periods will see a gradual change, without any undue service gaps arising. Differential pricing policies can be used to move passengers into these periods where there is some spare capacity available; increasing peak capacity is much more costly for the operator.

PEARS

See Paladin Data Extract And Reporting System.

Pee Wee System

See Portable warning equipment.

Peg

Railway slang for a signal.

Penalty Fares Regime

A means of reducing ticketless travel, by insisting that passengers purchase a ticket before travelling. Failure to do so results in payment of a fare at a penalty rate. Such schemes apply in designated areas only.

A simple test applies:
- Has the passenger got a valid ticket for the whole journey being undertaken?
- If not, was it impossible for him to buy a ticket (or authority to travel) at the start of the journey? Impossible means just that, not that there was a long queue at the ticket office. An out-of-order ticket machine at an unstaffed station, with no alternative, is a valid reason.
- Were the statutory notices in place at the station of departure, warning that Penalty Fares were in operation?

If the answer to the first two questions is 'no', and the third question 'yes', a Penalty Fare is payable except in very limited defined circumstances. These include the journey starting outside the Penalty Fares Area, in which case the passenger could not have been expected to know about the conditions.

People on the railway

The following groups have been identified by HMRI:
- *Passengers*
  Any person who is on railway property and is travelling, or intends to travel, or has recently completed travelling on the railway. Passengers may be on the station premises (waiting to buy a ticket, waiting for a train, etc) or on a train. Note that people can be classified as passengers before they buy a ticket, and that this can sometimes be done on board the train.
- *Workers*
  Staff and contractors directly employed on the railway, including the train crew, station staff, signalling staff, etc, and contractors employed in the supply industries, maintenance facilities and disposal organisations. The workers may be employed at a fixed location or move about the railway.
- *On business*
  Those who visit railway premises as non-travelling 'passengers' such as people meeting or seeing off passengers, customers of station retail units, etc and (according to HMRI), train spotters. Also, those who are official visitors to the railway.
- *Level crossing users*
  Those crossing the railway on or at a level crossing. This includes pedestrians, horse riders and occupants of road and agricultural vehicles.
- *Trespassers*
  Those people who are on the railway who have no right to be there.

Performance allowance

An additional allowance which may be made when timing trains.

Performance And Loading Analysis Database of Information (PALADIN)

Provides a record of past train movements, showing 'actual against planned', details of any delays and their causes, which is available to all rail industry users.

Performance regime

That which rewards or penalises a TOC on the basis of its timekeeping and whether or not it runs all of its timetabled services over each four-weekly accounting period. While the approach appears reasonable and has many supporters, there are problems. These include the inhibitions on terminating a train short of destination as the best way of recovering from delays. Even if another operator is in a position to convey the passengers, the result of such an action is that the train is deemed not to have run at all.

Periodic review

The process under which the Office of Rail Regulation establishes Network Rail's revenue requirements for a five-year period.

Permanent speed restriction

A length of track over which the maximum permitted line speed is reduced permanently for a variety of reasons, such as track curvature or level crossing siting distances. The starting point of such a restriction is marked by an indicator, at the track side showing the speed permitted in mph (eg 50), and another where line speed is regained. Differential speed limits may apply to different classes of train.

Permanent way

A 19th-century term still in widespread use to describe the items which together provide the guidance and support systems for the railway. The term is often shortened to P Way, and includes rails, sleepers and their fastenings, the ballast underneath, plus any blanketing material and associated drainage.

Permanent way slack (PWS)

A temporary speed restriction, which may be applied to a section of line before, during or after work on the permanent way is undertaken. Before, due to the condition of the track and thus the cause of the work, and after, to give the formation time to bed down.

Permissive working

Arrangement where, in certain specified circumstances as authorised, more than one train can be in the same signal section at any one time. Station platforms are one example, if trains are to be separated or joined together. Another is goods trains or empty passenger trains awaiting entry to their respective depots on lines set aside for this purpose, and it is desirable to keep them as bunched up as possible to avoid tailbacks obstructing the running lines elsewhere.

Permit to travel Ticket Issuing machine (PERTIS)

Installed at stations where a Penalty Fares Scheme is in operation, these machines (which work only when the ticket office is closed) issue value 'tickets' in exchange for coins, minimum 5p. This receipt, which carries the name of the issuing station, time and date, as well as the amount paid, is prima facie evidence of the originating point of the passenger's journey. On presentation at a manned ticket office or to travelling staff, the passenger is then charged the normal fare (net of any Railcard discount), less the amount paid. Failure to produce such a receipt (or other authority) will incur a Penalty Fare.

This is aimed at those without tickets who arrive at (say) Victoria and who have come from Brighton, but claim to have come from Battersea Park. It does however depend on manual or machine checking at some point during the journey and the collection of any excess. If there are no checks, even an honest passenger has no way of paying any balance due if the ticket office at the destination station is also unmanned.

Personal track safety (PTS)

The duties and responsibilities of those whose work requires them to be present or to work on or around the track for which a Personal Track Safety Certificate (PTSC) must be held.

PERTIS

See Permit to travel Ticket Issuing machine.

PFI

See Private Finance Initiative.

Physical needs break (PNB)

For footplate staff, guards and conductors only; a guaranteed break in a turn of duty to allow the taking of refreshments and toilet visits. Also used informally by other staff, usually as initials, to indicate a need.

Pick-up shoe

A sprung device enabling an electric train to pick up traction current from the conductor rail in a third-rail system. The shoe is mounted on the bogie and slides along the conductor rail. A number are distributed throughout the train, on both sides, to allow for the conductor rail changing sides for pointwork or other reasons, and to avoid gapping (which see).

Piggyback

The carriage of a road semi-trailer, complete with wheels, on a rail wagon. Fairly common in the United States, this system is not employed extensively in Britain at present, owing to loading gauge restrictions.

P

Pilot locomotive

1. A locomotive in a depot, station or yard, usually a diesel shunter and semi-permanently stationed at that point. The pilot is used for moving vehicles within the area for duties such as re-forming trains or repositioning rolling stock for maintenance. It is, effectively, the shunting power on call.

2. A locomotive which is sent out with the appropriate staff to inspect the line in advance of revenue-earning traffic after (say) severe overnight weather conditions, to ensure that it is free from obstruction and safe for use.

3. A locomotive which is added to double head a train is said to be piloting the train locomotive.

Pilotman

Person provided to accompany a train driver where a train is to be diverted over a route of which the driver has no route knowledge, or to manage rail traffic over a single line during equipment failure or similar circumstances.

Pinch bar

A long bar which can be used to move rail vehicles manually over short distances within sidings or similar, by using it to exert pressure at the wheel/rail interface.

Pinch point, bottleneck

A location on the rail network where the number of train movements is close to, or is projected to exceed, the capacity of that location. In nearly every case, the limitation is time specific, albeit that it may last for large periods of the operating day. Often, such locations are where the cost of providing extra capacity would be phenomenal, there might be serious environmental objections, or both. Examples are between Manchester Piccadilly, Oxford Road and Deansgate, where the two track railway is carried on brick arches through the centre of the city, or in the Welwyn area where four tracking requires the construction of a second Digswell Viaduct, the doubling of two tunnels, and the reconstruction of Welwyn North station. (It should be noted that the cases cited are not engineering problems as such.)

Piped (only)

Dating back to days when automatic brakes controlled from the locomotive were an exception, the piped wagon was a compromise. It had no automatic brakes itself, but was through 'piped' and fitted with connections to allow continuity of braking from the locomotive to the other fully (brake) fitted wagons on the train on either side. See also Brakes.

PIXC

See Loading of trains.

Plain line

The basic track formation, which is not interrupted by junctions or other features of a similar nature.

Planning and Resource Monitoring System (PROMISE)

A system to provide the controller of diesel units with the current status of all units regarding location and distances run since last maintenance. The planning mode is used for producing timetables on a 'what if' basis as well as unit diagrams, and a means of costing each option examined.

Plasma torch

A vehicle-mounted device which improves adhesion by the removal of contamination from the rail surface.

Platform

A raised structure from which passengers can join or alight from trains. May also be used for goods, but this is usually known as a dock.

Platform

Right: Platform width is all important when dealing with large crowds, especially when they are joining trains. Those alighting disperse quickly; those joining will wait, in ever increasing numbers, until their train arrives. This is Betws-y-coed, probably in the early 1960s, with a 'Derby Lightweight' unit disappearing in a cloud of exhaust towards Blaenau Ffestiniog. Today, there is but a single platform, that in the foreground. *BR/Author's collection*

Below right: The simple single terminal platform is used here at Glossop, Derbyshire, although this station used to have two platforms. It is at the rather awkward end of what was the 1,500V dc suburban service from Manchester Piccadilly. Trains need to reverse here to also serve Hadfield, which is the real terminus of the line today. This is 25kV ac unit No 323235 on 12 June 2002. *John Glover*

Platform to train stepping distance

Bottom right: The gap between platform and train is dependent upon the length of the vehicle, track curvature and its cant, and the relative heights of each. This is demonstrated in this 1995 picture by some 23m MkIII coaches of Irish Rail, which show that the problem can become substantial. *John Glover*

Platform coping

The stones or concrete slab which forms the track side edge of a station platform.

Platform furniture

Semi-permanent items such as bars for securing bicycles, CCTV cameras, clocks, lighting, public address systems, seating, signage, telephones, ticket machines, timetable boards, train running displays, etc; also moveable items such as A boards for chalked messages and similar.

Platform ramp

The slope at the end of the platform, provided to avoid accidents to passengers accidentally stepping off a vertical edge, especially after dark, and injuring themselves.

Platform to train stepping distance

This is a function both of the height of the floor of the train relative to the platform surface, and the horizontal distance from the platform edge to the nearest point within the train. The problem of the horizontal distance is exacerbated when platforms are on curves, and it affects the ends or the centre of the rail vehicle depending on whether the curve is concave or convex.

PNB

See Physical needs break.

Point clips and scotches

A manual means of securing the position of a set of points, often used in the event of power failure. A metal clip (or clamp) secures the closed switch rail (the part that moves) to the stock rail (that which is fixed), and is padlocked. A large tapered wooden scotch is also inserted between the open switch rail and the stock rail, thus preventing the open switch rail from closing. Such long-standing methods illustrate well the traditional 'belt and braces' approach to railway safety.

Another use for a scotch is to place it between a wheel of a wagon and the railhead, to stop the wagon from moving.

P

Point heater
Top: Gas-powered point heaters, showing the considerable length of rail which needs to be heated to make them effective. *BR*

Points and switches
Above: This double slip is immediately outside London Liverpool Street station on the east side. While later practice preferred to place two simple turnouts back-to-back to achieve similar ends, this more complex construction uses far less longitudinal space. In some locations, and this is one of them, such space is at a premium. Extending the station platforms into the concourse area would have its problems too! *BR*

Point ends
The toe end of the point, which is worked by the signaller. One lever (or switch) may operate more than one point end. Thus, in the case of a crossover between two tracks, the two points are interlinked and need to move together. They thus become 'double ended' and are given A and B suffixes to the same number on the lever frame, as in 12A and 12B. They are still referred to as 'No 12 points'.

Point heater
Used to keep running lines operational in very cold weather, though not applied universally. May be electric, in which case the power supply can come from mains or batteries, or gas from the mains or nearby storage tanks. Both types are thermostatically controlled and activated when the rail temperature falls below freezing, to be switched off again when it rises to 3°C.

Point machine, point motor
Devices used to move the point blades to the position required. Usually electric, these need to detect the present position of the point blades and unlocking/relocking their clamplocks, as well as providing the impulse for actual movement from the position serving one route to the other. The clamplocks perform the same functions as point clamps.

Point-to-point times
See Sectional Running Times.

Point winding
The manual action of moving point blades which are normally powered with a crank handle, which locks into the mechanism.

Points and switches
Alternative terms for the construction of two fixed rails and two moveable rails plus a crossing, by which means trains may be directed from one track to another track. In general, the term 'points' is used by operators and signal engineers, and 'switches' by civil engineers.

Points, facing and trailing
These are terms used to describe the direction in which a set of points is encountered. Thus, if approached from the end which allows a choice of routes to be taken (the toe), they are said to be 'facing'. If approached from either of the other two converging ends, they are described as 'trailing'. Hence expressions such as 'trailing through a set of points'.

Points, facing point lock
Points on passenger running lines which are normally approached from the toe end must be locked in position before they are used, and there needs to be a positive detection to confirm that this is so. Point locking ensures first that the points are fully over to the required position, and then that they are locked into that position. It is achieved through the use of a stretcher bar fastened between the two switch rails, in which two notches are cut. These correspond with the two possible positions of the points. The signaller unlocks the points by withdrawing a bolt in one of the positions, moves the points, and places the bolt into the other position.

Points, mechanical
Those operated without any form of power assistance, from a signalbox, a shunting frame or an adjacent lever in the yard.

Points, position
All points are deemed to have two positions: 'normal' and 'reverse'. 'Normal' is the way which points are likely to spend most of their time in a mechanical system — probably the straight-on position. By pulling the point lever, the signaller will put the points into 'reverse'. This has no connotation in terms of the direction of movement of the train.

Points, turnouts
Both these terms are used for the track formation where one route diverges from another, controlled by the movement of the point blades.

Points, uncontrolled
Points which in normal circumstances are approached only in a trailing direction, and the weight placed on them by the leading set of wheels of a train is deemed sufficient to move the points to the required position (if they need to change). Normally used only in relatively low speed applications; if the points are to be used in the reverse direction of travel, they must be clipped and scotched on each occasion.

Portable Ticket Issuing System (S)PORTIS
A smaller version of the ticket office APTIS machine, worn around the neck by mobile staff for use on pay trains, or mounted on a desk in a small office. The range of tickets issued is necessarily more restrictive, and these are on paper rather than thin card. Credit card transactions may be made. The (S) denotes a modification to accept credit card transactions.

Portable warning equipment (Pee Wee System)
This system provides an audible warning of an approaching train from a Distant Lookout to a Site Lookout and hence a gang working on the track. This uses a cabled telephone link and loudspeaker. When the Distant Lookout's plunger is depressed, the 'Safetone' is replaced by a continuous warning sound, the receipt of which the Site Lookout acknowledges by telephone. Other warning devices use track circuit occupation or involve vibrators that are worn by the staff.

Portal
1. Type of overhead line support, from its shape.
2. Entrance to a tunnel.

Portion working
Where a train is divided into two (or possibly more) separate portions as it proceeds along its route, each with its own destination or calling pattern, or maybe for part of the train to terminate short of final destination. Similarly, trains in the reverse direction will be joined up.

PORTIS
See Portable Ticket Issuing System.

Positive train identification
Where a train transmits its reporting number rather than let the signalling system work it out for itself from the occupation of track circuits.

Possession
The railway is normally considered to be open for traffic, whether or not any trains are running. The main occasion when this is not the case is when engineers (of any discipline) take the possession of a specified section of railway. This enables work to be carried out

Points, facing point lock
Above: A facing point on the West Coast main line electrification, operated by the motor on the left-hand side through mechanical linkages. Centre is the locking bar, which ensures that once set, the point blades don't move. *BR*

Left: The point motor and facing point lock are prominent in this view of the South Eastern line north of Grove Park on 5 March 2005. Also noticeable is the sizeable length of track over which there is no third rail for electrical pick-up for trains. This however is more a problem for locomotives, since multiple-units are much less likely to become gapped.
John Glover

which it is not possible or safe to undertake when the railway is open for traffic. Such possessions will normally be pre-arranged, with alternatives made available for the duration for both passenger and freight traffic. The physical lengths (limits) of possessions, which may not be for all running tracks where there is more than one, will be related to the incidence of crossovers and other features needed to run a restricted commercial service.

The limit of a possession is marked at each end by a double-sided indicator displaying the word 'Stop' on a red sign, with red lights.

The engineer may run his own trains within the possession limits. It must also be appreciated that civil engineers (in particular) frequently need to have at their command the use of trains carrying materials into

Left: The replacement of old signalling by new has to be strictly controlled. This is Rugby on 12 September 1964, with a bracket semaphore being dismantled to the extent of having its arms removed. The replacement colour light signal carries an 'X' to indicate that it is not yet in use. The new power box is in the background. *BR*

Below left: The operations console of the power box installed at St Pancras in 1957, showing the 205 route setting switches and the illuminated track diagram above. It controls, however, no more than the station area, whereas the West Hampstead power box which replaced it and others, controls the Midland from Moorgate through to Sharnbrook, over 60 route miles. *BR/Author's collection*

the site, and others for the disposal of waste, for which access to and from the possession has to be made available. This may also apply to on-track machinery.

There are frequently a number of separate work sites within a single possession, thus making cost effective use of the period of railway closure.

At the end of the possession, the line is 'given up' to the operators.

Power signalbox (PSB)

The large number of relay-operated power signalboxes built during the 1960s and 1970s eliminated much of the mechanical signalling then prevalent. The new control areas were of unprecedented size, albeit that trains were controlled by signallers using push buttons on an illuminated diagram of the signalled network. Each train, and the route set for it, was indicated by a path of lights which changed colour as it progressed. Signals returned to danger automatically. To aid the signallers, the eNtry-eXit (NX) system was introduced. By depressing a button at the point where the train entered the panel (or a specific part of it) and another button at the exit point, the relays set up the routeing without further signaller involvement. The result could of course be overridden if thought inappropriate for any reason, but the system did reduce the pressures on signallers considerably. Such power boxes are now in course of replacement.

Generally, in the first generation power signalboxes, all the interlocking was located in the PSB, with hard wiring running out separately to each lineside connection. Later generation installations used a computerised interlocking in the PSB with single pair data-transmission wires only to lineside equipment. See Solid State Interlocking.

Powers and duties of public bodies

In the UK, other than at central Government and Parliamentary level, public bodies, including the Office of Rail Regulation, local authorities and PTEs are created by statute. They are invested only with the powers and duties contained in statute. Unless specifically authorised so to do, they cannot 'invent' additional powers or duties which they wish to carry out. There is a distinct difference between duties, which they are *obliged* to undertake, and powers, which they *may* exercise if they so wish. In either case, the enabling legislation may specify the objectives of such action, how funding will be carried out, the methods to be used, and any other requirements or constraints.

PPM
See Public Performance Measure.

PPP
See Public Private Partnership.

Predictors
A form of high-tech track circuit, which is independent of the signalling system. Predictors use the rails to transmit audio frequencies. Effectively, the rails form a long inductor. Predictors may be used to activate a level crossing protection sequence (as an alternative to conventional track circuit control with treadles etc). The Predictor is so called as four seconds after an approaching train has entered the level crossing area, it predicts when it will reach the crossing itself and so adjusts the operating cycle to fit. Conventional systems have to allow for a range of speeds, which increases the time the crossing is closed to road traffic. Predictors can also inhibit the sequence if the train stops at a station on the approach to the crossing, holding the road warning until the train moves off.

Preserved railways
Railways which have been closed and are thus no longer part of National Railways, but have been acquired by groups who use them to operate services re-creating scenes of the past. Usually partly or totally operated by steam traction.

Preserved railways and Network Rail
Standard gauge preserved railways fall into four categories:
- Those where there is a running connection with Network Rail. Example: Norton Fitzwarren, West Somerset Railway.
- Those which meet Network Rail at a point where passengers can change trains at the same or an adjoining station. Example: Alton, Mid-Hants Railway. In such situations there is also likely to be a physical rail connection.
- Those which, at present, are remote from any operational part of Network Rail. Example: Bluebell Railway, which has ambitions to reach a new station at East Grinstead and hence Network Rail.
- Those which are remote from Network Rail and likely to remain so. Example: Avon Valley Railway.

The existence of a connection does not necessarily imply that it is in regular use, nor that it is suitable for use by trains carrying passengers.

Pressure ventilation systems
Pressurised heated air is fed, at thermostatically controlled temperatures, into the coach at seat level. There is no separate distribution of cool air. The aim is to provide a better distribution of warm air than is achievable with radiant heaters. Quantity production was first seen with the early MkII builds of coaching stock.

Private Finance Initiative (PFI)
PFI was introduced by the Conservative Government in 1992 and '93. It allows the public sector to contract with the private sector to provide services on a long-term basis, typically 25-30 years, to take advantage of private sector funding and management skills incentivised by having private finance at risk.

The private sector takes on the responsibility for providing a public service against an agreed specification of required outputs prepared by the public sector contracting body. The private sector can thus carry the responsibility and risks for designing, financing, enhancing or constructing, maintaining and operating

Preserved railways and Network Rail
Virgin Trains' CrossCountry DEMUs reach some unexpected destinations; here, a Virgin 'Voyager' No 220001 forms a local Bishops Lydeard to Minehead service on 10 May 2003. It was photographed leaving Watchet station, West Somerset Railway, as the 14.48 departure during the railway's Cross Country event.
John Glover

capital assets, to deliver a service in accordance with an output specification.

Typically, the contracting body pays for the project through a series of performance or throughput related payments (based on usage or availability). These cover service delivery and return on investment. The London Underground Public Private Partnership for infrastructure maintenance and renewal are interesting examples.

See also Public Private Partnership.

Private sidings
A siding or a group of sidings connected to the national network. These provide access to commercial premises, such as factories, although there are relatively few such sidings nowadays. On a larger scale are power stations, which receive coal by rail, or oil refineries which despatch by train petroleum products which have arrived there by sea. These sidings may be owned by a company, a group of companies, or perhaps a body such as a dock or harbour authority. They are not part of the national network and are thus outside the control or responsibility of Network Rail. The point where ownership changes is likely to be marked, perhaps by a gate. Larger siding complexes may use their own (or hired) locomotive power for internal movements, but the use of the train engine from EWS (or other supplier) to carry out limited supplementary moves is more usual.

Private sidings
A traditional private siding complex north of Redhill, Surrey, with its own diesel power. In the background is the Quarry line, avoiding Redhill. In the foreground are the premises of Hepworth Minerals & Chemicals, leading to the sand pits beyond the rail bridge in the background. The whole is, or rather was, accessed from the original Redhill line. *BR*

Proceed
Green signals give the driver permission to proceed, without restriction. Yellow or double yellow signal aspects still allow the driver to proceed, but are themselves indications of a red danger signal either one or two signals ahead and thus the need to control the speed of the train so that it may be stopped at the red. Permission to proceed is tempered with the rider 'if it is safe to do so'.

Profit centre
A separately identified revenue-generating activity which may consist of single flows of traffics, groups of flows or passenger services.

Project manager
The manager responsible for the delivery of the project to the timescale and budget specified.

PROMISE
See Planning and Resource Monitoring System.

Propelling
The act of moving a train using a locomotive other than at the front, which has obvious limitations because of the position of the driver. See also Driving van trailer and Push-pull operation.

Protection
Basic protection is afforded to a train by the signalling system. However, in the case of a train failure or other cause which prevents it from being moved in an unusual location, ie from where it has come to an unscheduled stop, or if it is involved in a derailment or more serious accident, additional protection needs to be secured to prevent another train from hitting it or any part of it.

PROTIM
A computer-based system for train timing and pathing. Train planners enter details of the stations at which a proposed service will call, and journey timings are produced as timetables in a variety of formats.

PSB
See Power signalbox.

PSR
See Passenger Service Requirement and Speed restrictions, permanent (PSR).

PTSC
See Personal track safety.

Public Performance Measure (PPM)
The statistical compilation required by the SRA for a specified group of rail passenger services in terms of how their actual times of arrival at their final destinations compare with those advertised in the public timetable. Separate measurements are made for each four-weekly financial period. Results are presented as the percentage of trains arriving at their destinations within five minutes of scheduled time, or ten minutes for long distance trains, and are the basis of levying penalties.

Public transport, integration
The rebuilding of Feltham station was to provide a much improved bus interchange, especially that to Heathrow Airport. This is a view of the forecourt on 31 July 2000.
John Glover

Public Private Partnership (PPP)

PPPs are a development of the Private Finance Initiative (PFI) introduced by the Labour Government in 1997 as part of its strategy for delivering public services. The term is used internationally to refer to PFI-type arrangements. With private sector finance, PPPs bring together a public body and a private company, usually in a long-term contract, for the delivery of high-quality public services. They bring additional investment resources for investment in the public sector, and the management of that investment.

The Government recognises from experience that the public sector is not always best placed to procure and deliver major investment projects, and that the private sector can bring benefits such as:
● A challenge to inefficiency and the development of imaginative approaches to delivering public services.
● An incentive to invest in the provision of high-quality assets to optimise long-term maintenance and operating costs (whole life costs).
● A strong incentive to manage the risks associated with completing complex investment projects to time and on budget, and providing quality services thereafter, as payment occurs only when the assets are complete and the service is being delivered.
See also Private Finance Initiative (PFI).

Public service contract

A contract regulated by EU law between a transport undertaking and a competent authority (of an EU member state) in order to provide the public with transport services additional to those which would be offered commercially, and for which state compensation (subsidy) may be paid.

Public transport

Transport by rail, bus or other mode, whether publicly or privately owned, providing a scheduled and generally available service to the public on a regular and continuing basis. Services which are not available to the general public (for instance, chartered operations) are not normally considered to be public transport. Opinions vary as to whether or not taxis are public transport as they do not fit such a definition, so it is preferable to refer to public transport including (or excluding) taxis, to ensure the meaning is clear.

Public transport, adequacy

To be considered under the four headings of Affordability, Availability, Accessibility and Acceptability. (*DETR, July 2000*)

Public transport, integration

An integrated public transport network is one which includes:
● More through ticketing.
● Better facilities at stations and other places for interchange.
● Better connections between and co-ordination of services.
● Wider availability and provision of information on timetables, route planning and fares.
● A national public transport information system available over the telephone, internet, etc.
(*Future of Transport White Paper, Cm 3950, July 1998*)

Pull off, pulled off (a signal)

The signaller (or the system) operates the signal to give a proceed rather than a stop indication. Derived from the physical action in a mechanical signalbox.

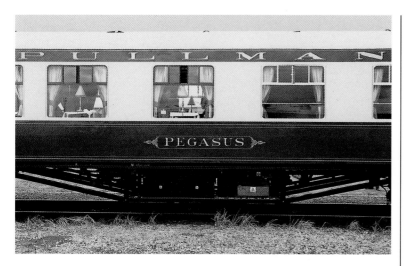

Pullman cars

The Pullman Car Co owed its existence to George Mortimer Pullman and his works in Chicago. Pullman pioneered the idea of luxury train travel, and his dining cars were first seen in Britain in 1874. Later, the cars were all built here. Supplementary fares were always charged for Pullman travel, with its 'at seat' service. The British company became a wholly owned subsidiary of the British Railways Board in 1963, but eventually the name Pullman represented only a style of service in ordinary vehicles.

However, the name lives on in the British operations of Venice Simplon-Orient-Express, offering quality days out, and in the dining operations of some preserved railways.

Push-pull operation

Push-pull operation has a long pedigree, but current use is to enable what is nominally a locomotive-hauled train to be driven from the other end. This avoids the time (and space)-consuming running round ritual at each terminus, and also in some cases the need for a turnover locomotive.

To do this, a driving trailer with full cab is required, and a means of connecting this to the locomotive to relay the driver's commands. The jumper cables between vehicles, provided originally for train lighting and public address systems, are used for Time Division Multiplex (TDM), an electronic data transmission system, which fulfils these requirements.

Major users are GNER with its Class 91s and Driving van trailers, and One Anglia's operations from Liverpool Street.

Push out (a train)

May be used in the event of a failure, when the succeeding train is used to push the failed train to a location where it can be got out of the way.

Put back (a signal)

This could be the action by the signaller of returning the signal to danger, in the normal course of events. However, the term usually implies that it is done to stop a train for which the route has already been set.

Such action has its problems, in that the train may have already passed the signal, or if not, it may be too late for the driver to stop at the signal. Putting back a signal should take place only in an emergency, or otherwise in strictly controlled conditions. If, for instance, a train has inadvertently been wrongly routed, there has to be a way of remedying the situation, but that does not include putting the signal back in the driver's face when he is travelling at speed.

Put inside

Diverting a train onto the slow line or into a passing loop, to get it out of the way of higher priority traffic.

PWS

See Permanent way slack.

Q-path

Q is a shorthand term for 'runs as required'. Such paths are incorporated into the Working Timetable on the basis that if they are needed for traffic or other operational reasons, they can be activated easily and without causing repercussions to the normal booked services. An example would be football traffic, in the sense that a timetable footnote might read 'runs only when Spurs are playing at home at White Hart Lane'.

Many Q-paths are provided for freight services which do not run every day or only when traffic is available.

Q-Trains

Special additional trains used by BT Police, which appear 'normal'. They are used when tackling route crime on the railway and stop to allow Police to pursue trespassers.

Quadruple track

Where there are four running lines, normally two for each direction. They may be arranged up, down, up, down, or up, up, down, down.

Quiet coaches

Those so designated, in which passengers are requested not to use mobile phones (in particular, but also radios and personal music players), so as not to disturb others.

RA

See Route Availability.

Race trains

Special trains run in connection with racing events, eg to Newbury, which is endowed with a special station (Newbury Racecourse) or, more generally, extra trains to destinations such as Epsom, which has a suburban-type service frequency anyway. Another approach is to insert special stops in trains as at Plumpton, where the service during the day is normally very sparse, but it happens to be on the main line to Eastbourne. Trains may also be strengthened.

Radio Electronic Token Block (RETB)

Traditional signalling on single lines requires the driver to carry a unique token of authority, which he holds during his passage of the single line section. This is given to him by the signaller at the entry to the single line section, and surrendered by the driver to the signaller at the exit point. This is the basis of all such systems of which there are several varieties, but what all have in common is the need for a signaller at each end of the single line section.

To reduce staffing costs, an answer developed during the 1970s and '80s was the Radio Electronic Token Block system (RETB). The signaller issues the driver with an electronic token, by radio. Thus signallers can control long routes without the expense of lineside cabling, extended traffic hours are possible at reduced cost, and engineering possessions can be given with minimal disruption to traffic. On the other hand, each driving cab has to be fitted with radio and other equipment, and journey times are slightly extended. RETB is suitable only for lightly used lines due to the volume of oral radio transmissions.

It was installed on the East Suffolk line, the Cambrian, and several lines in the Scottish Highlands.

Rail

Lengths of rolled steel, commonly 60ft (18.288m) and of a determined cross-sectional profile and weight per unit length, pairs of which in parallel support and guide the flanged wheels of a railway vehicle.

Rail creep

The longitudinal movement of rails caused by traction and braking forces, associated particularly with jointed track. This results in the rail 'bunching up' at some locations and gaps opening out at others. This causes dangers of buckling in hot weather and strains on the rail joints respectively. In both cases, track adjustments are then necessary.

Rail grinding

Action carried out by on-track machinery to remove corrugations in the rail surface and thus to extend the life of the rail. This is a noisy process, creating many sparks. The immediate effect of these corrugations is vibration, raising the noise level in trains and giving rise to that phenomenon which is often known as 'roaring rails'. In turn, the vibration causes damage to the track through the loosening of fastenings and deterioration of the geometry.

Rail Industry Forecasting Framework (RIFF)

A replacement of the Passenger Demand Forecasting Handbook to reflect the inadequacies found in the latter in explaining demand growth since the late 1990s.

Rail joint

The connection between two adjoining rail ends, made by the use of fishplates, to provide a continuous running surface.

Rail Journey Information Service (RJIS)

A computerised train service information system available to booking offices, NRES staff and on-line enquiries. It is sourced from the Train Service Data Base and allows journey information queries to be made and seats to be reserved. Amendments are down-loaded daily to cater for engineering work, other short term alterations and any new timetable.

Rail skate

Where a vehicle has a wheel which is seized and will not rotate freely, this small, two-wheeled device is attached to provide guidance along the railhead and thus enables it to be moved at reduced speed.

Rail Settlement Plan (RSP)

The ATOC scheme which allocates revenue from ticketing and arranges the settlement of accounts between TOCs.

Rail Vehicles Records System (RAVERS)

See Rolling stock library.

Rail, bull-head (BH) and flat-bottomed (FB)

The traditional rail used on British railways was the bull-head section, with a railhead of rather deeper dimensions than the base. The whole rested in cast-iron chairs attached to the sleepers, and was held in place by sprung steel or wooden keys. Latterly, British Standard (BS) rails weighed 95lb/yd for main line renewals and 85lb/yd elsewhere.

The introduction of flat-bottomed rail offered a rail less prone to lateral distortion as a result of greater stiffness and a broad, flat base. It is capable of carrying heavy trains at high speed and at reduced maintenance costs. Rails are secured to the sleepers with the use of the Pandrol clip, an 18mm diameter spring steel bar (or equivalent). Anchorage is provided by a shoulder which is cast into the sleeper during manufacture. The standard FB rail now weighs 113lb/yd (56kg/m), but it is being replaced gradually by the more robust 60kg/m version.

Rail, bull-head (BH) and flat bottomed (FB)
Top: A well-maintained section of track using bull-head rail, with all the wooden securing keys correctly in place, holding the rail to the supporting chair. The very neat edge to the ballast shoulder may be noted. *Ian Allan Library*

Rail, flat bottom
Above: A demonstration cross-section of flat-bottomed rail showing why it is thus called and how it is secured to a concrete sleeper by Pandrol clips. Or, as the back of the print declares, somewhat unhelpfully: 'A still from the British Transport Film *British Rails are Long and Fast.' Author's collection*

R

Rail, continuously welded (CWR)
Right: The inherent flexibility of steel allows lengths of rolled rail to be welded together in depots and then transported to the site where they are to be installed. This reduces considerably the time spent on site, during which time the railway has to be closed to traffic. Six long lengths are being moved here on bogie bolster wagons. *Ian Allan Library*

Rail, lubricators
Below right: Rail lubricators can make a considerable mess of their surroundings if they are on the generous side in their dispensation of grease. This one is at Tir Phil, seen on 7 April 1984. *John Glover*

Rail, continuously welded (CWR)

Continuously welded rail is the result of welding together lengths of standard rails of 36m lengths, to form one long and unjointed length. The first phase is undertaken in the depot by the flash butt welding process. Rails are then transported to site, where they are installed and then welded together into longer lengths using the Thermit welding technique.

The advantages of CWR over jointed track are:
- Up to a third longer rail life.
- Maintenance costs around one half of jointed.
- Fewer rail breakages by eliminating cracks from fishbolt holes.
- Saves around 5% of traction energy costs.
- Increases sleeper life.
- Improves ride quality.
- Permits higher speeds.
- Reduces vehicle wear and tear.
- Eliminates rail joint noise, pleasing local residents.

See also Rail, stress

Rail, lubricators

These are grease dispensers located on the outside of sharp radius curves, and their objective is to reduce abrasive wear on the rails. The principle of operation is that when activated by passing traffic, a charge of lubricant is deposited on that part of the rail that will come into contact with passing wheels, which then distribute the lubricant along the rail.

Rail, stress

It is important to avoid the problems of stress due to varying ambient temperatures, leading to the buckling of continuously welded rail (CWR). This carries with it a considerable risk of derailment.

Stress in rails is dealt with on installation at the site, and is carried out by stretching CWR to reach the length it would be at a temperature of between 21°C and 27°C. It is then secured by clips, which hold the rail in place on the sleepers and at that length.

Where other lengths of rail abut the CWR section at either end, expansion joints (also known as adjustment switches, or breathers) may be installed. At these places, each rail is tapered to provide an overlapping joint, so that the pair of rails may slide together or apart for several millimetres, while still maintaining a continuous running surface. In such a way the thermal forces which cause longitudinal rail movement are dissipated.

Similar measures may be required at features such as long underbridges, which themselves are subject to expansion and contraction due to the same thermal forces.

Rail, stress restoration

Where continuously welded rail (CWR) is disturbed for reasons of maintenance, it needs subsequently to be restressed, so that the stress-free temperature is the same as it was before the CWR was disturbed.

Rail, welding

This is a butt weld between rail ends made by a flash butt welding process in a workshop. It is achieved by passing an electric current of around 30,000 amps through the rail ends. They become red hot, and are then forced together to form a fused joint. The excess metal is sheared off and the rail is ground smooth with a special grinder.

Railcar

Colloquial term for a diesel unit (one or two vehicles) on lightly used lines. The usage of 'car' is in the transatlantic sense and not that of a motor car. In the late 1950s when British Railways bought 22 small lightweight four-wheeled vehicles for branch work with around 50 seats each, they were termed Railbuses.

Railcards

Ticket which gives the holder the ability to purchase rail tickets at a reduced rate, usually with a discount of one quarter or one third on the fares available to the general public. There may be substantial restrictions on the range of tickets available, the times at which they can be used, and minimum fares payable. Railcards need to be purchased and are valid for 12 months. Those available to Senior Citizens, Young People and Forces personnel are protected; others such as the Family and Network Railcards are purely commercial. Some area railcards are available to their residents only.

Railhead

1. A rail passenger terminal which is publicised and marketed as a focus for accessing trains. This will often have additional facilities such as extra parking, good bus interchange, and higher quality waiting facilities. Railheads may sometimes cover substantial areas, for example St Austell, Cornwall, and Windermere, Lake District. See also Parkway stations.
2. A similar type of freight facility, serving a wide area.

Railway

A system of transport employing parallel rails which:
(a) provide support and guidance for vehicles carried on flanged wheels, and
(b) form a track which either is of a gauge of at least 350 millimetres or crosses a carriageway (whether or not on the same level), but does not include a tramway.
Transport & Works Act 1992, s67(1).

Railway Group Safety Plan

A plan setting out the collective health and safety performance and objectives of Railway Group members and the activities planned to deliver those objectives, particularly those related to good practice and co-operation.

Railway Group Standards

The mandatory operational and engineering standards for ensuring safety on the network, as administered by the Rail Safety and Standards Board (RSSB), a standalone company which is a wholly owned subsidiary of Network Rail.

Railway services

Defined by the Railways Act 1993, s82(1) as those for the carriage of passengers or goods by railway, light maintenance, or network services.

Rail, welding
Flash butt welding is carried out in permanent way depots, in this case at the Underground one at Ruislip as seen here on 18 May 2004.
John Glover

R

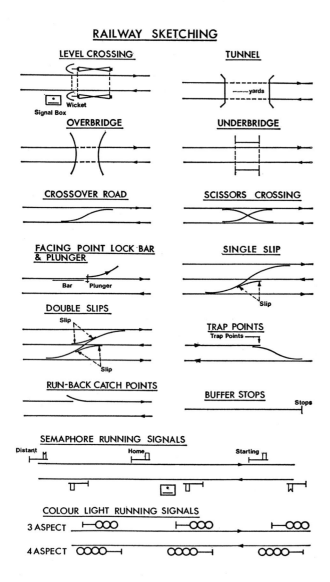

RAILWAY SKETCHING

LEVEL CROSSING

Wicket

Signal Box

TUNNEL

...........yards

OVERBRIDGE

UNDERBRIDGE

CROSSOVER ROAD

SCISSORS CROSSING

FACING POINT LOCK·BAR & PLUNGER

Bar   Plunger

SINGLE SLIP

Slip

DOUBLE SLIPS

Slip

Slip

TRAP POINTS

Trap Points

RUN-BACK CATCH POINTS

BUFFER STOPS

Stops

SEMAPHORE RUNNING SIGNALS

Distant   Home   Starting

COLOUR LIGHT RUNNING SIGNALS

3 ASPECT

4 ASPECT

Railway sketching
Above and far right: The preferred means of denoting various railway features when making sketches, as portrayed in the General Appendix, 1972. *BR/Author's collection*

Railway Safety Case
Each member of the Railway Group is required to have a Railway Safety Case as a prerequisite for running trains on railway infrastructure. It is a formal statement of the way in which safety related matters will be handled. A safety case is required by statute to be produced by all train and station operators and by all infrastructure controllers, the acceptance of which is a condition of the relevant operator's licence. A key item is an assessment of the associated risks.

Railway sketching
There are clear advantages in consistency in the symbols used in sketching suggested changes or incidents,

and the accompanying diagrams show some of the features more frequently encountered.

Railway station
See Station.

Railway time
Long obsolete, but still referred to occasionally. In the earliest days of railways, towns and cities across Britain kept local time. Thus in 1847 Carlisle was 12 minutes behind London, Edinburgh 15 minutes and Glasgow 17 minutes. The coming of the railway brought with it the need for standardisation (at Greenwich time), although this was not confirmed by legislation until 1880. However, 'railway time' was given out by the telegraph across the system at 10.00 every morning (or thereabouts). This enabled all signalbox and station clocks, and guards' watches, to be synchronised as part of a daily ritual. Hence the passenger-unfriendly response: 'I don't care what your watch says, we keep railway time here.'

Railway vehicle
'Anything which, whether or not it is constructed or adapted to carry any person or load, is constructed or adapted to run on flanged wheels over or along track.' Railways Act 1993, s83(1).

Rake
A term applied to a group of coupled wagons (sometimes coaching stock) implying it is probably complete and ready for the next movement to be made, or the term may be used purely descriptively for some future requirement.

RAVERS
See Rolling stock library.

Re-sleepering
The replacement of not more than one in three sleepers in the course of maintenance, known as 'patch', 'spot' or '1 in 3' re-sleepering.

Reach stacker
See Container handling.

Reach wagons
Where access to a siding is limited by bridge strength or track curvature, the use of reach wagons avoids the need for the locomotive to enter the area. Old wagons with bodies removed are kept nearby. Their sole purpose is to provide a buffer between the locomotive and the wagons to be propelled into (or drawn out of) the sidings concerned.

Real pricing
That part of a price increase which is in excess of inflation since the previous change.

Real Time Passenger Information System (RTPI)
Information to passengers on trains or stations that is updated to compare the actual progress of a train and the time it is expected to arrive, with the scheduled progress. Global Positioning by Satellite (GPS) transmissions are one way, but not the only way, of achieving this.

Reception sidings

Sidings adjacent to major yards or privately owned facilities (eg Ministry of Defence sites), used to receive or despatch a complete train. This recognises reality in that an arriving train cannot always be dealt with immediately, while a train which is made up and ready to go may still have to wait until the time of its booked path. However, should a slot become available earlier, it may be allowed to leave ahead of time.

Recessing

To recess a train is to get it out of the way of following (and by implication faster) services, normally by putting it into a loop or possibly a siding. The practicality of recessing depends critically on the availability of suitable facilities, and the time taken so to do. The loop, or siding, must also be long enough!

Recovery time

Additional time built into a timetable to allow for planned engineering works and associated speed restrictions during the currency of that timetable. Recovery time is then inserted where appropriate. However, the location will often move as the work progresses. Rather than make specific amendments to passing times at the usual timing points, which will become outdated, an additional allowance of x minutes is given over longer stretches, and is shown as such in the WTT. This approach is more difficult with stopping services, due to publicly advertised station departure times. Adjustments are usually made at the end of the journey, with the result that a train which leaves Finsbury Park five minutes late may miraculously arrive at King's Cross one minute early (on a good day). See also Pathing time and Performance allowance.

Rectifier

Apparatus for converting alternating current to direct current.

Red Card

The 'Not to go' red defective wagon label, which means it needs on-the-spot attention and is not fit to travel. See also Green Card.

Red Zone working

A site of work if it is on or near the line and it has not been possible to set up a Green Zone.

Refuge

A place of safety for employees to stand in tunnels, on viaduct parapets and in retaining walls, where recessed positions are cut into or extruded from the structure at intervals, or more generally alongside high speed lines and elsewhere if clearances are limited.

Refuge siding

A siding where a freight train can be placed temporarily, clear of all other traffic.

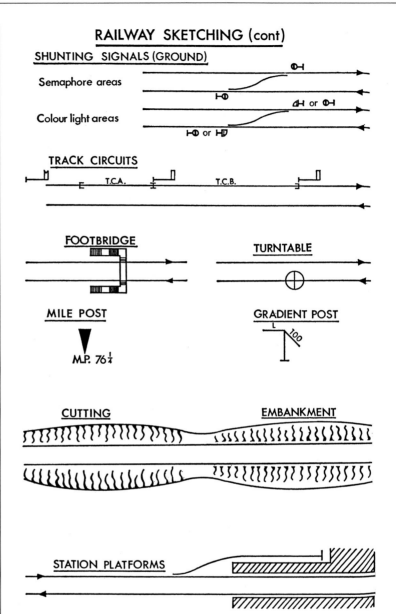

RAILWAY SKETCHING (cont)

SHUNTING SIGNALS (GROUND)

Semaphore areas

Colour light areas

TRACK CIRCUITS

T.C.A.   T.C.B.

FOOTBRIDGE

TURNTABLE

MILE POST

M.P. 76¼

GRADIENT POST

CUTTING

EMBANKMENT

STATION PLATFORMS

Refurbish

A major modification to an asset within its basic framework/body which improves its environment. Also applied to mechanical refurbishment when major modifications are made to improve performance.

Regenerative braking

A means of braking an electric train by harnessing and feeding back the energy which would otherwise just be dissipated. The traction motors are switched to become generators and the power they produce is returned to the traction current supply for use by other trains. However, for this to be effective, the other trains need to be taking current at the same time, and the electrification infrastructure configured to receive power.

Most urban timetables are regular interval, or as close to this as can be managed given physical layouts and the demands of other traffic. The West Yorkshire Airedale and Wharfedale services have to deal with electric services from both Leeds and Bradford to both Ilkley and Skipton, as well as between Leeds and Bradford themselves. Shipley station has platforms on all three sides of a triangle. Here, No 333012 forms the 15.15 Skipton to Leeds on 6 March 2003.
John Glover

Regional Planning Assessments
Produced by the SRA, each Assessment establishes the core functions of the railway in a region, and how these should evolve over the next 20 years. They also set out the priority passenger and freight markets, and what levels of capacity, frequency and journey times are justifiable. They will give the SRA's view on the best way of achieving them, including potential areas for capital investment.

Registration arm
The anchor for the contact wire in the overhead electrification system, which is a sliding fit on the support arm itself. This enables the position of the contact wire in relation to the track to be adjusted. This does not follow the centre line of the track but zigzags gently, the purpose of which is to even out the wear on the pantographs.

Regular interval timetable
A timetable similar to a clockface one, but although the services are regular, they are not necessarily evenly spaced. A service at 00, 05, 30 and 35 past each hour comes into this category. It should perhaps be added that there are a number of good reasons why this might happen, but it is generally undesirable if it can be avoided. See also Clockface timetable, and Trains per hour.

Regulation of trains
The giving of priority of one class of train over another, and the procedure to be adopted when services are running out of sequence due to lateness or otherwise. Such decisions are implemented by signallers, but the decisions may be made elsewhere. The overall objective is to minimise overall delays. Variants, strictly by agreement between all operators concerned, are applied on a geographical, a timeband, or individual train basis.

Thus Centro local trains are held for no more than three minutes on the Birmingham-Coventry corridor in favour of Virgin Trains in the peaks, but for longer at other times. Also, the 'Master Cutler' may get priority as a headline journey time service. See also Classes of trains.

Regulation tickets
Where passenger traffic is very heavy as the result perhaps of a special event, it is desirable to even out the loads between trains as far as possible. One possibility is to require all passengers to hold a regulation ticket, allocating them to a specific train but not to individual seats. This is more easily accomplished if tickets have to be purchased in advance. Alternatively, regulation tickets can be issued at the barrier for free, or perhaps on the outward journey of a train in respect of the return journey. Also known as boarding cards.

Relay
An electro-mechanical switching device used in many types of signalling systems. It 'relays' the instruction (eg set prescribed route for passage of train) to signals and points. The instruction however is activated only if certain prescribed circumstances are fulfilled, such as the route being clear of other trains. Now being replaced by solid state interlocking.

Re-laying
Renewal of some, or maybe all, of the components of a section of the permanent way.

Release
1. To allow a locomotive detached from a train at a terminal platform to escape via a crossover and a 'release road'.
2. A signalling term used in respect of actions needed (say) to free a ground frame for local control.

Relief line

Term used by the Great Western for the slow lines where there are multiple tracks, and which still applies today on the lines from Paddington. Trains on the GWR were never 'slow', or at least this was never admitted officially!

Reminder appliance, lever collar

Traditionally, a collar placed on a lever in a mechanical signalbox which prevents it from being released. It is put there to remind the signaller that there is some reason why it should not be operated, or operated only under certain conditions. By extension, similar reminders placed over control buttons or switches in power signalboxes or signalling centres.

Renewals, like for like

The restoration or refurbishment of an item, or replacement with an operationally equivalent new item, without any fundamental design change. This is, and always has been, a difficult area. Many railway assets have very long lives, and whether a similar item is available to replace one perhaps 25 years old is a question in itself. And even if it is, a prudent business might prefer to install a more modern asset which takes account of technical and design advances in the interim. The problem is that this can turn straightforward renewals into capital investment, hence the caveat in the first sentence about an equivalent item of the same basic design.

Repeaters (of signal indications)

A repeater arm in a mechanical box is an electrical indicator to the signaller that confirms the position of the semaphore signal controlled, in the relatively rare situation that it is not easily visible from the conventional signalbox installation.

Restaurant car

A coach which offers sit down meals to customers from an adjacent kitchen which may or may not be in the same vehicle; there is no counter service implied. It is usually necessary for passengers seeking such a meal to go to that particular vehicle.

Restricted clearances

Where these apply between track and lineside structures, these are indicated by a 300mm square red and white chequered board bearing the notice 'Warning, limited clearance'. If line speeds are greater than 100mph, a similar blue and white sign may appear with the notice 'Warning – no refuges'. In this case, they will be provided on the opposite side of the line.

Retail Price Index

Index of retail prices for a defined basket of goods which is published by the Office of National Statistics on a monthly basis.

Retail Price Index (RPI-x or RPI+x factor)

The RPI-x formula has been used by the Regulator to determine how the charges of a company such as a TOC's fares may be allowed to vary over time. It refers to the Retail Price Index, less a percentage 'x'. Thus if the RPI is running at 3.5%, and 'x' is determined to be 1%, the maximum price increase that the company can make in that year is 3.5%-1%, or 2.5%. In itself, that does not determine each and every individual fare. The usual approach is to apply the control to a basket of popular fares, the average increase of which equals RPI-x, or less. More recently, this has reverted to RPI+x.

Retaining wall

That needed to prevent earth slippage either onto or away from the railway.

RETB

See Radio Electronic Token Block.

Return conductors and booster transformers

These are provided on most overhead line electrification installations to reduce interference between the electrification system and signalling and communication circuits, both railway and non-railway. (Some OHLE schemes still have just a return wire.)

Revenue protection

Management action taken, mainly through an inspectorate, to reduce the amount of ticketless and fraudulent travel, and thus increase actual revenue.

Reverse

All sets of points have two possible positions: the route for which they are usually set (normal), and for the other route (reverse). This is reflected in the positions of levers in a mechanical signalbox.

Reverse curve

A curve which changes from a clockwise direction to an anticlockwise direction, or vice versa — an 'S' shape, without any intervening straight track.

Reversible signalling

A line (other than a single line) so signalled that trains may progress in either direction under the normal control of the signaller. Reversible signalling need not apply to all the parallel lines between two given locations.

Reversing siding

Any single-ended length of track used for reversing trains such that it does not block the running lines whilst stationary. See also Centre siding.

Rheostatic braking

The energy generated by the traction motors is dissipated in resistors (similar to large electric fire elements). The heat produced can be used to warm the train in cold weather, providing a degree of energy recovery.

RIFF

See Rail Industry Forecasting Framework.

Right side failure
The failure of a piece of equipment in a way that does
not compromise safety.

Right time
A train's scheduled (or booked) time of arrival or departure.

Ring fencing
A limiting condition applied to the provision of capital
funds, or any other funds or resources such as people,
which can be used only for the purpose intended.

Risk
The combination of the magnitude of the consequences of a defined hazard and the chances of its
occurrence. Greater accuracy in assessment will allow
risk to be controlled more precisely.

RJIS
See Rail Journey Information Service.

Road
Colloquial term used for running line, as in 'you've got
the road' to a driver when the controlling signal
changes from a stop to a proceed aspect.

Road learning (also route learning)
The process by which train crew become familiar with
the route over which they will work. This includes gradients, track layouts, and station and signal positions.

Road-rail vehicles
A motor vehicle which is equipped both with flanged
steel wheels for rail use, and with pneumatic tyres for
road use. One set is retracted when the other is being
used. The approach was pioneered as long ago as 1932
by the LMS with their Karrier 'Ro-Railer' bus. This ran
on the branch from Blisworth to Stratford-upon-Avon
and thence by road to the LMS-owned Welcombe Hotel,
a duty which lasted a mere two months.

Today, road-rail vehicles are used only for engineering work and may be found in all sorts of guises,
for instance excavators. They require the use of an
access point to and from a road (or lineside location)
but, most importantly, strict control needs to be maintained over their access to and egress from the track
and to receive suitable protection. It should also be
noted that such machines cannot be relied upon to
operate track circuits, and so often work only within
a possession.

Rodding
The mechanical system of rods and arms connecting
the point operating mechanism (manual or powered)
to the points themselves.

Rolling motorway
Where a whole unit, road tractor and trailer (or a rigid
vehicle) is driven onto a flat rail wagon, to be transported as a whole to its destination. The lorry drivers
travel separately in a carriage which forms part of the
train. No specialist lifting equipment is required, merely suitable loading and unloading platforms at each
end. The only use of such arrangements in Britain is
at Cheriton for Channel Tunnel freight shuttles to
Coquelles, Calais. Generally, the restrictions of the
British loading gauge prevent such operations from
use for domestic transits.

Rolling stock
The total rail fleet, often divided into locomotives
(although some would exclude them), hauled passenger vehicles, diesel units, electric units, freight vehicles and service stock for clarity. Rolling stock is
defined by the Railways Act 1993, s83(1) as 'any carriage, wagon or other vehicle used on track and
includes a locomotive'.

1. Rolling stock companies (ROSCOs)
The three rolling stock companies, present names
Angel Trains, HSBC Rail (originally Eversholt Leasing)
and Porterbrook Leasing, were sold to the private sector at the beginning of 1996. Each inherited from

British Rail a mixed portfolio of passenger rolling stock of different types and ages.

These vehicles are leased to the TOCs to provide franchised services. Each ROSCO is responsible for securing its own finance for the acquisition of any new rolling stock or the procuring of heavy maintenance for its fleets. Most TOCs have dealings with more than one ROSCO and are likely to have short-term leases on a proportion of their fleets to offer some flexibility. There is no obligation on TOCs or others to procure new rolling stock through a ROSCO.

One important effect of this arrangement for the TOCs is the transfer of rolling stock acquisition from capital to revenue account, so the large sums needed for outright purchase are no longer required.

Freight locomotives are generally owned outright by the freight companies, and the wagons by themselves or their customers.

2. Rolling stock leases

A lease is a contract between two parties in which one (the lessor) conveys to the other (the lessee) the use of an asset for a predetermined period in exchange for a periodic payment. This carries with it defined responsibilities such as its maintenance and general upkeep, insurance against various perils, the uses to which it may be put, and its condition upon the expiry of the lease when it is returned to the lessor.

At privatisation, a distinction was drawn between light maintenance (the responsibility of the operator) and heavy maintenance (the responsibility of the ROSCO). More recently, leases have become 'wet' leases, where the user is absolved from any responsibility for vehicle maintenance, and 'dry' leases where the lease is just a financing arrangement and the operator takes the maintenance responsibilities at all levels.

Thus the Alstom-built Class 170 trains in the North West are let on a wet lease, with the maintenance subcontracted to the manufacturer at Chester depot, while the Alstom Class 175s for First Great Western are on a dry lease, with the TOC undertaking all the maintenance itself.

3. Rolling stock examination

The aim of periodic examination is:
● To ensure the stock remains in a wholly serviceable condition.
● To examine elements of the stock not accessible in normal usage, for damage and degradation.
● To check and adjust wearing parts and consumable items to ensure they remain serviceable within defined limits.
● To check secondary protective structural devices.

The intervals between successive examinations are determined by the rate at which consumables wear out, and the time it is considered prudent to run the stock before having a good look underneath. In short, the aim is to make sure that nothing falls off.

With consumables, the time between replacements can be increased, but it must be recognised that the rate of wear depends upon the use made.

Thus, if a brake block is not fully worn when it is replaced some wastage will result, but this is unavoidable on a time interval based system rather than usage.

Additionally, rolling stock returning to service following maintenance needs to be tested, to guard against matters such as the incorrect renewal of wiring, which could induce wrong side failures.

4. Rolling stock heavy maintenance and repairs

The maintenance required to be performed on rolling stock under the relevant programme, including correction of corrosion of body shells and underframes necessary to ensure structural soundness. Heavy repairs include rectifications or modifications in connection with defective heavy maintenance, design or endemic faults, major faults and mandatory modifications.

5. Rolling stock library

A computer program devised by the BRB and used to record maintenance and engineering details of vehicles and components. This central register records all rolling stock, ensuring that no numbers are duplicated and attempts to maintain a logical approach to the grouping and sequencing of the various vehicle types and their number series.

Roster

A sequence of diagrams including rest days for crews.

Rough shunt

The act of shunting vehicles with insufficient care, causing damage as a result. See also Shunting.

Roundabout working

A track arrangement, the use of which returns the train to its place of origin. Examples include the Cathcart and Hamilton Circles, out and back from Glasgow Central, the Fife Circle, out and back from Edinburgh, or the Kingston and Hounslow roundabouts, out and back from London Waterloo.

Rodding
Point rodding and signal wires can be substantial tripping hazards, especially on a dark, wet and windy night. The problem is particularly acute outside mechanical signalboxes as this picture shows. *John Glover*

Route Availability (RA)

This is a system which originated on the LNER, in which all sections of route are classified by Network Rail on a scale RA1 to RA10. The highest number is the most restrictive and is based on the maximum single axle weight or the maximum equivalent load effect of a whole vehicle for underline bridges and structures. Over 80% of the network is in the RA7-9 group.

Each vehicle is allocated a corresponding route availability code (eg RA7), and may not be used on a route where the RA is lower (in this case RA1 to RA6). A vehicle with availability RA1 can go anywhere. See also Axle load.

Route crime

Criminal acts of trespass and vandalism etc associated with a defined section or geographical area of the railway. Nationally, accidental trespasser fatalities (as opposed to suicides) run at about 60 per year.

Route knowledge

It is a formal requirement that all train drivers must have been trained on all sections of route to be used by the train of which they have charge. If this is not the case, the driver must be accompanied over those sections by a pilotman with that knowledge.

Route miles (or km)

The distance between two given points along the length of the railway, irrespective of the number of tracks (see track mile). It is traditionally measured in miles and chains (1 chain = 1/80 mile or 22 yards), and mileposts (painted yellow unless made of concrete) are provided at $^1/_4$-mile intervals at the side of the track. Some of these are not infrequently missing. In interpreting the number of miles thus shown, it is necessary to know the location of the zero point from which they are measured. Many of these have more to do with railway history than present-day operation, but the system does make a coherent whole. Measurement in route km is still relatively rare.

Route modernisation

A term associated with major investment projects aimed at updating substantial sections of railway, for instance West Coast Route Modernisation. Note that there has to be a linkage with the trains that run on it; there is little benefit in building trains capable of 140mph (225km/h) route if the infrastructure is limited to (say) 125mph (200km/h). This has happened on both the East Coast and West Coast main lines.

Route Utilisation Strategy (RUS)

Individual strategies developed at line of route level, within the framework provided by the Capacity Utilisation Policy (Network Utilisation Strategy [NUS]). The aim is to provide properly performing train services which accommodate aspirations for growth in a way that maximises value for money and is affordable. They focus on short to medium term (three to ten years) railway service provision and on corridors where network capacity is constrained and there is pressure for further development of rail services.

RPI

See Retail Price Index.

RSP

See Rail Settlement Plan.

RTPI

See Real Time Passenger Information System.

Rule book

The book which incorporates the rules to be observed by personnel working on railway property, and those for the safe operation of the network. The latest version was brought into force on 6 October 2003, when its structure was changed to a series of task-based modules. The intention was to make it relevant to tasks performed in a fragmented and privatised industry.

Rules of the Plan

Network Rail's rules regulating, for any part of the network, the standard timings and other matters necessary to enable trains to be scheduled into the Working Timetable. Bids for paths by train operators must be compliant with these Rules, although there is a change procedure. These rules apply also to any bid from any train operator for additional paths.

Rules of the Route

For any part of the network, the rules agreed between Network Rail and the train operators for the imposition of speed restrictions or temporary line closures which are needed for infrastructure work. This includes the inspection, maintenance, renewal or repair of any track, or section of track, or any other railway asset, within that part of the network.

Ruling gradient

The ruling gradient is the steepest on a given section of line. This in turn determines the greatest load which can be worked over that line by a given locomotive at a given speed.

Run down, running down

Situation when a faster train catches up a slower train in front on the same line, to the extent that the driver of the second train receives caution signals and needs to reduce speed accordingly.

Run round

The track layout which allows a locomotive to be detached from its train at a terminal, move forward, then proceed on the adjacent track to a point beyond the former rear of its train, reverse again and couple up. Hence also the term 'release road', this being the track used by the locomotive in running round and without which (or if it is occupied by another train) the movement could not be made.

Run through

When a locomotive or train approaches a set of points from the trailing direction, and the points are set for the other direction, such action forces the switch blades over. The locomotive is then said to have run through the points. In itself the action is unlikely to cause danger, although there may be severe consequences in terms of a collision with another train in the vicinity. The cause may be anything from a signal passed at danger to a wrong indication by a hand signaller.

Running gear

That which is associated with actual movement, essentially most of those elements below floor level. It includes wheels, axles, axleboxes, bogies, brakes and suspension systems.

Running lines

The lines on which trains are run in traffic from place to place, as opposed to those in yards or sidings. They can be further divided into passenger lines where all types of traffic may be operated, and goods lines which are restricted to freight traffic. The distinction recognises a less rigorous safety requirement for goods lines, on which trains may stand one immediately behind another in the case of congestion, rather than being bound by a separate signalling section, as with all passenger trains.

Running rails

Those on which the train actually runs, as opposed to conductor rails, check rails, etc.

Running time

The scheduled time which a train of a given description and performance is expected to take between two given locations, without any additions or adjustments, and normally timed to the half minute. Times will vary according to whether the train stops at, or passes, any stations.

Point-to-point times are a more specific use of the same concept, usually implying that the two points concerned are the timing points used by timetable compilers and are those adjacent to each other.

RUS

See Route Utilisation Strategy.

S&C

See Settle & Carlisle, or Switches and crossings.

Safe walking routes

Routes on the railway infrastructure which are so designated as being the best available and with the least risk of being run down by a train, which suitably qualified staff or contractors are authorised to use. They should be clearly marked. By definition, such routes will be close to the operational railway, and may involve crossing it. Crossings (other than by bridge or subway) must be protected by train-operated warning systems wherever possible, but a minimum of 15 seconds' warning of a train's approach must always be available. Routes which are considered unsafe will sometimes be expressly forbidden.

Safety

The freedom from unacceptable risks of personal harm, that is the avoidance of accidents and incidents.

Safety case

See Railway Safety Case.

Safety critical defect

A defect, the assessment of which is deemed to be an immediate threat to the safety of trains, the public or the staff, and warrants trains being stopped or cautioned until remedial action is undertaken. The railway term 'cautioning a driver' is used in the sense of a need to take extra care; it is never used in the disciplinary sense.

Safety critical work

That which has the potential to affect adversely the safety of the railway and hence its users, or the health and safety of individuals undertaking that work.

Safety duty

All railway operating companies owe a duty to passengers, workers, railway neighbours and trespassers not to cause them harm. The duty is the same for all four groups, and the requirement is to reduce the risk to each of them to a level which is as low as reasonably practicable (ALARP). However, what is 'reasonably practicable' is not necessarily the same for each group, or within each group. The threshold is set by the Courts to reflect society's demands, which themselves change over time. (Duties arising under the Health & Safety at Work Act 1974.) Operators of railway infrastructure, trains, stations and light maintenance depots are required to have a safety case (to be replaced by safety certificates).

Safety Risk Model (SRM)

The Safety Risk Model is based on the quantification of the risk resulting from hazardous events occurring on the main line railway that have the potential to lead to fatalities, major injuries or minor injuries to

S

Sand drag

Right: At the west end of Rye station, where there is a passing loop on the line from Ashford to Hastings, the line becomes single track again. A sand drag is provided (right), so that any down train which starts away from the station platform (in the distance) without authorisation will be diverted into the sand drag. Depicted on 25 May 1999. *John Glover*

Seating arrangements

Bottom: A generous 2+1 seating arrangement as used in the first class of Anglia's Class 170 units, in this case No 170203, seen on 25 June 1999 when these units were new. *John Glover*

passengers, staff or others. This aim is achieved by identifying and analysing various hazardous events, grouped within the incident categories: train accidents, movement accidents and non-movement accidents relevant to the operation and maintenance of the system.

Sand box

Receptacle on the locomotive etc, which contains sand used for improving adhesion.

Sand drag

An inexpensive and low maintenance device in which the rails approaching a stop block are surrounded by a trough for a distance of perhaps 20m. This is filled with sand up to the railhead level. It is an effective means of decelerating trains fast, causing minimal damage in the process. Often provided in connection with trap points, or in addition to stop blocks.

Sandite

This is a widely used slurry of antifreeze with suspended particles of sand. This abrasive gel is deposited on the railhead, where it is designed to improve adhesion. It is used during extreme winter weather conditions, and also during the leaf fall season. Special trains carry out the work, and these are often old diesel multiple-units which have had the seats removed to accommodate the storage tanks. Sandite S4 also contains steel shot, to assist in the operation of track circuits.

Sandite is effective; the main problem is that when temperatures are around freezing any rain will wash it off the rails, which then require new treatment. A similar product is known as Traction Gel.

Scotch

See Point clips and scotches.

Scratch set

A set of coaches, or multiple-unit(s), of a type or in an internal condition which may not be the ideal for the job in hand, but is the best that can be mustered, probably at relatively short notice.

SDO

See Selective door operation.

Season ticket

Ticket for unlimited journeys between two named points or within an area specified, which can be purchased for a period of one week, one month, or any number of months and days between one month and one year. The longer period tickets are heavily discounted, to the extent that an annual ticket is charged at 40 times the weekly rate.

Seating arrangements

Nearly all seats on railway vehicles on National Railways are arranged transversely rather than longitudinally. There are two basic layouts:

Face-to-face, with or without an intervening table.

Face-to-back, airline or bus seat style, with or without a folding table built into the back of the seat in front. These two styles may be mixed within any particular vehicle, especially the more modern ones. The seating types and their spacing may not be uniform on each side of the gangway.

Seats are usually arranged on each side of a central corridor in the vehicle, in pairs or threes. Thus two seats one side of the corridor and three on the other is usually abbreviated to a 2+3 arrangement; others often found are 2+2 and sometimes 2+1. Single seats are most often found adjacent to bulkheads with doors for access to the vestibule, which have the effect of reducing the available width in that part of the interior.

Vehicles designed with the needs of those with mobility problems in mind exhibit a variety of designs.

Seating capacity

The number of seats installed in a vehicle, subdivided by class of travel where appropriate, eg 12F, 56S, total 68. Such information may usually be found on the data panel on the outside ends of the vehicle, but unlike (say) a bus, there is no legal connotation in terms of its being a limitation in the numbers which may be carried.

Prime considerations are seating arrangements, the seat dimensions, the number and location of doors, the overall length of the vehicle, and the provision (or not) of toilet(s).

Seating dimensions

It is in the interest of commercial managers to maximise the amount of passenger accommodation in a vehicle, but passengers want sufficient seating space. Travelling first class, when available, purchases more spacious and comfortable seating. The main variables in seat sizes are:

● The seating pitch (distance from one seat back to the next in front, or the equivalent in a face-to-face arrangement).

● Cushion width plus the spacing between adjacent seats, which together determine the number of seats which can be fitted in side by side, allowing also for access from a central gangway or side corridor.

Section

1. The block of line between the section (or starter) signal of one signalbox and the home signal of the next.

2. A length of overhead line equipment which can be isolated from adjoining lengths of overhead line equipment by the operation of (a) switches in feeder stations and/or track sectioning cabins, (b) overhead line equipment switches.

Section gap

That between the point where one section of conductor rail ends and another commences.

Section insulator

Insulation introduced into a contact wire between two adjacent sections of overhead line equipment, arranged so that pantographs may pass at limited speed from one section to the other smoothly and without break of circuit.

Section switch

A switch mounted on a structure between two sections of overhead line equipment arranged to disconnect one from the other, but not designed to break current.

Seating dimensions

Top: Standard class seats in the Class 170 unit of Anglia have a seat pitch which gives good legroom, but these trains were intended for relatively long distance travel. Photographed on 25 June 1999. *John Glover*

Above: The Anglia Class 170 units have only a few seats and an accessible toilet in this section of one driving car. The unoccupied space is to allow for wheelchairs, but also the securing of bicycles. The net result, though, is a substantial drop in total seating capacity. This is unit No 170203 again, on 25 June 1999. *John Glover*

S

Sectional Appendix
The Sectional Appendix rendition of
Leeds City station, 2002, showing
general layout, directions in which
each line is signalled (most bi-
directional), permitted speeds in
each direction, platform numbers,
and mileages from King's Cross
(top) and Selby South Junction
(below). *Network Rail*

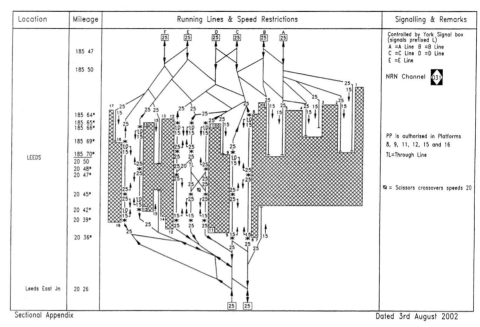

Sectional Appendix
A manual of operating information divided geographi-
cally into line sections. Information includes line
speeds, names of lines, whether lines are passenger,
goods or sidings, normal direction of travel, mileages
and where they change, position of features such as
signalboxes and level crossings, tunnels and their
lengths and the type of signalling in force.

Sectional Running Times (SRT)
Also known as point-to-point times. Derived from actual
measurements or calculations, the time taken for a train
to run between two identified fixed points (stations, junctions, summits, etc), and used in timetable compilation.
This will vary according to train performance, eg rate of
acceleration, while power/weight ratios will vary with
locomotive-hauled trains, especially with freight. There
thus has to be some averaging in the process, although
a distinction is drawn between various broad classes of
train and whether the train stops at either, or both,
points. SRT is compiled separately by direction as up
gradients become down, and for each track on multiple
track lines, since speed limits may vary.

Securitisation
Fundraising against expected or guaranteed future
revenue. This could be fares (eg season ticket income)
or access charges. The future revenue stream is 'sold'
to a third party. The latter pays a lump sum at the
commencement, in order to receive an income for a
set period of time. To be successful, the future revenue
stream from which such guarantees will be paid must
be correspondingly reliable.

Selective door operation (SDO)
The means adopted for opening (or releasing) only
those doors of a train which are on the platform, when

the platform is shorter than the train length, so that
passengers alight in safety. Systems can be either
manual, operated by the train crew, or automatic
using a train-based or a land-based system.

Self-discharging train
A train which carries with it the means of discharge,
rather than having to rely upon either permanently
fixed or mobile equipment at the lineside destination.
This can be particularly useful in the construction
industries, where many destination sites are likely to
have only a limited life, but is also used for ballast
delivery onto railway worksites.

Sensitivity analysis
The calculation of the effect of key planning assump-
tions turning out to be better (or, more importantly)
worse than that assumed in preparing a plan or eval-
uating its economic or business case.

Service application (of brake)
To cause a gradual and thus smooth reduction of the
speed of a train as a result of a normal brake application, in contrast to an emergency application in which
the rate of deceleration is likely to throw any standing
passengers to the floor if they are not hanging on, in
the interests of stopping as quickly as possible.

Service Level Commitment (SLC)
In franchise agreements concluded from 2004
onwards, the SRA specifies quite precisely the level of
service it requires an operator to provide during the life
of the franchise. The operator is not allowed to
timetable more or fewer services than those defined in
the SLC, unless expressly permitted by the SRA. The
SLC is a fundamental obligation in the Franchise
Agreement.

Service stock

Vehicles used solely for engineering purposes, and which therefore do not form part of the revenue-earning fleet. Traditionally, dating from the days of telegraphic codes, vehicles used for carrying track materials were given aquatic names. Hence Dolphin, Grampus, Mermaid, Sturgeon, Walrus and many more.

Set

A complete train, which should include the locomotive; otherwise it is a set of coaching stock, a set of hopper wagons, etc. There is an implication that each vehicle is of the standard type and composition used in the area, eg a Class 66 plus 36 HAA vehicles, or whatever. Also, a multiple-unit train, as in a 12-car train made up of three four-car sets.

Set back, setting back

To reverse a train a short distance, for instance to move the train back beyond a crossover and hence allow the locomotive to be detached and use the run round. Trains may also be set back over a longer distance, eg into a bay platform. Also used for reversing a locomotive onto the train which it is about to haul.

Settle & Carlisle (S&C)

The Midland Railway's magnificent bid for its own route to the north, built through the most difficult terrain at huge expense, and noted for offering spectacular views. It was opened in 1876, while attempts at closure in the 1980s were rejected, and the route carries both local and Anglo-Scottish traffic.

SFO

See Station Facility Owner.

Shed code plate

A relic of steam days, when each locomotive displayed a smalloval plate on the smokebox door indicating the shed to which it was allocated. Some locomotives, notably freight ones, still carry such codes low on the bodysides; these take the form of number (two digits maximum) and letter. Thus, 18A is Toton, 36A Doncaster, 71A Eastleigh and 81A Old Oak Common.

Sheet

Short for wagon sheet, a tarpaulin (or similar) of such dimensions that is suitable to be secured over the top of an open wagon to protect its contents from the weather.

Shoe

See Pick-up shoe.

Shop, shopping

To call a locomotive or other rail vehicle in for overhaul, or to commit it for overhaul, at the (work)shops.

Shore supply

An electrical source in a depot, not connected to any traction supply, to provide electric power for services on vehicles while in workshops etc. Special sockets are provided on vehicles to allow such connections to be made. Also used in stations to provide electrical power to diesel trains for heating, lighting, etc while their engines are shut down to reduce exhaust omissions.

Shunting

The movement of rail vehicles, usually within a yard or similar, to rearrange them for whatever reason.

Settle & Carlisle (S&C)
The isolation of the Settle & Carlisle line is emphasised by this view of the spotless Ribblehead station, which has staggered platforms in best Midland Railway style. This is the view looking north towards the viaduct of the same name on 3 May 2000. There is only a tiny settlement here, but an excellent pub and, amazingly, the train service makes it possible to commute the 52 miles to Leeds quite easily on a daily basis. Arrival in Leeds with a train starting from here at 07.14 is at 08.37, and you can leave Leeds to return at 17.56 or 19.19. *John Glover*

Shunting signal

A signal provided for shunting purposes only.

Side platform

The simplest and by far the most often found arrangement on double-track lines is that of two platforms, on each side of the lines, linked by a footbridge or subway, or perhaps via an adjacent level crossing. Exceptionally, a barrow crossing may be provided such as at Great Malvern and Winchester. All platforms on sections of single line are, by definition, side platforms.

Side wear

The wear on the head of a rail, reducing its width, caused by flange contact from the wheels of trains as they round a curve in the track.

Sidings

Tracks which are not part of any running line, used for the loading and unloading of goods but also to store locomotives and rolling stock. Sidings are found extensively in yards and depots, and on occasion may require the use of their own shunting locomotive.

Sighting distance

The distance at which a driver can first see a signal ahead, which thus represents the first occasion on which he can take action accordingly.

Signal, signal types

A lineside device visible to the driver of a train, advising him of the status of the line ahead and how he is to proceed. A signal on running lines consists either of a semaphore arm or a colour light display. The signal controls the movement of trains according to its position (semaphore), or the aspect of the colour light.

1. Semaphore signal

A mechanical signal worked by wire from a signalbox lever frame. Semaphore arms may be red or yellow; stop signals have a red arm with a white vertical band. If horizontal (on) this means 'stop', or inclined at an angle of 45° to the horizontal and usually upwards (off) indicates 'proceed'. The distant is a cautionary signal, yellow with a black chevron and a fishtail end. If horizontal (on), this means 'prepare to stop at the (red) home signal' (the first to be encountered in the next section). At 45° (off) it means 'proceed'.

At night, indications are by red, yellow or green lights through coloured glass on the inner end of the arm. The light source is traditionally oil, which gives a yellowish light. It may be noted that the glass associated with the clear indication is blue rather than green; however, green is displayed to the driver due to the effect of the light source.

Signals in which the 'off' position is 45° above the horizontal are known as 'upper quadrant', if 60° below the horizontal (a Great Western speciality) 'lower quadrant'.

The semaphore signal is derived from naval signalling with flags, representing an even earlier era.

2. Section signal

In an absolute block area the stop signal, also known as the starter, controls entry to the block section ahead.

3. Home signal

In absolute block, the first stop signal to be reached after passing the distant signal, on the approach to the signalbox. Occasionally, an 'outer home' may be reached first. It is *not* any red semaphore signal. See also Section signal.

4. Colour light signal

A signal displaying its aspect by coloured lights, which offers the same indication to drivers by day and by night. It is also relatively impervious to poor weather conditions in the sense of its visibility to train drivers. There are no moving parts. Signals may be of up to four aspects:

green	proceed
double yellow	preliminary caution, proceed but be prepared to find the next signal at single yellow
single yellow	caution, proceed, but be prepared to find the next signal at red
red	stop

An additional aspect of double yellow, flashing, may be encountered occasionally. It is used on high speed lines to indicate a diverging junction at which a lower speed applies on one route. The flashing indication means that the lower speed route has been set, and that the driver should regulate his speed accordingly.

Three-aspect signals omit the double yellow, while two-aspect signals are often replacements for semaphores and not part of a modern scheme. Single (red) aspect signals are rare, and found only in low speed areas in conjunction with a calling-on signal, for instance. Note that signal aspects are always red, yellow or green, and referred to in the Rules as such. The yellow should never be called amber.

See also Junction indicators.

5. Banner repeater signal

Banner repeater signals, nowadays solid state rather
than mechanical, are placed in advance of the signal
they repeat where for some reason the view of that
signal is (or may be) obstructed. A typical instance is
on a curved railway platform, so that it can be seen
easily by the guard of a train when the view of the
controlling signal is obstructed by the station canopy.
Banner repeaters show merely whether the signal
concerned has a proceed or a stop aspect, but it
allows the guard to know whether or not he can give
'right away' to the driver. To do so when it indicates
danger might end up with the driver passing a red
signal. This is known as the 'ding! ding! and away'
type accident.

Banner repeaters may be used at other locations
where the signal which they repeat cannot for some
reason be seen easily by the driver. These consist of a
white disc with a horizontal black band in the centre
which is tilted 45° to the left to indicate proceed.

S

Position light signal
Position light signals can be quite insignificant in size when they are located, as here, at ground level. This example is at Longbridge, where it was photographed on 22 October 1997. *John Glover*

6. Disc signal
Small mechanical disc shunting signal at low level, usually a red horizontal bar on a circular white background, which inclines to 45° from the horizontal when cleared. A yellow bar signifies 'stop' to movements in the direction for which the signal can be cleared, but other movements may pass the signal without it being cleared. Known as a 'Dolly' in LNER terminology, but also as a 'Dod', 'Tommy Dodd', or 'Dummy'.

7. Position light signal
A low-level shunting signal which displays lights rather than a disc. When set to clear, the signal displays two white lights set at 45° inclined to the left; at danger, one red light (on the left) and one white light, horizontal.

8. Calling-on signal
A subsidiary signal on a running line which authorises the driver to pass the main signal which is at danger, but advising him to proceed at caution as there is an obstruction before the next signal is reached. A common usage is when two trains are to be joined together at a station platform; the calling-on signal is used to allow the driver of the second train to approach the first.

9. Fixed distant signal
A distant signal which displays the caution indication permanently as, for instance, on the approach to the terminus on a line with one train working. In such cases, there may be no other signal.

Signalboxes and signalling centres
Buildings from which the day-to-day operational control of railway movements in a given area is regulated to achieve a high and effective throughput of trains, with safety. Traditionally, mechanical signalboxes were placed at the lineside at intervals, but today's power boxes and similar may be located in faceless buildings relatively remote from the railway. In such cases, the term signalling centre is more appropriate.

Signal gantry
A structure supporting fixed signals, other than those on individual vertical posts. Gantries often span one or more tracks. A more modest structure is known as a bracket.

Signal Passed at Danger (SPAD)
Signals Passed at Danger make a significant contribution to railway risk; they are also one of the criteria on which the safety of the network is measured. It relates to the occasions where a train passes a signal at which it should have stopped.

A range of existing and emerging hardware systems either prevent SPADs or mitigate their consequences, eg, ATP, ERTMS and TPWS. Another important component in reducing SPAD risk is ensuring that drivers are provided with consistent information to enable them to control their approach to signals.

SPADs are classified as to their seriousness; there is less danger, for instance, in a short over-run of a signal protecting the section in front on plain line, and a longer overrun at a signal protecting a converging junction. Specifically, a Category A SPAD occurs when a stop aspect or indication (and any preceding indications) was displayed correctly, in sufficient time for a train to be stopped safely at a signal. A Category B SPAD occurs when a stop aspect or indication was displayed because signalling or level crossing equipment had failed or malfunctioned, or it was returned to danger in error, and so on.

Signal post telephone (SPT)
A telephone located on or near a signal, which provides direct and secure connection to the signaller controlling that signal. The box in which it is located is designated by diagonal black and white stripes.

Signal sighting distances
The distance at which a driver can see a signal, free of obstructions (such as an overbridge or electrification masts), and at which he may be expected to be able to react appropriately to whatever it indicates. Sighting distances need to allow for variations in weather conditions, as well as between day and night time.

In mechanical signalboxes, the signaller has a 'fogging point', usually a signal some distance from the box. If this can't be seen, the signaller introduces the more restrictive method of working required during 'fog, mist or falling snow'.

Signal status
1. Automatic signal
The traditional automatic colour light signal is one in which the normal aspect displayed is green for proceed rather than red for danger. The signal displays a more restrictive aspect only when there is a train in the section in advance, as determined by the occupancy of track circuits.

With more recent installations, automatic signals are maintained at danger following the passage of a train and only clear shortly before the departure or passing time of the next. The function however remains automatic.

Automatic signals are much used on busy sections of main lines without junctions, crossovers, etc, and obviate the need for continual route setting by the signallers. An automatic signal carries a white, rectangular plate with a horizontal black bar on the signal post. See also Controlled signal and Semi-automatic signal.

2. Semi-automatic signal

A variation on the automatic signal occurs where there is, say, a trailing crossover between the lines, which sees occasional use only. If this is to be used, the signal needs to be controlled, even if at other times it can be used perfectly satisfactorily in automatic mode. The post for a semi-automatic signal carries a white, rectangular plate with a horizontal black bar and the word SEMI. See also Automatic signal and Controlled signal.

3. Controlled signal

A controlled colour light signal is placed to danger by the passage of a train through the operation of track circuits, but it then requires positive action by the signaller to clear it for the next move. See also Automatic signal and Semi-automatic signal.

Signalling, absolute block

'A', 'B' and 'C' represent three consecutive signalboxes, and the process of signalling a train from 'A' towards 'C' is as follows:

- Prior to the despatch of a train from 'A', the signaller there, provided he has received the *Train out of section* signal for the previous train and the block indicator for the line to 'B' is in the *Normal position* of 'line blocked', must call the attention of 'B' with a single stroke of the bell (1).
- The signaller at 'B' repeats the call attention signal (1) back to 'A'.
- The signaller at 'A' sends the *Is line clear* signal appropriate for the type of train, for instance three beats, pause, one (3-1) for a stopping passenger train.
- If the line is clear at 'B' the signaller there acknowledges the signal by repeating it back to 'A' (3-1) and places his block indicator to the *Line clear* position. This action also places the relevant block indicator in Box A to the same *Line clear* position. (If the line is *not* clear, the signaller at 'B' does not acknowledge the signal, and the line remains blocked.)
- This action will electrically release the starting signal at 'A', which the signaller at 'A' may now clear for the train to leave 'A'.
- On the train leaving 'A' the signaller there must send the *Train entering section* signal, two beats (2), to 'B'.

Signal sighting distances
The north end of Nuneaton station is shown during the 1960s resignalling, which proceeded concurrently with the West Coast electrification. Here, the semaphores are still in place, although the ones on the right are somewhat obscured by the overhead equipment. Curiously, the signal arms have not been removed, although colour light NN26 is displaying a red aspect. This picture perhaps demonstrates the difficulties in ensuring that each signal displays a clear, unobstructed and unambiguous message to drivers at all times. The scene here, with all signals at danger, may have been photographed during a total engineering possession. *BR*

The movement of each train is recorded currently in a Train Register Book held at each signalbox, and in this the bell codes used and the times at which they are exchanged (or refused) are shown. The system might nowadays seem antiquated, but it works and works well. However, the number of such installations is decreasing steadily.

Signalling assets
In the year 2003/04, those on Network Rail were recorded as follows:

- Signalling centres   256
- Mechanical signalboxes   650
- Signals   38,017
- Point mechanisms   14,786
- Train detection systems   60,994
- Level crossings   8,612

Signalling assets, lineside
These comprise:
- Signals, colour light and semaphore.
- Point operating mechanisms, which may be electric, hydraulic, pneumatic or mechanical.
- Train detection systems, whether track circuits or axle counters.
- Level crossing barriers or gates, and associated warning systems.
- Train protection systems of various types, including associated equipment cases and cabling.

Signalling assets, signalboxes and similar
These comprise:
- Control systems, which are operated by signallers to monitor the state of the railway and control train movements.
- Train describers, which record the identities of trains and track their movements through the network.
- Interlockings, which process train position information and execute the safety logic, which translates route setting requests from the control system into computer-based and electro-mechanical commands to move points and operate signals.
- remote control systems, which allow control and indication data to be transmitted for long distances along the lineside.
- Mechanical signalboxes, of which approximately 650 remained in use in 2004.

Signalling, evolution and purpose
'When an engine follows another on the same line of rails, the driver of the engine shall keep at the distance of at least 500 yards from the first engine.' *Rule Book of the Eastern Counties Railway, 1840.*

Such was the method of traffic regulation in the earliest days of railways, which had some obvious shortcomings even in simple situations, such as when the line goes round a curve or during the hours of darkness. From this evolved the establishment of the time interval system between the despatch of trains and the use

- The signaller at 'B' acknowledges the signal by repeating it back to 'A' (2), and places the block indicator at both to the *Train on line* position.
- Provided he has received the *Train out of section* signal for the previous train, and the block indicator for the line to 'C' is in the *Normal position* of line blocked, the signaller at 'B' must then call the attention of 'C' with a single stroke of the bell (1).
- The signaller at 'C' repeats the call attention signal (1) back to 'B'.
- The signaller at 'B' sends the *Is line clear* signal for a stopping passenger train (3-1) to 'C'.
- If the line is clear at 'C' the signaller there acknowledges the signal by repeating it back to 'B' and places his block indicator to the *Line clear* position. This action also places the relevant block indicator in Box B to the same *Line clear* position.
- This action will electrically release the starting signal at 'B', which the signaller there may now clear for the train to leave 'B'.
- When the train has arrived at and then passed 'B', the signaller at 'B' sends the call attention signal (1) to 'A'.
- The signaller at 'A' repeats the signal (1) back to 'B'.
- The signaller at 'B' sends the *Train out of section* signal of two beats, pause, one (2-1) back to 'A'.
- The signaller at 'A' repeats the signal (2-1) back to 'A'.
- The signaller at 'B' returns the block instrument in both boxes to the *Normal position* of line blocked.

Signalling assets
Mechanical signalboxes are rapidly diminishing in numbers – Coventry No 1 is clearly in the way of the remodelled junction, and the new Coventry Power Box can be seen under construction in the background. Soon, there will be signs of overhead electrification. This undated photograph was probably taken around 1963.
BR/Author's collection

of flags to instruct the drivers, based on the semaphore signalling practised by the Royal Navy of the period.

The main purpose of signalling as we know it today is to maintain a safe distance at all times between all trains on the running lines. The secondary but also very important aim is to make the best use possible of the railway infrastructure, so that the throughput of trains achievable in total meets the operational and hence the commercial requirements of the business.

Signalling, moving block
A moving block system compares the position of trains, their direction of travel and speed to determine the safe space ahead of and behind each train. To compute the position, direction and speed, a system of continuous, or near continuous, train detection or reporting is required.

Thus the block of line which contains the train moves with it, rather than the blocks being between a succession of fixed points. The principle of not more than one train being in any one block at any one time remains inviolate.

Recent work has attempted to substitute a 'moving block' for fixed block signalling, in which the train is deemed to be in an invisible envelope. Continuous cab signalling measures train speeds, constantly recalculates the safe stopping distance available in front of each train, and advises the drivers (or takes direct control) accordingly. Lineside signals can thus become redundant.

The principal gain of moving block from a traffic regulation point of view is its effect in increasing line capacity. It does this by tailoring the blocks to the railway traffic prevailing at the time, rather than their

being imposed to a generalised and fixed standard at the design stage. Moving block is not however a straightforward development. Thus braking distances depend upon variables such as track gradients. Wet rails, high winds and their direction, snow and ice will all have an effect, while locomotive-hauled trains (particularly freight) will vary in their braking performance according to the weight of the load. Train lengths are another variable, and there are many more. The trick is to devise a system which takes sufficient account of adverse circumstances, but which is not unduly restrictive when conditions are generally favourable.

SIMBIDS
See Bi-directional line, bi-directional signalling.

Single-lead junctions
Installed in the later years of the 20th century, these are the simple junctions for use when a double-track line diverges.

Approaching the junction from the main line and assuming the less important line diverges to the left, the first to be encountered is a trailing crossover, followed by a facing point. The latter marks the beginning of the branch to the left, which may of course be single throughout. Alternatively, this gives way to a second facing point, which restores double track.

The advantage is that the diamond crossing in a traditional junction, which can pose maintenance problems, is eliminated. However, the restriction on movements which can take place simultaneously at single-lead junctions is quite severe and a number have been removed, eg Filton Junction outside Bristol.

Singling
Above: Here, track restoration is taking place; the single platform track at Princes Risborough is having an additional platform constructed, together with a connecting footbridge on 12 November 1998. Subsequently, full double track capability was restored from here through to Aynho Junction, Banbury. This was the only available means of providing sufficient track capacity on the route to cater for the proposed traffic levels, given the need also for service reliability. *John Glover*

Slab track (PAved Concrete Track)
Far right top: Research into new forms of maintenance-free track was a major activity of the Railway Technical Centre, Derby. This view shows a Class 105 Cravens DMU on a new, 60m length of Paved Concrete Track installed experimentally on the Grantham-Nottingham line at Radcliffe-on-Trent. This particular design (one of six) was intended for Channel Tunnel use. The most immediate use of PACT was in newly electrified areas as a means of increasing vertical clearances. *BR*

Sleeping cars
Far right below: These 23m MkIIIa vehicles look their length, and more. This air-conditioned sleeping car has 13 compartments each with a fixed lower berth and a hinged upper berth and weighs in at a very substantial 43½ tonnes. This view is of the berth as opposed to the corridor side. *BR*

Single line
The situation where only one running line exists between two points, which must therefore be used for traffic in both directions. Since a head-on collision between trains is one of the most destructive possible, the development of signalling systems able to handle this situation safely has been a priority from the earliest days.

Single manning
Manning the cab with one driver only (ie without a driver's assistant), although this is not permitted where train speeds exceed 110mph without ATP or the equivalent. There may be other train crew elsewhere, such as a guard on passenger trains. See also Driver-only operation.

Singling
The reduction of double track to single line but with passing places, in order to match capacity provided more nearly with the lower levels of traffic on offer. This saves on renewal and maintenance costs. A variation is to retain some sections of double track, as on the Cotswold line between Oxford and Worcester, which enables trains in opposite directions to pass at speed, and is less restrictive in terms of timetabling than being able to pass at only a few selected stations. See Dynamic loop.

This was much practised in the latter days of British Rail, but with the concomitant effect that if traffic levels rose again subsequently, the track capacity might not be available. A second reason for singling, as on the Hastings line, was the limited tunnel clearances with double track. Singling made the tunnels passable with standard rolling stock. Similarly, singling in tunnels can allow higher freight loads to occupy the centre of the arch, where clearances are enhanced.

Six foot
See Track gauge.

Skip stopping
The practice of speeding up passenger trains which call at all stations, by omitting alternate stops on one service and the other stops on the succeeding one. This can be all but essential in terms of making the best use of line capacity, but care needs to be taken to avoid a situation in which it is never possible to make some local journeys. Passengers do not take kindly to being told that the only way to get from Newark to Retford (18½ miles) for several hours is via either Doncaster or Grantham, with a fare to match.

Slab track (Paved Concrete Track)
The replacement of conventional sleepers with a concrete slab, it was hoped, would reduce construction costs. In the event, this aim was not realised; one particular problem being that in the event of a derailment, the track might be comprehensively destroyed over a considerable distance, and would take some time to replace. One area in which it did prove to be superior was for new works electrification, as it enabled the track bed to be lowered in restricted areas and to give increased clearances while minimising bridge reconstruction. It was used thus in the Argyle Street electrification through Glasgow Central Low Level, parts of Merseyrail, and also for the Widened Lines to Moorgate in London.

SLC
See Service Level Commitment.

Sleeper
A beam of wood, concrete or steel. Sleepers are placed beneath the rails and at right angles to them at regular intervals, with the purpose of:
- Spreading the wheel loads over the ballast.
- Holding the rail to gauge and inclination within tolerances.
- Preventing the rail rolling over sideways from weight of traffic.
- Resisting lateral track movements, or buckling.
- Insulating the rails from each other.

Sleeper material
The traditional sleeper for British conditions was the wooden or timber one, and it is always a useful standby when conditions are awkward. An example of this is a drain cover close to the track, which requires a couple of sleepers to be shortened a little. This is a much easier task with wood than concrete!

Cost and the availability of suitable woods have told against them, but wood has continuing advantages for switch and crossing work, where the position of rail fixings and sleeper lengths will vary from one to another. Wooden sleepers have a continued application as 'second-hand' items from main lines downgraded to siding use.

Concrete sleepers came into their own when the pre-stressed, pre-tensioned monobloc sleeper was perfected, and pre-fitted with fastening systems. Concrete sleepers are also virtually maintenance free, although if damaged replacement is the only real option.

More recently, all-steel sleepers have again found favour, while the twin block sleeper consists of two concrete blocks connected with a steel bar. With both steel and concrete sleepers, electrical insulation matters have to be resolved.

Sleeper pumping

A track movement associated with the presence of liquid slurry, as a result of shortcomings in the original construction, or dirty ballast. The result is a loss of vertical rail alignment (a 'wet' spot) and this can be a major problem. A sleeper which does not offer adequate rail support is useless, and increases the effective distance between the adjacent support points for the rail. In turn, this sets up bending moments. Pumping was a particular and widespread problem for Northern Ireland Railways on the Dublin main line south of Belfast, which had to be remedied before faster timings could be introduced.

Sleeper services

The market for medium-distance sleeper journeys such as London-Leeds has long gone, due to the increasing speed of daytime trains plus early/late departures, while the *en suite* accommodation now much demanded is simply not feasible in the space available and given the limited water-carrying capacity. Longer distance markets such as London-Scotland have also been affected by cut-price airline competition, although these are the main routes today. The other is London-Penzance.

Sleeping cars

Passenger vehicles used for overnight transits and containing full bedding. Sleeping cars have a turbulent history; the most recent MkIII build in the early 1980s by BR was for 217 vehicles, of which fewer than one third remain in regular use today. The problems are those of dubious economics with vehicles able to hold only 24 or 26 passengers (or 12/13 if in single occupancy), the high staffing costs of several attendants, operational costs which include laundry, and the ability to make only one revenue-earning journey in a 24hr period.

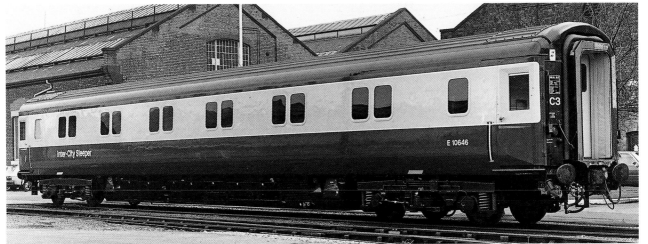

Slew, slue

A general term meaning to move sections or panels of track bodily sideways. This may be undertaken to correct misalignments which have been caused by wear over a period of time, as part of a track layout remodelling scheme, or to enable trains to bypass a temporary obstruction caused, for instance, by a landslip. Movements may thus be to make new connections, or to restore the track to its original position. Such work may be undertaken manually or by machine.

Slipstream effect

An induced airflow which begins after the head of a train passes and continues until after the tail of the train passes. The airflow produces an unsteady, or gusty force, which is felt by any person or object nearby. Its strength is dependent upon the train speed, distance from the train, ambient wind speed and direction, and the shape and surface finish of the rolling stock. The greatest effects are caused by container trains at their 75mph maximum speed, while wheeled objects on station platforms, such as pushchairs which are not being held are the most likely to move.

SLU

See Standard Length Unit.

Small wheels

Introduced to enable higher loads to be carried, especially containers. However, the trend to smaller wheels has increased wheel/rail contact loads. Larger wheels have the benefit of relieving contact stresses.

Smoking

A barometer of social values, smoking accommodation accounted for three quarters of the total (then) third class accommodation during the 1950s. In the 1960s this was reduced to a half, which made a mockery of the colour-coded seat covers of red for smoking and green for non-smoking. In more recent times, smoking accommodation fell to a quarter at the very most, and now all TOCs ban smoking on trains altogether. It is also banned, by law, on stations subject to s12 of the Fire Precautions Act, 1971.

Social cost/benefit studies

In 1963, a study was made of the social case for building the Victoria Line of London Underground. Although there were reasons why the new line would be unprofitable from the commercial point of view, society would benefit from its construction, principally because of the (quantified) effect it would have on the relief of road congestion. Since then it has become normal practice for Government to require similar justifications for major transport projects; similar studies have been used to investigate the case for retaining unprofitable parts of the railway network. Much use is made of the value of time to users and non-users; less traffic congestion speeds up journeys for the remaining road users.

Solebar

Outermost and principal longitudinal structural member of a vehicle underframe.

Solid State Interlocking (SSI)

A processor-based system for controlling the interlocking between points and signals, as well as communication with lineside signalling functions. First installed at Leamington Spa, 1985.

Southern Electric

The lines radiating from the London stations of Blackfriars, Cannon Street, Charing Cross, London Bridge, Victoria and Waterloo to the south coast, from the Thames Estuary to Weymouth. All are electrified on the third-rail system, save only the branch from Hurst Green to Uckfield, the Ashford-Hastings link and most of the line between Reigate and Wokingham .

SPAD

See Signal Passed at Danger.

'Sparks effect'

The surge in passenger traffic which allegedly follows from the electrification of a railway, beyond that which the improvement in the service alone would warrant.

Special Traffic Notice (STN)

Advance notice, usually issued weekly, of changes to, additions to and deletions from the normal service. It may, for instance, give the timings for special excursion trains, confirm dates at which 'as required' trains will run, provide for additional stops in trains as a result of sports fixtures, give details of any freight flows, and specify any consequential alterations such as the make-up of trains (eg two four-car sets replace three four-car sets) as a result of any or all of the above.

Speed restrictions, permanent (PSR)

The maximum speed permitted on any localised section of track below that of the line speed, and denoted by a lineside sign to that effect. This may vary between different lines at the same point, eg 'up' and 'down'. A cause of such restrictions might be track curvature. See also Line speed.

Speed restrictions, temporary (TSRs) or emergency (ESRs)

Restrictions of a temporary nature imposed by the infrastructure controller on the movement of trains, for reasons which are foreseen and notified in advance to the operating companies. The cause may be the condition of the track, structures or overhead line equipment, or changes in the signalling arrangements. Another reason might be to offer some additional protection to staff who need to be on the track for a particular reason.

They are termed emergency speed restrictions when they are not notified in advance.

Spent ballast

That which has been removed from the track as no longer fit for purpose.

Splitting and joining
The act of forming or re-forming a train to consist of the numbers and types of vehicles required for its next duty. In these days of multiple-units and fixed train formations, this technique, which can take up considerable time and need the help of a shunting engine, is much less used than formerly. Splitting and joining may also take place at stations, with each portion of the train serving different destinations.

Sponsor
The manager accountable for the establishment of the business case and output specification for a project.

SPORTIS
See Portable Ticket Issuing System.

Spreader
See Container handling.

Spring points
A set of points which are spring loaded to force the point blades back to their original position after a wheelset has passed through them in a trailing direction.

'Sprinter'
A generic name for the fleet of Classes 150-159 bogie diesel units built for British Rail in the decade from 1984, the delivery of which allowed many of the first-generation diesel units to be withdrawn.

SPT
See Signal post telephone.

SR (Southern Railway)
See Railways Act 1921.

SRM
See Safety Risk Model.

SRT
See Sectional Running Times.

SSI
See Solid State Interlocking.

Stabling (of trains)
The temporary storage of trains which for the time being are not required, often in sidings provided for the purpose, with the implication that this is likely to be relatively short term (eg between the peaks, overnight, or over the weekend). It is important to know the condition of such trains before they next enter service. Thus do they need cleaning or have they been cleaned internally or externally, do the water tanks need refilling, have any minor defects been reported, and so on.

Stagger
1. With OLE equipment, the practice of varying the distance of the contact wire from the track centre line. The contact wire is staggered from side to side (within limits), with the objective of evening out the wear on the train pantographs.
2. Platforms are said to be staggered where the one on the up line is offset by anything up to its entire length from the one on the down line.

Stakeholders
Those with a vested interest in a company and the service it provides (eg local government).

Standard Length Unit (SLU)
Formerly Standard Wagon Lengths, this is a measurement of train length and also that of loops and sidings. There are obvious problems if the train length exceeds the length of the siding into which it is to be put. One SLU equals 21ft (6.4m). Also, Extra Length Unit (ELU), defined as one tenth of an SLU (2.1ft or 640mm)

Starter signal
See Signals.

Static vehicle profile
See Gauge, structures and vehicles.

Station
A place constructed for passengers (originally also for goods and/or parcels) to gain access to trains and to allow them to join or alight in safety. Nearly all stations have lighting, which allows them to be used at all times of day, and shelter for waiting passengers. Many have ticket offices and some have other staffed presence. Stations may also have other facilities such as car parking and retail units, but these may be outside the immediate premises. A well-sited station will maximise the catchment area and attractiveness of the railway system for the benefit of local communities. Depending on the context, the term station does not necessarily include the permanent way, signalling or any electrification plant.

Station
One of the most distinctive stations anywhere, London St Pancras dates from 1868. This is the former hotel, later offices, on the Euston Road as it was on 20 October 1998. The train shed is behind. The whole is presently inaccessible due to the conversion work in progress to make it the London terminus of Eurostar services as well as Midland Main Line and some domestic services from Kent. *John Glover*

The word station has long been prefixed when necessary by the word 'railway' to distinguish it from a bus station, fire station, police station, etc. To the intense annoyance of many, the term 'train station' has come into use more recently.

Station, sub-surface
A station of which more than half of any one platform is within a tunnel or under a building (HMRI definition).

Station access agreement
A regulated access agreement by which one Train Operating Company obtains permission from the station facility owner (usually another TOC, but Network Rail at a major station) to use that station, or parts of it.

Station condition index
A Network Rail measurement in which all stations on the network are classified from Grade 1 (as new) to Grade 5 (dire). The scale represents a combination of the degree of deterioration, and a comment on the timescale in which renewal or extensive rebuilding will be needed. Numbers in each condition grade in 2005 were:

Grade 1	151
Grade 2	1,766
Grade 3	582
Grade 4	6
Grade 5	0
Total	2,505

Station Facility Owner (SFO)
The Station Facility Owner is the tenant under a lease from Network Rail (or Network Rail itself at the 17 major stations). The SFO is normally the sole Train Operating Company using that station, or the TOC with the most services using it. Other TOCs may call there, a privilege for which they pay access charges to the SFO as contributions to lease charges and running costs. The SFO is responsible for providing facilities there, and these must meet the standards that are specified in the franchise agreement. They include matters such as signage, cleanliness, passenger information and lighting, public communication systems and waiting accommodation. A specific licence to operate a station is required, and two TOCs (Gatwick Express and Virgin CrossCountry Trains) do not require one as all the stations they use are operated by other parties. See also Station ownership.

Station Facility Owners are identified in the Station Index of the National Rail Timetable.

Station limits
The area within the direct control of a single signalbox on the absolute block system, in which movements under the control of the signaller can be carried out without reference to any other box. Specifically, it is the portion of line between the home signal and the section (or starting) signal on each of the running lines. Although referred to as 'station limits', there does not have to be a station in the vicinity.

Station names
Each station name should be unique, and distinguished from others in the locality by a suffix rather than a prefix. Thus, while there is nothing at all wrong with the name South Acton, it will not come up in an alphabetical list of names under Acton, in the way that Acton Central will. This can cause considerable difficulties in ticket offices. Sadly, some TOCs have omitted the previously applied suffixes. Thus St Albans City is now plain St Albans; this gives no clue to the passenger that there is also a St Albans Abbey station. Similarly, Dorking North is now Dorking, never mind Dorking Deepdene and Dorking West.

Stations with direct interchange with shipping services
The facilities at railway stations serving ports vary enormously — this is the modern but basic scene at Ardrossan Harbour, seen here on 24 July 2004. Strathclyde PTE-liveried No 334037 has just arrived at 15.09 with the 14.15 from Glasgow Central, to provide a connection into the 15.15 Calmac sailing to Brodick on the Isle of Arran. It also caters for the 1350 sailing from Brodick arriving Ardrossan at 14.45. *John Glover*

Station openings

There have been about 145 station openings on the national system since 1948, including nine at airport locations:

Birmingham International (1976), Gatwick Airport (1958), Heathrow Terminals 1, 2, 3 (1998), Heathrow Terminal 4 (1998), Luton Airport Parkway (2000), Manchester Airport (1993), Prestwick International (1994), Southampton Airport Parkway (1966), and Stansted Airport (1991).

Some stations have been rebuilt on new sites, and these include Bradford Interchange and Stevenage (both 1973).

Station ownership

The vast majority of stations owned by Network Rail are leased to passenger Train Operating Companies, but 17 major stations are owned and operated directly by NR. These are: Birmingham New Street, London Cannon Street, London Charing Cross, Edinburgh, London Euston, London Fenchurch Street, Gatwick Airport, Glasgow Central, London King's Cross, Leeds, Liverpool Lime Street, London Liverpool Street, London Bridge, Manchester Piccadilly, London Paddington, London Victoria and London Waterloo (but not Waterloo East or Waterloo International). There are also other stations used by trains on the national rail network which are not the responsibility of Network Rail.

● leased by Network Rail to TOCs and operated by them	2,488
● major stations owned and managed by Network Rail itself	17
total, Network Rail	2,505
● Owned and operated by London Underground Ltd*	13
● St Pancras and Waterloo International, owned and operated by London & Continental	2
● Prestwick International Airport, owned and operated by the airport	1
● Heathrow T1,2,3 and Heathrow T4, owned and operated by Heathrow Express	2
● Warwick Parkway, owned and operated by Chiltern Railways	1
total	2,524

Also, Eurotunnel's British terminals at Cheriton, not strictly stations in the conventional sense, are wholly owned by that company.

Station services

Any service relating to the provision or operation of a station, irrespective of by whom it is provided.

*These stations are Amersham, Chalfont & Latimer, Chorleywood, Rickmansworth, Harrow-on-the-Hill, Greenford, Kentish Town, West Brompton, Farringdon, Barbican, Moorgate, Old Street and Highbury & Islington.

Stations with direct interchange with shipping services

Clockwise round Britain, starting on the east coast: Harwich International, Folkestone Harbour (out of use), Portsmouth Harbour, Lymington Pier, Fishguard, Weymouth Quay (out of use), Holyhead, Heysham, Stranraer, Ardrossan Harbour, Wemyss Bay, Gourock, Oban and Mallaig.

Statistics

Quantified presented data. Available from a number of industry sources but also from Government, particularly for comparative figures with other transport modes. Thus the annual bulletin of Public Transport Statistics, Great Britain, is a mine of information on rail, light rail and bus operations and performance, and includes an Annex detailing the key events over the last 20 years or so.

STN

See Special Traffic Notice.

Stock rail

The fixed rails on each side of a set of points, distinguished from the point blades, which move.

Stoneblower

On-track machine designed to make good the deficiencies of tamping machines, which can only rearrange the ballast but not introduce new material. The Stoneblower blows a stream of small stones under the sleepers, using very high pressure to ensure that they are tightly packed to a controlled geometry. The aim is a level and maintenance-free track profile.

Stop board

Provided on platforms, especially where train lengths vary, to indicate to drivers of passenger trains where the front of trains should be stopped. They usually take the form of a prominent figure, eg '4', and the words 'car stop'.

Stop block

The physical impediment placed at the end of the line to prevent further progress by a train. Normally provided with a red lamp or equivalent, the more elaborate examples at terminal stations may include hydraulic buffers which contract on impact and are themselves designed to be pushed backwards. If a train runs into these, the buffers will absorb the energy as the train is decelerated. This energy will then be released by pushing the train back in the direction whence it came. Clearly, this can only be fully effective at low closing speeds, but in any event damage would be reduced. In the majority of locations, where there is little in the way of real safety hazards, the stop blocks will only withstand minor misjudgements made during shunting, for instance. Also known as buffer stops.

Stops

Railway abbreviation for buffer stops, as in 'the driver just managed to avoid hitting the stops'.

Substation
This is Codmore Hill substation near Pulborough, installed in 1938 as part of the Portsmouth via Chichester electrification scheme by the Southern Railway. The Electrical Control Room was at Havant, nearly 30 miles away. *Southern Railway*

Stored value ticketing
The principle by which a passenger pays an amount in advance for future ticketing transactions (at present within a growing number of pre-defined areas), which is then credited to a swipe card. Each time this card is used, it is swiped at a card reader on entry to and again on exit from the system. The fare payable for that journey is decremented to that card (ie the balance available on the card is reduced by that amount). The card can be recharged with additional funds as the balance available diminishes. Good customers can be given incentives, for instance half price travel next Saturday or Sunday if you paid over £x in the preceding week. Smartcards may also be used for other transactions, such as bus or metro fares or, depending upon the originator, even payment for school meals. These are still early days, and the smartcard potential will take some time to materialise.

Straddle carrier
See Container handling.

Straight air brake
A simple compressed air brake fitted to locomotives and for use on the locomotive only.

Strengthening trains
Adding extra coaches or another unit to provide more capacity, but only to the extent that platform lengths or other operational constraints are not exceeded.

Strike-in point
The location on the approach to an automatic level crossing at which a train initiates the operating sequence, such as setting off the visual and audible warnings and, later, the descent of the barriers (where fitted).

Strike-out point
After a train has crossed an automatic level crossing with barriers and, irrespective of the train's length the whole of the train is completely clear of it, the point at which the barriers are lifted.

Structure
A bridge (road, rail, etc), viaduct, retaining wall, tunnel or similar, signal or electrification post or gantry, station construction such as a platform wall, track drainage manhole or cable pit, and any other construction on Network Rail-controlled infrastructure.

Structure bond
A bond to connect the steelwork of an overhead line equipment structure, bridge or other metal structure to the running rails.

Structure gauge
See Gauge, structures and vehicles.

Subgrade
The prepared surface of natural ground on which the permanent way is to be laid, or upper surface of fill material.

Substation
Substations contain electrical equipment for controlling the supply of electricity and, for dc traction systems, converting alternating current to direct current. They may vary in size from a few square metres to those covering many hectares.

Summit
The top of an incline.

Super elevation
See Cant.

Supervisory control
An electrical system for the remote control of unattended substations and track sectioning cabins.

Surface water drain
A drain designed to collect water from the surface and/or from the surrounding ground continuously along its length.

Swap-body
The swap-body is in effect the body of a lorry (containing goods) which can be 'swapped' onto another road vehicle or rail wagon. Unlike ISO containers, these cannot be stacked one above the other. They are also known as 'caisse-mobiles'.

'Sweeper up'
Railway term to describe the last train of the day, often long distance, which calls at all principal stations in order not to leave any passenger stranded due to missed connections etc.

Swept envelope
See Gauge, structures and vehicles.

Swing bridge
A bridge where part or all of the deck is designed to rotate through 90°. Associated with rail crossings of rivers or inland waterways, their purpose is to allow water traffic to pass where there is otherwise insufficient headroom. Notable examples exist at Norwich Trowse (where the railway is electrified at 25kV ac) and at Selby, where the bridge is on the former route of the East Coast Main Line. Signalling arrangements have to encompass giving a clear indication to river traffic as well as to trains.

Swing-nose crossings and switch diamonds
Higher speeds bring a need for less obtuse turnouts, but this also brings a more difficult situation at the crossing, where one track finally leaves the direction of the other. The angles between the two sets of rails reduce, and the theoretical ability of a wheelset to take the wrong road increases.

The solution adopted is to eliminate the gaps between the rails, by substituting a rail which 'swings' across the nose of the turnout, powered by an electric motor. The continuous surface thus obtained gives the wheels solid guidance at all times, to the extent that the check rails normally provided to keep the wheels in place are no longer required. The flangeway at the nose is arranged to open or close according to which way the points are set.

A similar situation arises with a switch diamond, which has switch blades that can be moved to fill the gaps that would otherwise occur.

Such are the requirements associated with faster speeds, but the additional complications come at a cost.

Swing bridge
Right above: The swing bridge over the River Wensum at Trowse, Norwich, was one of the more interesting challenges in the electrification of the Anglia main line. As can be seen, the short section over the reconstructed bridge was singled. This is the view looking towards Norwich with Crown Point Depot in the distance. The signalling and the bridge are controlled from Colchester, 62 miles distant. *Brian Morrison*

Swing nose crossings and switch diamonds
Right: The swing-nose crossing gives the train a continuous set of rails on which to travel, albeit that it complicates the operation considerably to provide the movement and its detection. There is thus additional cost. This example was seen on 27 September 2001 on the Rome to Naples high-speed line before commissioning. The absence of any check rails will be noted. *John Glover*

Switches and crossings (S&C)
Switches and crossings together make up points and
turnouts. They consist of specially machined rails and
other components and are the means whereby trains can
be diverted from one track to another track. They need
to be reliable, and there is no substitute for a good
design, well installed. The ability to inspect and maintain
such equipment is related to the ability to access the site
in the gaps between trains, and this in turn depends on
their location and frequency of use. Otherwise, a possession may be required. See also Points and switches.

Switchgear
Equipment used to control the supply of power.

Switching
The operation of circuit breakers, isolators or other
methods of making or breaking an electrical circuit.
High voltage (HV) switching is carried out only on the
instructions of the electrical control operator except for
routine or emergency switching.

Switching out
The ability to close certain boxes on an absolute block
signalled line when traffic levels are low, in which case
signals controlled from the box to be closed are placed
at clear and trains proceed directly (in a signalling
sense) between the boxes on either side.

System security
This covers all activities associated with providing
security to passengers and the protection of railway
property, including supervision and clerical support.
Also included is the patrolling of vehicles and property during revenue operations, access to depots, yards,
buildings and structures, monitoring of security
devices and reporting security breaches.

TAA
See Track Access Agreement.

Tail lamp, tail light
A red light carried on the rear of each and every train
at all times to show a) that it is complete and that no
vehicles have become detached, and b) to signify its
presence to any following train. Today, such lamps are
built into many passenger vehicles, and must be illuminated at all times if at the back of the last vehicle
on the train. In the event of a failure and no replacement being available, a Bardic hand lamp (which has
a lamp bracket built in) may be substituted. If a signaller observes a train with no tail lamp displayed, he
must stop the train.

Tamper
A track maintenance vehicle which runs on rails. It
is designed to raise, align and level the track, while
at the same time consolidating the ballast underneath and at the side of the sleepers. The aim is to
produce track which is smooth, level and safe; in
short, to maintain the correct geometry. See also
Stoneblower.

Tare (or unladen) weight
Tare weight is that of the wagon itself, when empty,
measured in tonnes.

TASS
See Tilt Authorisation and Speed Supervision system.

TCB
See Track circuit block.

TDM
See Time Division Multiplex.

TE
See Tractive effort.

Temporary speed restrictions (TSR)
See Speed restrictions, temporary (TSRs) or emergency (ESRs).

Ten foot
See Track gauge.

Terminal
Any passenger station, freight or parcels depot. The
reference is to a place where passenger journeys or
freight transits may start or end, rather than the end
of the railway itself. This can easily lead to confusion,
especially with passenger stations, and the term needs
to be used (and interpreted) with care.

Terminal loop

A track arrangement in which trains call at their traffic objective and subsequently continue in the same direction without reversing, to rejoin the main line and return whence they came. This can cause considerable land take, but such arrangements are the key to merry-go-round coal to power station operations. They can also be found on passenger railways, notably on Merseyside. Trains from the Wirral call at the below ground station at James Street, then successively at the single platformed Moorfields, Liverpool Lime Street and Liverpool Central deep level stations, then James Street again.

Terminating board

See Commencement board.

Terminus

The station at the end of the physical line, for instance London Charing Cross, Holyhead or Thurso. This is not a foolproof description; Manchester Piccadilly might reasonably be described as a terminus, and so it is for most of the platforms. However, there is also a large island platform, physically separate, from which trains proceed through to Manchester Oxford Road and beyond. A more precise definition would be a terminus with some through platforms. Similar problems arise in many other places.

Thameslink 2000

The proposed linking of the present Thameslink and the Great Northern outer suburban services north of the Thames on a high-frequency basis of 12-car trains to the Wimbledon and Sutton services, and others via London Bridge, to destinations south of the Thames. Essentially, this is a capacity enhancing scheme. The original Transport & Works Act case was rejected by the Office of the Deputy Prime Minister due to the extent of land take in the London Bridge area where the existing viaduct would need to be widened.

Thermit, thermit welding

Thermit is an aluminothermic reacting material often used to weld rails together. Thermit welding is the on-site welding of rail into longer lengths at a temperature of 2,500°C. This can be carried out only during a total track possession. Welds have to be trimmed and ground, with track clips replaced, before the line is reopened to traffic. The first such welds in Britain were made in 1935 by the Great Western Railway.

Throat, station throat

The complex arrangements of tracks and junctions at the approach to major stations, particularly termini, the layout of which has the ability to expedite (or throttle) the movement of traffic. The problem of multiple conflicting moves is at its most acute when physical space is limited, as at King's Cross where Gasworks Tunnel is only a short distance beyond the platform ends.

Terminus
The vastness of Glasgow Central has only a few short trains visible in this view of 1 August 2004. There are 13 platforms on the surface, plus two at low level. This is valuable real estate in the centre of Scotland's largest city; does the railway really need so much space?
John Glover

Through lines

Normally those at a main line through station, without platforms of their own (or little used if they have them), for fast non-stop traffic. Sometimes, these will have been built subsequently to the rest of the railway infrastructure.

Through platform

Term used at larger stations to distinguish such platforms where trains may arrive from one direction and depart in the other, from those which end in buffer stops and are for terminating trains. Examples of such stations are Crewe and York. The signalling may also permit a through platform to be used reversibly, so that trains can depart in the direction whence they came.

Through ticket

Tickets for a journey which involves the trains of more than one operator. These latter are not necessarily rail operators; they might be for ship or bus/coach journeys. The fares may be a straight summation of those applicable to each part, or some reduced fare for the whole journey as may be determined on a commercial basis. The important point is that the ticket(s) for the entire journey are purchased in one transaction.

The issue of through tickets for (say) a rail+ship journey avoids large numbers of people queuing up to buy tickets at the ferry terminal and either delaying the ferry departure or perhaps missing it altogether. There are thus good operational reasons for through fares.

Throw

Throw represents the position which a straight vehicle takes up on curved track. There are two types, end throw and centre throw, which are the opposite of each other.

- End throw is the extent to which a rail vehicle hangs out at the ends on the outside of a curve.
- Conversely, centre throw is the extent to which a rail vehicle hangs in at the centre on the inside of a curve.

The nearer the bogies are to the vehicle ends, the less the end throw. However, this also maximises the centre throw. Similarly, the nearer the bogies are to the centre of the vehicle, the greater the end throw but the less the centre throw. Shorter vehicles will have less throw altogether.

Throw brings substantial problems, notably at station platforms in the stepping distances between platform and train. It may also be noted that cant in the track will tip a vehicle away from the outside of a curve when stationary. This can make boarding a vehicle at a centrally placed door position decidedly difficult. The corresponding effect of end throw with a platform on the inside of a canted curve tends to be less problematic, though still inherently unsatisfactory. In such cases, the sharpness of the line curvature is critical.

It is for reasons such as these that straight platforms are much to be preferred whenever possible and vehicle lengths are usually limited to 20m or 23m.

Ticket

A ticket represents the contract between the carrier (a train operating company) and the passenger, and the conditions under which that contract is made. Reference to that contract should always be found on the face (principal side) of the ticket. Both parties are bound by the National Conditions of Carriage, which relate to the carriage of passengers on National Railways for domestic journeys within Britain. They are available for inspection at any ticket office, and copies are usually available on demand.

Where the ticket includes travel by other operators, such as London Underground, a bus or ferry company, that portion of the journey is made subject to the terms and conditions of that company.

The purchase of a ticket to travel by the payment of a fare gives the holder the right, subject to any restrictions applicable to that description of ticket such as limitations on the time of travel, to make one or more journeys on the network as may be specified (whether or not in conjunction with other rights). A ticket holder is entitled to be carried between the points stated, or as provided for by the ticket. The open rail ticket does not, on its own, entitle the holder to be carried on any particular train, or to the use of a seat.

Other rights might include seat reservations, entitlement to refreshments, or other benefits as may be agreed between the parties. For some types of ticket, the holder may also be required to travel on a nominated day by a nominated train and to occupy a nominated seat. Some or all such entitlements and restrictions may be stated on a single travel document.

There will be a stated period of validity, usually one day or one month for ordinary tickets, after which the ticket ceases to be valid.

From the carrier's point of view, the issue of that ticket creates a debit in the accounting system, against which an offsetting credit is needed in terms of cash or a debit/credit card transaction. At all times, the ticket remains the property of the issuing company, although its collection at the end of the journey is nowadays often forgone.

Ticket barriers, barrier control

The purpose of ticket barriers is to restrict entry to and exit from station platforms to those with a valid ticket, and the collection of used tickets and excess fares as necessary. But it doesn't help with passengers travelling on trains for which they have not paid, or out of class. Staffing costs are also high. So, the move has been to replace manned ticket barriers with occasional comprehensive spot checks, plus either regular or occasional on-train ticket inspection, and the extensive use of penalty fares legislation. Efforts have also been made in some areas to provide passenger-operated ticket machines, for use when the ticket office is closed, or on-train issue where stations are unstaffed.

Automated ticket barriers can 'read' tickets and control entry and exit to platforms, but while their costs can often be more than met through reducing revenue loss, for safety reasons they do require a member of staff to oversee them when operational, to ensure emergency egress and to collect fares where appropriate.

Ticket interavailability
Where a ticket can be used between two given points by more than one route, even if this involves using the trains of another company. In a small number of cases, it may be possible to use (say) the return half on a bus rather than a train.

Ticket office
See Booking office.

Ticket On Departure (TOD)
Where a ticket has been ordered by telephone or online, but is then collected from a travel centre or from a ticket machine at the departure station.

Ticket snippers
The hand-held tools used by ticket examiners to mark the ticket, showing that it has been inspected. Holes in tickets are less desirable nowadays, as they may puncture the magnetic strip used to activate the gates for journeys which include travel on London Underground or gated TOC/Network Rail stations.

Ticketing and Settlement Agreement (TSA)
The rules that deal with fares setting, fares distribution, through fares and interavailablity, retailing, ticket branding, payment methods, conditions of carriage, revenue allocation and settlement between the parties.

Tilt Authorisation and Speed Supervision system (TASS)
This controls where tilting takes place on trains so equipped and supervises the maximum speed at any location, using a series of balises which are registered by the approaching train. Where additional signals are provided for wrong direction running, extra balises will be installed. If a wrong direction movement is made in other circumstances, the driver needs to isolate (and subsequently reset) the TASS system, as it will read the balises in the wrong order.

Tilting trains
Today, the tilting train fleet consists of Virgin Trains' Class 390 electric 'Pendolinos' on the West Coast main line, and its Class 221 diesel 'Super Voyager' units on CrossCountry. The first British train to tilt with paying passengers on board for 20 years did so over 17 miles in Oxfordshire on a Bournemouth to Manchester CrossCountry service, on 29 April 2004. Tilting enables curves in the track to be taken at a higher speed, with no passenger discomfort. With electric trains, it is essential that when the body of the train tilts, the pantograph too must tilt, but in the opposite direction. Otherwise, dewirement will take place.

Time Division Multiplex (TDM)
A control system which allows a large number of remote signal interlocking relays to be controlled from a signalling centre using one set of wires. Each item is allocated a brief time slot in a continuously repeated scanning cycle. Every time an item's time slot comes round, it is connected to the main highway to the control centre. In this brief instant, any necessary control signal is sent and indications are returned showing that the equipment has responded by updating the presentation of signal aspects, point settings and track circuit occupations on the signaller's control panel.

Timetable
The document published from time to time by an operator, setting out the train services to be provided for a specified period in advance.

Timetable database
The Journey Planner facility which allows the public to view timetable information either remotely through the internet or through Visual Display Units at stations.

Timetable symbols, public book
Many of these have been long lasting, such as those listed here:

Bank Holidays	BH
Saturdays Only	SO
Saturdays Excepted	SX
Train does not run full period of timetable	wavy line between train times
Arrival time	a
Departure time	d
Stops to set down only	s
Stops to take up only	u
Train stops on request only	x

There are also many pictograms. Others vary, including this example of reversed notation. Trains with second class only accommodation used to be identified by a stylised 2 at the head of each column. That didn't work when second was reclassified as standard class, so now any train with first class accommodation is singled out to be represented by a stylised 1.

TOD
See Ticket On Departure.

Token, tablet, staff
The physical authority, made of wood or metal, given by a signaller to a train driver to enter a section of single line which is signalled by the Electric Token Block system. Each token (or tablet, or staff) is inscribed with the names of the locations at each end of the section of line to which it relates. The token also carries a locking device, and the signalling equipment at the other end of the line cannot be operated without it. This is to ensure that another train cannot enter the single line in the opposite direction.

The driver surrenders the token to the signaller on arrival at the end of the single line section and, if necessary, collects one for the next section.

Top
'Top' is the term for the longitudinal profile of the track, which is affected by differential subsidence along its length. The objective of top maintenance is to produce a quality which meets the standards laid down for the speed and weight of traffic using the line, and which is also durable.

T

Token, tablet, staff
Token exchange takes place at
Quay Crossing, Bridlington, on 30
May 1981 as the driver of the
Class 101 unit holds out his arm
for the loop to be slipped over it by
the signalman. This will cover him
for the ten miles of single track
thence to Hunmanby where double
track is resumed as far as Filey.
Care must be taken not to drop the
token, to avoid losing time while it
is retrieved. *John Glover*

'Top-and-tail'
Running trains with a locomotive at each end, usually during disruption to services, so that should a
reversal be necessary, time is not taken up by running round movements (the facilities for which might
not be available where needed, anyway). Also much
used on engineering trains, by excursion trains visit-
ing destinations with no run-round facility and by FM
Rail.

TOPS
See Total Operations Processing System.

Total Operations Processing System (TOPS)
British Rail introduced the TOPS system progressively
from 1972; it originated with the Californian-based
Southern Pacific RR. It is used to monitor the planned
movement of trains and the maintenance and state of
repair of those trains.

Each item of rolling stock was given a unique number (TOPS number) on the database. Movements of
that vehicle are input as to its current whereabouts
and status (ie available for traffic, refuelled, under
repair, etc). Freight wagons are also recorded as
loaded or empty, and with which commodity. Various
reports can be produced and also made available to
customers if required. The whole offered something
approaching a current record of the ups and downs of
the production side of the railway business, which represented a vast advance for its day.

Today, TOPS is the prime source of train movement
information for other systems, providing as it does a
comprehensive system for monitoring a train's complete movements.

Total Operations Processing System (TOPS), number series

Different sections of the TOPS classification system are used to distinguish vehicle types. Other number series are not used.

- 01-69   diesel locomotives
- 70-79   dc third-rail electric and electro-diesel locomotives
- 80-97   ac overhead electric and dual-voltage locomotives (except 89/1-5)
- 89/1-5   private diesel locomotives certificated to operate on Network Rail
- 98   steam locomotives permitted to run on Network Rail
- 100-139   diesel units, first generation*
- 140-199   diesel units, second generation*
- 200-249   diesel units, electric transmission
- 300-399   ac overhead electric and dual-voltage units
- 400-599   dc third-rail electric units
- 900-999   service and test units

TPH
See Trains per hour.

TPWS, TPWS+
See Train Protection Warning System.

Track Access Agreement (TAA)
An agreement, with conditions attached, under which a train operator obtains permission from Network Rail to use the latter's track. The agreement defines the number of movements and type of rolling stock that can be operated, in addition to rights in relation to the timing of train movements. It also defines Network Rail's contractual obligations to the operator.

The agreements, running over a number of years, enable operators to bid for train paths. These are translated into trains, ultimately appearing in the finalised timetable. Network Rail may need to resolve conflicts with other operators who want to use the track at the same or similar times. In the case of disputes between most operators and all TOCs which cannot be resolved, the Office of Rail Regulation is the final arbiter.

Track bond
A bond, either bolted or welded, across the joint between two running rails.

Track circuit
The use of the rails to form a low voltage electric circuit, which is short-circuited by the presence of a train. It thus detects the presence or absence of a train on a given section of line, and has been the prime basis of safety for generations of signalling equipment. Track circuits may be ac or dc, a necessary require-

*The expression 'first generation' refers to those diesel units procured in the late 1950s/early 1960s and now virtually extinct. 'Second generation' are their replacements dating from 1980 onwards. See also 'Pacer' and 'Sprinter'.

ment being to avoid interference with, or from, other electrical systems in the area.

Track circuit block (TCB)
A development of the Absolute Block System, in which track circuiting is applied throughout. A train may proceed to the next stop signal as soon as the line is clear, determined by the operation of the track circuits, provided the overlap beyond that signal is also clear.

Track circuit clip
A simple but effective protection device which simulates the presence of a train on any track-circuited line. Two metal spring clips, connected by a wire bond, are placed (or rather stamped) onto a pair of running rails. This results in a short circuit, placing signals controlling that section at danger. It is of particular use to trainmen should a derailment (or other event) result in the adjacent line being blocked, and is quick and easy to apply.

A variation with handles is used on electrified lines with a conductor rail.

The track circuit clip is said to have had its origins in the Great Train Robbery of 1963, when a homemade version was used to bring a Travelling Post Office train to a halt at a remote signal location of the robbers' choosing at Ledburn, Bucks.

Track gauge
The distance between the inner faces of a pair of running rails, nominally 4ft 8$\frac{1}{2}$in (1,435mm). Colloquially, this is known somewhat inaccurately as the 'four foot'. The distance between one running line and the adjoining one (between the outer running rails of each) is likewise the 'six foot' or, where the distance is increased where there are four parallel running lines, the gap between the two pairs is widened to the 'ten foot'.

Track gauge spread
The widening of the track gauge which can occur if rail fastenings fail due to damage or otherwise, and the rails move apart from each other. This has the potential to cause a derailment.

Track gauge widening
Increasing the distance between the two running rails on curves below 200m radius to ease the movement of vehicles around the curves, by up to 19mm in the most severe cases. The manufacture of special sleepers may be necessary to accommodate the revised positions of the rail fixings. See also Check rails.

Track geometry
Track geometry is measured by track recording vehicles that record the vertical and horizontal alignment of the rails. Track quality is expressed as a standard deviation (in mm) for each unit length ($\frac{1}{8}$ mile).

Track irregularity
A feature of the permanent way geometry, the size of which exceeds permitted thresholds specified in the standards.

T

Track panel

Above: A re-laying exercise in the Severn Tunnel using pre-assembled panels of track is under way. Physical limitations as here are often a feature of railway work, and have a large part to play in determining the methods to be used. *BR*

Right: The pre-assembling of complex formations gives everybody the chance to check that everything is as it should be before movement to site. This layout has been manufactured in manganese steel, for extra durability. It was put together in Low Fell Yard in 1949, prior to being moved to the junction at the east end of Newcastle Central station. *BR*

Track lowering

A course of action designed to increase clearances (for overhead electrification, or higher wagons) as an alternative to bridge or tunnel reconstruction. However, this can create its own problems in terms of track levels or drainage, to say nothing of what services may lie beneath the existing formation.

Track mile (or km)

The distance between two given points along the length of the railway on a single track. Thus a single track distance will be doubled if a second track is installed, and so on, while the incidence of extra platform tracks at stations, loops, sidings, etc will all increase the number of track miles (or km). This is primarily a measurement of the assets employed in the business, as opposed to route miles which show the extent of the network.

Track panel

A pre-assembled length of track complete with rail, sleepers and fastenings, of such a size that it can be transported to site and installed 'as is'. The rails themselves may be no more than scrap rail, which is there only to hold the whole panel together at the correct spacings. When laid in position, this rail is removed, and replaced by long lengths of continuously welded rail. Such techniques can reduce the site occupancy time considerably.

An alternative approach with a large and complex formation is for it to be assembled off site to ensure that all parts are present and correct, and that they fit as intended. It is then dismantled for transport, but such preliminary work ensures that any site problems when it is finally reassembled are minimal.

Track paralleling hut (dc)

A building containing high voltage electrical switchgear and the equipment used for connecting together a number of sections of third-rail equipment.

Track sectioning cabin (ac)

A building containing high voltage electrical switchgear and the equipment used for connecting together a number of sections of overhead line equipment (OLE).

Track sharing

Track sharing is usually taken to mean the use of the same infrastructure by light rail and heavy rail vehicles. As yet, the only instance of this in Britain takes place between Pelaw and Sunderland with the Tyne & Wear Metro. While there can be many good reasons for this, including costs, there are both technical and safety problems to be overcome. These include the general incompatibility between lightweight trams and heavy rail trains, differences in vehicle widths and the resulting gap to the platform edge, electromagnetic interference affecting signalling, wheel/rail geometry, power sources (especially if the heavy rail line is electrified), and platform heights where the 915mm above rail level used by Network Rail is very different from the 350mm preferred with modern light rail schemes, which also run on streets.

Track sharing can also mean parallel or adjacent running by light rail vehicles on part of the heavy rail formation, but over completely separate tracks. This latter is relatively common and can be found in nearly all the present British light rail schemes. There are fewer problems with this, but the track maintenance staff of each will be working alongside each other and an intervening fence may be provided.

In both cases, staff training and certification has to cover the action to be taken in the case of an incident, especially if this requires a tram to be evacuated.

Traction current

That supplied for the purpose of electric traction, collected either by pantograph from the overhead supply, or by collector shoe from the third rail.

Traction knowledge

It is a formal requirement that all train drivers must have been trained on the type of vehicle which they will drive. This includes handling characteristics (acceleration and braking) plus fault finding and rectification.

Traction maintenance depot (TMD)

Place where diesel and/or electric locomotives are maintained.

Traction motor

Electric motor used to provide the final drive to a locomotive or train axle and used in electric and diesel-electric applications.

Traction motor rating

The continuous rating of a traction motor is the horsepower it can deliver continuously without its temperature rise exceeding a limit. The one-hour rating allows a higher output but sets the temperature rise that must not be exceeded after the motor has been working for an hour.

Tractive effort (TE)

The force exerted by a locomotive at its wheels. Normally quoted as continuous tractive effort, that which the equipment can take for long periods without overheating, as opposed to that for short periods of time as when accelerating a train.

Traffic statistics, passenger

Those identified by the British Railways Board for comparison over time were:
● Receipts per loaded train mile.
● Receipts per passenger mile.
● Passenger miles per loaded train mile.
● Loaded train miles per passenger vehicle.

Trailer car

A passenger vehicle in a multiple-unit train, diesel or electric, which is itself unpowered. It relies on a motor car for traction. It may, or may not, have a driving cab.

Train

Any vehicle or combination of vehicles which run on the railway and thus including some form of traction. Therefore, a train may consist of a single vehicle or a number of vehicles coupled together, including any locomotives or power units. A train may be for passenger or freight purposes, also maintenance and construction work. It also includes on-track machines, engineer's trolleys, cranes and other plant while operating on a railway.

Train crew

The driver, driver's assistant, guard or conductor.

Train describer

The apparatus which ensures that the identity of each train is displayed on the signalbox panel together with the indication of that train's presence. This is also the source of TRUST data recording train running. Train describers are not used in IECC areas.

Train heating, electric train supply index (ETH, also ETS)

Power used on trains for saloon heating or otherwise is derived from the locomotive. Since the number of vehicles may vary, it is essential that the locomotive has the ability to meet the total power requirements of the vehicles it hauls. Each type of hauled rolling stock has an ETS index, the total of which must not exceed that of the locomotive.

Although still commonly known as ETH (electric train heating), in practice this nowadays represents also the power needed for air conditioning, cooling fans, kitchen equipment and any other auxiliary service requirements. There are some incompatibilities in ETS equipment between different types of stock.

Locomotives used primarily for freight work are unlikely to have any ETS capabilities.

Steam heating is now defunct (except in the preserved railway sector), and any steam heat only coaching stock is unlikely to find a locomotive able to supply it.

Train line

Cabling running the length of a train for control or power purposes, and connected between vehicles by jumpers or through the couplers.

Train operator

A body authorised and licensed to operate trains over the railway network, and which has an accepted Railway Operator's Safety Case and a Rail Operator's Licence.

Train paths

Train paths are the space taken up in the timetable by the passage of each and every train, allowing for safety margins. Trains of different performance characteristics and stopping patterns each produce different requirements for their passage, and an objective of timetable compilation is to allow all trains passage without delaying (or being delayed by) other trains in the process. Thus a stopping passenger train will take longer over a given length of line than an express, and the train path required has to reflect this.

Where critical conditions arise in terms of the total track capacity available, some difficult decisions in terms of relative priorities may be needed. It is important to realise that a train path is a variable and not a fixed quantity, so a section of track cannot be described as containing 'x' train paths.

Train plan

Part of the train services database, the train plan covers the operation of trains and their formations (eg one two-car Class 144 'Pacer' unit or two) in accordance with the company's timetable.

Train preparation

The aims of daily train preparation are to check that a train is in a safe and proper condition when entering service, and to ensure that defects reported by operators are acknowledged and addressed.

Train Protection Warning System (TPWS, TPWS+)

TPWS is a development of the AWS system. It automatically applies a train's brakes if it approaches a signal at danger too fast, or if it is travelling too fast on the approach to certain speed restrictions and buffer stops which are so fitted. It therefore reduces the risk of collisions between trains and of derailments through overspeeding.

TPWS is designed to stop a train in the signal overlap rather than at the signal itself. The effectiveness of the system depends on the speed of the train and its braking performance. At speeds above 75mph, TPWS is unlikely to stop a train in the overlap, but it may still provide adequate protection by stopping the train before a collision occurs.

Train Protection Warning System (TPWS, TPWS+)
The Train Protection Warning System installed between the tracks at Braintree, depicted on 16 November 2001. *John Glover*

Fitment at 12,000 sites and to all rolling stock was completed by the end of 2003. An enhancement, TPWS+, which gives protection up to 100mph, is to be fitted to a further 400 locations.

Train Ready To Start button (TRTS)
A button on the platform which, when pressed, is an indication to the signalbox that platform duties have been completed and the train is ready for the road to be set up for departure (if this has not been done). There is no point in the signaller setting up a route for a train which isn't ready, especially if another train is.

Train register book
A detailed record book kept by signallers in Absolute Block areas (and more simply elsewhere) to record who was on duty and when, the passage of each and every train, the times associated with the transmission of each bell signal, and to record any exceptional circumstances. Now mostly recorded electronically.

Train re-marshalling
The reformation of trains to meet changing traffic needs, for instance doubling up the number of cars in a train for peak operations. Such work may be undertaken in depots, or at termini – in which case additional turnround time will be needed. Similarly, where a train is split at an intermediate station for two (or more) destinations, additional time will be needed. Care also needs to be taken that all passengers are in the correct portion.

Train Running System on TOPS (TRUST)
TRUST is an operational system used by Network Rail which records train running performance and compares it with the schedules as monitored by TOPS (Total Operations Processing System).

Train Services Data Base (TSDB)
Holds all available data about planned train services which have been agreed by Network Rail management teams throughout the country, ensuring as far as possible the reliable running of the railway network.

Train Staff and Ticket system
A method of ensuring safety on single lines. Unlike Electric Token Block, there is only one authorisation for movement over the single line. This is in the form of a train staff, normally a piece of wood or metal about the size of a chair leg, on which is engraved or a plate affixed to confirm the section of line to which it relates. The staff, or token, is carried by the driver as his authorisation to be there, and there are token instruments in the signalboxes at each end.

Should there be a need for two or more trains to follow each other in the same direction, the driver of the first train is shown the staff, but given a written ticket of authority to proceed. This is handed to the signaller at the far end in the same way that a token would be. This procedure can be repeated, but the driver of the last train is given the staff itself.

The shortcoming is that the number of successive trains in either direction must be known in advance, or the token ends up at the wrong location. For this reason, it was customary to make sure that a bicycle was available for a member of the station staff to take the token back to the other end if needs be.

Train station
See Station.

Trainload operation
The operation of a complete train for a single end user, as in coal from a pit (or port) to a power station, or container flats from one Freightliner terminal to another. By definition, there is no intermediate marshalling of the train, so such operations require heavy volumes of goods.

Trains per hour (TPH)
A measurement of train service frequency or line capacity, according to context. The result is however heavily influenced by the mix of traffic. Since they obstruct each other, there can be far fewer alternating fast and slow trains over a given section of line in a given time period than if they were all fast or all slow. This measure is at its most useful when all trains have similar characteristics and stopping patterns, as in most heavy urban or metro-type operations. See also Regular interval timetable.

Traintaxi
From stations so designated in the timetable, either:
- There is a taxi rank from which taxis will usually be available, or
- a cab office/taxi rank is located within 100 metres, but pre-booking may be advisable.

Transformer
Apparatus for changing high-voltage electricity to a lower voltage supply.

Transformer/rectifier
Equipment to convert a high-voltage ac electricity to a lower voltage dc supply, as for 600/750V third-rail use.

Transhipment
The physical movement of freight between a rail and a road vehicle (or ship), other than by the use of containers, swap-bodies or similar. While it may allow more specialist and hence more satisfactory vehicles to be used in each case, the transhipment has to be quick and cheap to maximise the cost savings possible from the use of rail.

Transition curve
An elegant solution to linking a straight line of railway to a curve of given radius, minimising the possibilities of a lurch in the train's movement. Strictly, a curve of constantly changing radius, used to connect a circular arc to a straight line, or to an arc of different curvature.

T

Treadle
A treadle on the inside of the running rail, pictured at Ely on 8 November 1999. Passing wheel flanges depress the treadle, signifying the approach of a train and causing secondary effects such as the lowering of level crossing barriers. *John Glover*

Transmission-based signalling
A system in which the driver is authorised to proceed by radio, alternating current sequences through the rails, or by balises, rather than by observing lineside signals.

Transponder
Equipment fixed between the rails which transmits data to a passing train when interrogated by the train-borne equipment.

Transport 2010 (The Government's Ten Year Plan)
Published in July 2000, this set out the Government's priorities for transport. For railways, the vision was summarised thus:
'A bigger and better railway with reduced journey times, higher standards of safety, service and comfort. We want to see a 50% increase in passengers and an 80% growth in rail freight over the next decade.
● Around 6,000 new carriages and trains.
● Modernisation and upgrading of the East and West Coast main lines.
● The Channel Tunnel Rail Link completed.
● Train Protection Warning System throughout the network, with full automatic train protection on higher speed lines.
Many of the objectives and targets were later abandoned.

Trap points
Facing points installed at the exit from a siding, a loop or other converging line, which will direct a train to the 'trap' when the route is not set for it and the movement is thus not authorised. The points may consist of no more than the switch blades. A train which is wrongly started by its driver will enter the trap. This may consist of a sand drag, or just stop blocks at the end. The result is likely to be a derailment in a relatively safe position, or the train becoming embedded in a sandbank, depending on the speeds involved. The main line is not obstructed.

Travelator
A means of providing mechanical assistance for passengers in connecting two areas, in a station for instance. Requirements are that those points are some distance apart, and that the gradient (if not flat) is sufficiently shallow that steps are not required. The effect is that of a stepless escalator, and many users will walk along the moving path.

Travelcard
The London ticket available for one-day peak, one-day off-peak or for continuous periods between seven days and one year. Tickets are divided into six concentric zones, central London being Zone 1, and tickets may be purchased for combinations of two or more adjacent zones. These give the holder the use of (effectively) the entire London public transport system of rail, Underground, light rail and bus for the period and zones selected. Travelcard revenue is divided between the participating operators.

Gradually, the Travelcard is being superseded by Oystercard, a Transport *for* London product which allows the value of the card to be decremented with use.

Treadle
A lever operated by the passage of the wheels of a train which make an electrical contact. This enables the train's presence to be detected. It is often associated with level crossings or axle-counter signalling installations.

Trespass
On the railway, unusually but not uniquely, trespass is a criminal and not a civil offence. This reflects the long recognised dangers of entering railway land unlawfully, due to the speed at which a train can approach and the lack of sound often associated with it. Trespass on the railway may take place from station platforms, from other points where the public have legitimate access such as highway or footpath crossings, or from a breach of the railway fence.

Triangle (of track)
A track arrangement which forms that geometric shape that can be used to turn locomotives, items of rolling stock, and even complete trains, depending on the lengths of each of the three sides of the formation. To do this, the train runs forwards, then reverses along the second side of the triangle and then forwards again on the third side, back to where it started.

Tribometer
A device for measuring the adhesion between wheel and rail.

Tribute
A PC-based ticketing system widely used to replace APTIS. It may use similar magnetically encoded credit card sized tickets, or much larger ones which have the ability to show train and seat reservation details.

Trip length (miles/km)

The distance a passenger covers on a single trip, which may include one (or more) changes of train. Clearly, trip lengths vary considerably according to journey type and journey purpose, but may be relatively constant within (say) an urban transport network. Measurement can be carried out simply through analysing ticket sales, but this assumes that the passenger is able to buy a throughout ticket for a point-to-point journey. Interview surveys are an alternative but expensive approach. Further complications may arise if the passenger uses another form of transport such as a bus for part of the total journey.

Trip working, tripping

Usually, the movement of relatively small numbers of wagons between a yard where the long distance train calls, and their point of origin or destination such as a customer's private siding. By extension, the term 'trip' is used to refer to any fairly short distance movements made with a locomotive and a small number of vehicles of any type and for any purpose.

Troughing

Protection runs in which power, lighting and signalling cables may be placed at the side of the line. They will be covered, both to protect the cables and to avoid creating a hazard for staff needing to walk alongside the track.

TRTS

See Train Ready To Start button.

Trunk route

One of the principal arteries of the rail system, for instance the London to Brighton main line.

TRUST

See Train Running System on TOPS.

TSA

See Ticketing and Settlement Agreement.

TSDB

See Train Services Data Base.

TSR

See Speed restrictions, temporary (TSRs) or emergency (ESRs).

Tumblehome

The shape often associated with the side of a passenger car body, in which the lower part curves inwards towards the solebar. Its usual purpose is to give the maximum width possible in the car body for its occupants between their shoulder level and the seat, while reducing the width lower down in order not to foul platforms.

Tunnels

Structures provided to allow a railway line to pass under higher ground. There was no standardisation of construction methods or dimensions in the early years, so there are considerable variations. Tunnels may have been excavated without disturbing the ground surface (bored), or constructed by cut-and-cover methods (a literal description), particularly in urban areas. What constitutes a tunnel rather than a bridge is formally designated, since tunnels carry slightly more onerous operating rules. A minimum length of 50m is normally required.

There are 700 tunnels on the network today, with a combined length of about 200 miles.

Turn

Instance of staff duty, as in early turn, late turn, etc.

Turnback

A facility which enables a train to reverse its direction, often using a 'turnback siding' beyond a passenger platform, where a passenger train can reverse without blocking running lines for the time it spends there before returning.

Turning a train

Causing the train to be turned *in toto*, so that the entire train faces in the opposite direction. This may be achieved by the use of triangular track layouts with two sets of reversals, or by the use of routes which have that effect. The classic case is that at Newcastle, where Central station can be accessed from the south either via King Edward Bridge (the normal route across the River Tyne) or the High Level Bridge. In the first case, the train will arrive in the station facing the north; in the latter case, it will be facing the south. The extra time taken for the latter move is minimal.

Turnouts

The whole track assembly where one track 'turns out' from another; often known as points.

Turnover locomotive

A spare locomotive provided at a train reversal point, to take the train forward, or on its next duty. This may be necessary if the locomotive hauling the incoming train is trapped at the stop blocks and there is either no run round or it is blocked by other traffic. After departure, the original train locomotive becomes the new turnover locomotive.

Turnround time

Time scheduled at the end of each trip before the next trip to allow train crew to change ends or to be relieved by a new crew, to attend to physical needs, and to make a judicious allowance to recover from any late running. However, turnround time also depends on the availability of platform space, and departures may also need to accord with the maintenance of a regular interval operation.

Turntable

A device found in depots for turning steam locomotives or, occasionally, other rolling stock such as a single coach. It consists of a brick or concrete pit with a central bearing assembly, on which is balanced a steel girder bridge, or table, which is cantilevered out from the centre. The ends of this table, which carries the railway track, are supported by tracking wheels in the base of the pit. Operation is by hand or windlass, or from power derived from the locomotive's braking system. Now very rare.

Twistlock

The locking device used to secure containers onto rail and road vehicles. A locking pin device is turned manually to engage in fittings on the bottom corners of containers in order to secure them and prevent movement in transit.

Type approval

The process of giving approval to operate new types of equipment or infrastructure on the rail network. Once secured by a new locomotive type, for instance, it then applies to all subsequent production of that design.

Ultrasonic scanning

Rail flaw detection method, using a sound which is at a frequency higher than that which can be heard by the human ear. Ultrasonic tests can also detect flaws in axles.

Vandalism
Above right: While vandalism is to be deplored, some security measures now being taken do tend to produce a prison camp effect. This is the 'welcoming' secondary entrance to Abbey Wood station, down side, on 29 January 2001. *John Glover*

Right: South West Trains would like less litter on its trains; this was one car card displayed in inner suburban trains to try to promote the idea in 1997. *John Glover*

Unbalanced working
A train movement from which there is no revenue-earning potential in the return to the starting point or depot. The result is often to come back empty. This can be a feature of suburban peak operation, with a high level of services into town in the morning peak, but little traffic to be carried in the reverse direction.

Underframe
The frame which includes the buffing, coupling and running gear of a vehicle, used to secure and support the bodywork.

Unit
Abbreviated term for a multiple-unit, a completely self-contained passenger train of fixed formation, either diesel or electrically powered.

Unit cost statistics, passenger
Those identified by the British Railways Board for comparison over time were:
● Train operations expenditure per train mile.
● Train provision expenditure per train mile.
● Train maintenance expenditure per train mile.
● Terminals expenditure per train mile.

Unsafe track condition
A track irregularity or condition of such severity that it requires immediate action, which can range from the imposition of an emergency speed restriction (ESR) to

the complete closure of a line. Thus different forms of rail flaw require different response times to remove them, depending on their type and location, and based on risk analysis. See also Speed restrictions.

Up line
See Line designation, direction.

Vacuum brake
See Brake, vacuum.

Vandalism
The wilful or malicious destruction, injury or disfigurement of property without the consent of the owner, by cutting, tearing, marking, painting, drawing, or other means.

Variable costs
Those that vary with the level of output, eg fuel costs for a locomotive, as opposed to the fixed costs represented by the signalling system which has to be in place and manned as long as any rail traffic is in operation.

Viaduct
A bridge structure of multiple spans.

Viaduct
This striking view is of the 18.50 Stranraer-Carlisle freight on 25 April 1984 being headed over Pinmore Viaduct by Class 37 No 37195. Undulating countryside of this nature belies the efforts which may be needed to construct a reasonably level trackbed without undue horizontal curvature. Both are needed if a workable railway is to be the result. *Dr L. A. Nixon*

Vestibule
The entrance to Class 170 unit No 170203 showing the full unobstructed width available in the doorway, the positioning of the handrails, the passenger door open/close controls, and the emphasised step edges. This is at Norwich on 25 June 1999.
John Glover

Vehicle miles/km, hours, etc
The distance or time vehicles spend in service, most of which will be revenue earning but including running empty to and from a depot and as otherwise required. 'In service' includes the time spent at terminal stations in between making trips. This is a measure of vehicle usage, and is important in determining the intervals between distance or time related maintenance. A more important measure from the business point of view is the revenue-earning proportions of the total, during which the vehicles earn their keep. The word 'train' can be substituted for 'vehicle' here, where appropriate.

Vertical integration
Where the management of the provision of a good or service is under the control of a single company. Thus with the old British Rail, the infrastructure was controlled by the same organisation that operated the train services. On National Rail today, this applies only to the Island Line on the Isle of Wight. In contrast, vertical separation is where the different stages in the production of services (infrastructure, rolling stock, operations) are provided by different companies as now in Britain.

Vestibule
The area at the end of many types of passenger coach, usually containing external doors and a gangway to the adjoining vehicle. It is normally separated from the seating accommodation by a partition with a door. In other vehicle types, especially those used for suburban traffic, there may be one or two vestibules placed more centrally and forming the area containing the sliding doors. Most have the doors placed at positions one third and two thirds along the vehicle length.

Virtual quarries
Stockpiles of aggregates and ballast at strategic locations to be used for construction and engineering projects.

Voltage definitions
LV   Low voltage not exceeding 250V.
MV   Medium voltage exceeding 250V, but not exceeding 650V.
HV   High voltage exceeding 650V.

Wagon
Any railway freight vehicle.

Wagon codes, TOPS
The three-letter codes are based on the generic wagon type (first letter), the individual type within that grouping (second letter) and braking system (third letter). Thus HAA refers to a hopper, 32.5-tonne merry-go-round coal type, air-braked. Other first-letter prefixes include B (steel carrying, bogie), C (for covered bulk carriers), F (flats, as in Freightliner and others), O (for open wagons), T (tank wagons), V (for vans), Y (bogie service vehicles) and Z (two-axle service vehicles).

Wagon types
The main types are those for the following traffics:
● General merchandise, either open, curtain-sided or covered vans, including palletised goods.
● Flat wagons for the carriage of containers.

- Vehicles used for the carriage of road vehicle trailers, where suitable structural clearances exist.
- Coal hoppers for use on merry-go-round trains.
- Steel carrying, either as plate or in lengths supported by bolsters, or as steel coil.
- Tank wagons used for petroleum traffics, other liquids and gases, but also for other traffic such as powdered cement.
- Aggregates, stone, iron ore, etc.

Wagons for more specialised traffics, such as nuclear flasks, or cars.

Wagon, conventional

A rail wagon in which the freight is placed, for movement. The body, chassis and wheels are permanently united; it cannot be used as a bi-modal or intermodal vehicle. Such wagons form the majority of the fleet, and there are many different types.

Wagon, curtain-sided

A rail wagon, container or road trailer (or similar) whose sides consist of strong composite plastic sheeting that provides soft waterproof sides. These can be pulled back to allow side loading and unloading of goods.

Wagon, hopper

Wagon designed for a quick discharge of its load through the base of the wagon. Thus the bottom sections of the wagon slope are hinged, so that gravity only is needed to empty the contents, usually to a conveyor belt below.

Wagon, specialised

Those built for certain types of traffic, eg cement in bulk or the various types of petroleum traffic, which are not suitable for general use in the way of an open wagon or a van. While this confers many advantages, a less satisfactory characteristic of specialised wagons

is that they usually have to be returned empty after use to their starting points, as there is unlikely to be any possibility of a return load. Wagons may or may not be suitable for use on international transits; to do so, they must conform also to the requirements of the Continental systems concerned.

Wagonload

Where the volume of freight per shipment being moved is less than about 500 tonnes, this is unlikely to justify the use of a dedicated train. A wagonload operation assembles a number of smaller shipments from a selection of origin points, from which they are tripped to an assembly yard. From there they will be run as a complete train (trunked) to another yard, and then distributed by tripping.

Waist

The point of maximum width of the body of a passenger vehicle.

Waiting time

The time, often expressed as an average, that a passenger may expect to wait for a service. In high-frequency metro-type operations, it is usually half the headway.

Waiting (for) time

Holding a passenger train to ensure that it does not depart from a station where it is to pick up passengers earlier than advertised, for which there is no excuse. The position with freight is more complex, since if all is ready there is no commercial reason not to depart early. However, such out-of-course running can and does result in severe disruption to passenger services, and may devastate punctuality. Such problems can only worsen when networks get busier. Having said that, there can be occasions where early freight running causes few or no problems.

Waiting (for) time
Many customer information systems, as these here at Epsom on 9 December 2000, tell you not only the sequence of the next three trains to arrive, but also their expected arrival times. Some parts of the display scroll to achieve this.
John Glover

Wales-only service
A passenger service which starts and ends in Wales and does not make any other scheduled calls outside that country (and has not been excluded by the Secretary of State). See also Welsh service.

Walk on service
One on which no form of advance reservation is (or usually can) be made, as with nearly all commuter and local services. On longer distance services advance reservation is at least desirable in many cases, partly to take advantage of cheaper ticket offers, and partly to avoid the possibility of standing for much of a quite lengthy journey. In recent years, the growth of rail travel volumes has exceeded the supply of additional accommodation.

Warning board
A rectangular yellow board placed at braking distance from a temporary speed restriction ahead, showing the reduced speed required.

Warning panel
Concern was expressed about the visibility of the new forms of diesel and electric traction, which were being turned out in an overall dark green livery with little to embellish it. The main concern was those working on the track. A yellow panel was therefore applied to the ends of modern traction from the early 1960s. Later known as the small warning panel, this was increased in size at the end of the decade to cover the entire end of the locomotive or multiple-unit, and sometimes a bit more (full ends).

Despite the later mandatory fitting of high intensity headlights, the warning panel has remained on the basis that it must be safer with it than without it, although there is some evidence that it has been allowed to decrease in size. It is of note that London Underground trains have always been exempt from this requirement, although their corporate livery goes some way to redress the balance. This does not apply on the Isle of Wight where former London Underground trains providing National Rail services do have large yellow panels.

Washout
Where the ballast and other parts of the track or bridges etc have been washed away as a result of water erosion due to flooding or similar causes.

WCML
See West Coast Main Line.

Weave
The movement of a train on a four-track line from fast line to slow line and subsequently back to the fast line again (as crossovers permit), or slow to fast to slow. The usual reason is to facilitate engineering work on part of the line, but it can also be used to get round a failed train.

The effects on the overall operations may be severe, but this depends also on whether the line arrangement is down slow, down main, up main, up slow (less restrictive and as on the ECML) or down main, up main, down slow, up slow (as on the WCML or GWML, where any weave will affect both directions of traffic). However, the WCML arrangement is more helpful at terminals, since trains of a like nature are automatically grouped together.

Weekday, weekend
Words which have outlived their usefulness for railway purposes, due to their ability to be misunderstood. Weekday used to mean Monday to Saturday, but was banished from railway timetables as long ago as 1975, to be replaced by Mondays to Fridays or Mondays to Saturdays, as appropriate. Whether we really need so many different sets of timetables to cover normal operations on different days of the week seems never to have been addressed seriously.

Likewise, passengers arriving at Heathrow Airport on 'London weekend breaks' were reportedly dismayed to find that the London Weekend Travelcard would cover them for two days only. It has now been replaced by a three-day Travelcard which is marketed as such.

Weekly Operating Notice (WON)
A publication containing the engineering work for the forthcoming week and other related information.

Welsh service
A passenger service which starts in Wales, ends in Wales or otherwise makes at least one scheduled call in Wales. See also Wales-only service.

West Coast Main Line (WCML)
The main line from London Euston via Milton Keynes to Crewe, Preston, Carlisle and Glasgow, with the branches from Rugby to Birmingham and Wolverhampton, from both Colwich and Stafford to Stoke-on-Trent and Manchester, from Crewe to Manchester and to Liverpool, and from Carstairs to Edinburgh. This includes the route via Northampton. All these routes are electrified (25kV ac).

West London Line
An important cross-London route, especially for freight, linking Clapham Junction and Willesden Junction.

Wet spot
See Sleeper pumping.

Wheel burn
Wheel burn is a depression formed in the railhead as the result of a train trying to accelerate faster than rail conditions will allow, causing the driving wheels to spin. This is a particular problem at times of low adhesion. The heat generated can produce a metallurgical change in the rail steel in that area, making it hard and brittle. That part of the rail surface can then easily break up under traffic, but rarely to the extent of causing a rail fracture. The depressions have to be expensively removed by rail grinding, while the life of the rail itself is reduced.

Wheel flat

If a train skids when the brakes are on, the result is the wearing of a flat part on the running surface on the otherwise round wheel. The resultant hammering effect can cause serious damage to the rail surface and, in extreme cases, its structure. Damage to the wheel can be corrected only by use of a lathe to restore curvature; meanwhile it will provide a bumpy ride for the passenger. This is made worse if the same wheel has suffered such problems more than once without attention. Wheel flats can also be heard on a moving train.

Wheel slip protection

A device, where fitted, which aims to prevent skidding from leaves or any other source, and thus the problems caused by wheel burn on the railhead. It works by limiting the rate at which the wheels are allowed to accelerate or decelerate.

Wheel turning

The reprofiling of a wheelset consisting of two wheels on one axle to predetermined standards, to correct imperfections that have arisen during use. This is frequently carried out on a wheel lathe in running sheds, which does not require the wheelset to be removed from the vehicle. Each turning will result in the wheel profile becoming a little smaller, with the eventual result that the wheel will have to be retyred.

Wheel tyre

The outer part of a wheel which bears on the running rail and abrades with wear. It is formed of a separate steel ring (tyre) from the wheel itself and onto which it is shrunk, and is designed to be replaced when it becomes fully worn.

Wheelbase

The distance between the point of contact with the rail of the two sets of wheels on a four-wheel vehicle, or that of the outermost sets of wheels for bogie vehicles. Not to be confused with the length over buffers, which refers to that of the vehicle itself.

Wheelset

The combined unit of two wheels set to gauge on a single axle.

Whistle board

A lineside board instructing drivers of trains to whistle (nowadays use the horn) to give warning of approach or, on the Great Western, to *sound* a whistle (abbreviated to SW).

White line

That painted on platform edges to draw attention to them; not provided on the platform end ramps. Applied universally during the blackout conditions of World War 2 and subsequently made permanent.

White line
Lowestoft had an overall roof until recently; now it has three platforms, much longer than present-day requirements, as the white lining on the platform edges indicate. On 5 August 2003, trains will soon depart for Norwich (left) and Ipswich (right). *John Glover*

White space, white periods
Those spaces on the timetable graph which are not occupied by any scheduled train services, and are thus free to be used for additional services or, alternatively, for programmed engineering work.

Wicket gate
A small kissing gate at traditionally gated level crossings, which is left available for pedestrian use until the main gates are fully closed to road traffic, when it is locked from the signalbox.

Widenings
Where the original railway was built for perhaps single track, but was later widened to (say) double track. Such widenings rarely use the same construction materials or methods as the original, so the result is often far from uniform. This can have implications for the care of the structures and their eventual replacement, since their ages will also vary.

WON
See Weekly Operating Notice

Working Timetable (WTT)
The timetable to which the railway is worked by the staff, showing all trains and with detailed timings at regular intervals. These include passing times at points where the train is not scheduled to stop. Additional time may be allowed for various reasons, as follows:

[3]   Indicates number of minutes allowed for temporary speed restrictions or other engineering work.
(2)   Extra time for pathing requirements.
<1>   Performance allowance.

There are also symbols to indicate where the advertised public time in National Rail timetables is different from that in the WTT. This last can be the source of several additional minutes, which helps the punctuality statistics, while departures may be advertised $1/2$ minute earlier to ensure that passengers are ready and waiting when the train arrives.

As far as possible the Working Timetables, which are produced in a number of largely geographical volumes and separately for passenger and freight traffic, show every train movement on the network and are revised not less than twice a year. These are not published documents.

Timings in the WTT are in half minutes, but the public book shows only whole minutes.

Works plate
See Builder's plate

Wrong line working
On all running lines other than single lines, each is normally designated as either up or down. Wrong line working takes place when a train is authorised to move in the down direction on the up line, or in the up direction on the down line. In these cases, special conditions apply such as the provision of a pilotman, although such moves can be signalled. Lines may also be designated reversible. Hence, also the expression 'wrong direction'.

Wrong side failure
The failure of a piece of equipment in such a way that compromises safety.

WTT
See Working Timetable.

Yellow Book
The *Yellow Book* describes a proven and effective approach to Engineering Safety Management. It is not mandatory, but has been constructed as a distillation of best practice.

Yellow lines
These are to give waiting passengers protection from the aerodynamic effects of passing trains. Yellow lines, together with warning signs, are provided on platforms where the permissible speed on the adjoining line exceeds 100mph. They are to be positioned so that people standing immediately behind the yellow line are at least 1,500mm away from the platform edge. Note that there is no requirement for yellow lines where train speed does not exceed 100mph, though there are many such instances. Separate arrangements apply where speeds exceed 125mph.

APPENDIX A
LEGAL PROCESSES

This section is divided into two parts, that concerning domestic legislation and that for European.

British legislation

Statute Law

Statute Law dates from the earliest times. Unless Statutes contain specific references to an expiry date, whether of individual sections or the whole, they remain in force indefinitely or until such time as they are repealed. The procedure for new legislation is as follows.

Green Paper

In a Green Paper which is a completely optional publication, the Government sets out its ideas with a view to future legislation. This is essentially a consultative document, to which various groups, businesses and indeed individuals may respond.

White Paper

A White Paper, again optional, contains in-depth proposals which will form the basis of forthcoming legislation, on which the Government has essentially made up its mind. These may take account of any Green Paper consultation, to the extent that the Government so wishes.

Parliamentary process

A Bill (a draft law) may be introduced into either of the Houses of Parliament, where it needs to obtain a First Reading in order to proceed. It will then receive a Second Reading and be committed to a Standing Committee established for the purpose in the House in which it was introduced. At least one Minister from the Government Department concerned will be on the Committee. The Committee may amend the Bill of its own volition, or as a result of objections or other requests put forward by objectors or supporters. The amended Bill returns to the House, Report Stage, where further amendments may be made. It will then return to the Commons for a Third Reading, before progressing to the Lords, where a similar procedure is followed, although the Standing Committee is usually replaced by a Committee of the whole House.

The Lords and the Commons must agree the text of the whole Bill, and there are procedures to deal with any differences. The Bill is then submitted for Royal Assent, on receipt of which it becomes law, an Act of Parliament. The commencement date(s) of the new Act or individual sections of it will often be left to the Secretary of State concerned to determine through a subsequent Statutory Instrument.

Types of Bill

A Bill may be introduced by a Government Minister in pursuit of promises made in the election manifesto (Public Bill), on behalf of a company or similar organisation by a Member (Private Bill), or on a Member's own initiative (Private Member's Bill). Public and Private Bills have the most chance of being enacted, unless the Government is content to allow a Private Member's Bill to proceed and allows parliamentary time accordingly.

A Hybrid Bill is, as the name suggests, part Public and part Private; it is reserved for complex circumstances in which the interests promoting it are essentially private, but the implications are so extensive that it is unlikely to become law without Government backing. The Bill seeking the powers necessary for the construction of Crossrail is in this category.

Other needs by promoters and companies to acquire powers of this nature are dealt with using a non-parliamentary procedure by an application made under the Transport & Works Act 1992, which takes a similar form to that of a Planning Inquiry (used for example for Docklands Light Railway extensions).

Regulatory Impact Assessment (RIA) for forthcoming Bills

The RIA is the Governmental tool which informs policy decisions. The object is to provide an assessment of the impact of policy options in terms of the costs, benefits and risks of a proposal. It is Government policy that all departments and agencies where they exercise statutory powers should produce a Regulatory Impact Assessment. The RIA should provide a thorough cost benefit analysis of the Bill's proposals and an assessment of any risks to the effectiveness of its provisions.

General Acts

While each railway company had its own specific private Act, authorising it to be built and perhaps subsequent Acts to acquire additional powers for that company, all were subject to General Acts. The following classification of General Acts for railways is adapted from one first compiled in 1915:

- Those governing methods of construction, equipment and safety requirements.
- Those concerning rates, fares and charges.
- Those aimed at securing reasonable facilities for the public and providing that contracts should not be unfair or unreasonable.

- Those concerning amalgamations between companies.
- Those requiring railway companies to make financial and statistical returns.
- Miscellaneous provisions, such as those for the conveyance of the Forces, the carriage of mail, workmen at cheap fares, etc.

The same general divisions can still be made, the main additions being perhaps the ability of the State to use its own funds for railway purposes and direct the manner as to how such funds are spent, and those which stem from the separation of the operating companies and the infrastructure on which they run.

Statutory Instruments

A Statutory Instrument has the full force of law, but is usually limited to matters where the framework is established by an Act of Parliament. Thus an Act will determine the principles of the legislation, but the details of how these are applied are frequently left to the Secretary of State concerned. Broadly, the Act will set out what is to be achieved, but often delegates the detailed means of achieving it. This will be found in the Statutory Instrument.

An example is the requirements for Railway Safety Cases and the dates by which the various processes must be completed. Others might be the method of making a representation in a matter covered by the Act, or the charges levied for various matters prescribed in the Act. This approach has a secondary benefit, in that changes which are essentially of an administrative nature can avoid the full rigour of a change in legislation, if experience suggests that they should be altered. The Statutory Instrument procedure is very much quicker than that for primary legislation.

Statutory Instruments cover a wide range of topics under the various Acts of Parliament.

European Union legislation (EU)

There are three main bodies:

The **Council of Ministers** is composed of Ministers from Member States and its main function is to act as the Community's principal decision-making body.

The **European Commission** is the executive arm of the EU. It has the sole right to initiate legislation, which starts with a draft provided by the Directorate General (or Ministry) concerned. This is identified by a COM number, eg COM(2005)23 is the 23rd to be published in 2005. The Commission also implements Community policies based on the various treaties which establish the EU and which are intended to be replaced by the EU Constitution.

The **European Parliament** is composed of Members (MEPs) directly elected from each Member State.

Legal instruments

- *Regulations*
  These are binding in their entirety and are applied directly in all Member States without the need for domestic legislation.

- *Directives*
  These bind the Member States to achieve the results specified by transposing the Directives into domestic legislation in each State within a set time limit. They can create individual rights if not so transposed.

- *Decisions*
  These are binding on those to whom they are addressed.

- *Recommendations and Opinions*
  These are non-binding.

- *Communications and Policy Papers*
  These are also non-binding.

All the above are published in the weekly *Official Journal of the European Community* (OJEC), as are calls for tenders, etc.

It is a principle that the European Commission should propose action centrally at the EU level only if the desired result cannot be obtained more effectively at the national, regional or local level as appropriate.

APPENDIX B
ACTS OF PARLIAMENT AND REGULATIONS

Introduction

These Acts are those which have a bearing on the present-day railway and are arranged in date order, oldest first. Those referring to rates and charges, once a considerable element of railway law, have now been repealed for many years and are only mentioned in passing.

From the earliest days, railways were authorised individually by private Acts of Parliament. Railways were entrepreneurial projects undertaken for the private profit of the promoters, and were treated as such. The many hundreds of such Acts are omitted from consideration here. They laid down the basic conditions for the construction of the railway and the route to be taken, and conferred on the promoters the powers to acquire the land necessary. These Acts did not, however, contain any assurances on the quality or completeness of the capital works when they were opened, or how safely the railway would be operated. Following a number of accidents, the Railway Department of the Board of Trade was created by the Government, and legislation followed over the years.

This can only be a brief outline of a wide-ranging and complex subject, but it is hoped that it will form a useful reference.

ACTS OF PARLIAMENT AND REGULATIONS
Trespass has been a problem as long as railways have been around; this sign, which is now on show in the National Railway Museum at York, covers a situation which is unlikely to be of much consequence nowadays. Nevertheless, trespass is still a major cause of deaths on the railway. *John Glover*

Acts

Highway (Railway Crossings) Act 1839
Placed obligations on companies to provide gates at each intersection of the railway with a turnpike (trunk) road, and to employ proper persons to open and shut them.

Regulation of Railways Act 1840
This Act required the Board of Trade to be given one month's notice of the intended opening of any railway (but not to prevent its opening) and gave them powers to appoint Inspectors. Trespass on the railway became a criminal offence. Drivers, guards, porters, signalmen and others conducting traffic on the railway, or maintaining it, were prohibited from being drunk while so employed.

Regulation of Railways Act 1842
The Board of Trade was given power to suspend the opening of a new railway if, after inspection, it was not satisfied it could be operated without danger to the public. Serious accidents became reportable by the railway companies, whether they were attended by personal injury or not. All railway companies were put under an obligation to erect, maintain and repair fences along their lines.

The gates of all railway level crossings were to be kept normally closed across the road and opened as required 'in the interests of better regulation of railways and the conveyance of troops'.

Regulation of Railways Act 1844
Every railway company was obliged to offer at least one train daily in each direction, on all lines, calling at all stations, at a fare not exceeding one (old) penny a mile and at a minimum speed of 12mph, using covered accommodation. These fares were exempted from Passenger Duty. The same Act required the railways to carry troops.

Railway Clauses Consolidation Act 1845
The railways were obliged to fence their lines to delineate the railway boundary, protect livestock and prevent trespass from the railway onto adjoining land.

This Act made it a requirement to build a bridge where a railway crossed the highway, unless the authorising Act of the railway permitted the construction of a level crossing. Gatekeepers were to be employed to staff such crossings and operate the gates, but gates were normally to be kept closed across the road unless otherwise specifically authorised. An obligation was placed on railway companies of a train speed restriction of 4mph over level crossings adjoining stations.

The railway had to provide and maintain level crossings used as footpaths and bridleways. It was also necessary for accommodation crossings to be provided where a landowner's property was divided by the construction of the railway, or occupation crossings where the private way was in common ownership. Railway companies were given powers to make their own bye-laws.

Act for Regulating the Gauge of Railways 1846
Determined that the future standard gauge of railways in Britain should be 4ft 8½in, although the last bastions of the Great Western's broad gauge (7ft 0¼in) survived until 1892.

Railway Clearing Act 1850
Statutory recognition of the Railway Clearing House (RCH), which had been active since 1842. This consolidated the mutual arrangements between different railways, settling accounts between the 120 or so companies which existed before the First World War, when traffic passed from one company to another in the course of a single journey. For this, the mileage run

on each was the most important factor. The volumes stabilised at around 35% of the total receipts for goods traffic and 15% for passengers over many years. The RCH also established a common classification of goods, standardised signalling systems and telegraphic codes, implemented the common user system for wagons, and provided a neutral meeting ground for general managers to establish their pooling arrangements and rate conferences. At its zenith, the RCH employed over 3,000 staff.

Railway and Canal Traffic Act 1854
Introduction of 'undue preference', which required that where a facility or concession was provided for any one trader, the same conditions must be applied to any other trader requiring a similar service. This effectively destroyed the railways' commercial freedom on freight rates for, as it transpired, the century that followed.

Railway Clauses Act 1863
The Board of Trade was given powers to direct companies to erect bridges to replace level crossings, at their own expense, if this appeared necessary for public safety.

Regulation of Railways Act 1868
The installation of a means of communication between the passengers and the staff in charge of the train became compulsory in all passenger trains travelling more than 20 miles without a stop.

Tramways Act 1870
Regulation of the development of tramways. The Act gave local authorities the right to build but not to operate tramways, or to veto tramway development by others. It also gave them compulsory purchase powers 21 years after construction.

Regulation of Railways Act 1871
This Act specified the types of accidents which were reportable, legalised the holding of formal accident inquiries by the Inspection Officers, and provided for the publication of their reports.

Reportable accidents included all those to passenger trains, those to goods trains affecting passenger running lines, all cases of trains becoming divided or coupling failures on passenger running lines, mechanical failures which had caused or might cause an accident to a passenger train, all rail breakages on passenger lines, and accidents to people.

This Act also provided for the use of a judicial inquiry into accidents where Ministers so decided, and was first used following the collapse of the Tay Bridge in 1879.

Regulation of the Forces Act 1871
Gave the Government powers to take the railways under their own unified control. It was first exercised in the First World War.

Cheap Trains Act 1883
Made compulsory the offering of fares not exceeding 1d (0.4p) per mile, to which level third class fares were soon reduced. Such fares were exempted from Passenger Duty.

Regulation of Railways Act 1889
In this most significant piece of legislation, the Board of Trade was authorised to make orders to impose the following, where they were not already in force:
- The use of the block system of signalling on all passenger lines.
- The interlocking of points and signals on passenger lines.
- The fitting and use of the continuous automatic brake on all passenger trains.

This last requirement was for a brake which was self-applying and thus 'fail-safe' in the event of a change in air pressure in the system — for instance, if a train became divided. However, it did not specify air or vacuum braking.

It was also made a requirement for a passenger to produce a valid ticket on demand or pay the fare, and an offence to travel with intent to avoid payment.

Light Railways Act 1896
Allowed engineering and other standards to be reduced, and hence also construction costs, in exchange for additional limitations. The most important of these was a maximum permitted speed of 25mph. All today's preserved railways operate under the terms of a Light Railway Order, however they may have been constructed originally. This limitation does inhibit any attempt to provide reasonably speedy services, although speed is rarely a consideration in terms of the service offered.

Railway Employment (Prevention of Accidents) Act 1900
Safeguarded railway staff from the worst risks associated with railway operation. This gave the Board of Trade powers to make rules, under which it became mandatory to provide power brakes on all locomotives, to guard point rodding, and to provide a look-out man to warn staff working on the track. Railway Employment Inspectors were appointed.

It may be noted that the various Factories Acts offered no protection, since the railway did not come within the legal definition of a factory.

Safety principles
By the end of the 19th century and the formative period for the railway industry, three basic safety principles had thus been established:
1. The ultimate responsibility for the safety of operation must rest with the railway.
2. Once a railway has been opened, or new works approved, the railway administration is responsible for maintaining it to the safety standards necessary.
3. Responsibility for the safety of the design of structures built by the railway must rest with the railway.

Subsequent legislation has not altered these principles, although with the separation of infrastructure and operations one might question which organisation is meant by 'the railway'.

Ministry of Transport Act 1919
Creation of the Ministry of Transport, with wide powers of control over railways.

Railways Act 1921
The enabling Act for the grouping of 123 British railway companies from 1 January 1923 into what became known as the Big Four – the Great Western Railway, the Southern Railway, the London, Midland & Scottish Railway, and the London & North Eastern Railway. Private company status was retained. A primary aim of the Act was to enable the railways to benefit from economies of scale.

Finance Act 1929
Abolished Passenger Duty on first and second class fares, but with the proviso that most of the amounts thus saved by the railway companies would be capitalised and committed to infrastructure investment.

Road and Rail Traffic Act 1933
Railway undertakings were required to secure the authority of the Secretary of State for the opening of any new portion of a railway to passenger traffic, including the opening of any new running lines, or the opening of any railway for electric traction. (This was a tightening up and strengthening of earlier legislation.) The 4mph speed restriction across station level crossings was withdrawn and the Minister was allowed to direct that gates at specific crossings be closed across the railway (instead of across the road) either constantly or on such dates and times as he thought fit.

Railway (Agreement) Act 1935
To stimulate the national economy, the Government gave financial support for what became the Shenfield and Woodhead electrification schemes, although neither was completed before the Second World War.

Transport Act 1947
Nationalisation of the Big Four (and other forms of transport) from 1 January 1948 and the creation of British Railways. Administered by the Railway Executive under the aegis of the newly created British Transport Commission (BTC). The British Transport Commission was given the general duty in exercising their powers to have due regard to safety of operation.

Transport Act 1953
Abolition of the Railway Executive, and more power devolved to the (then) six Regions of British Railways.

British Transport Commission Act 1954
For the first time lifting barriers were permitted to replace swing gates at level crossings, with the consent of the Minister.

British Transport Commission Act 1957
The railway was no longer required to man highway crossings. This permitted automatic half-barrier and no barrier crossings, with suitable safeguards which included signing.

The pre-Grouping era (before 1923) lives on in many ways. Thus the entrance gates at Marylebone station which date from 1899 were still emblazoned with the initials of its then owners, the Great Central Railway, when photographed on 17 December 1998. *John Glover*

Transport Act 1962
Reconstruction of BTC finances, abolition of the Commission and creation of the British Railways Board (and others) from 1 January 1963. Its general responsibility was to provide railway services and to have due regard to efficiency, safety and economy of operation.

Transport Act 1968
Enabled the creation of the (eventually seven) Passenger Transport Authorities and Executives, and the introduction of grants for socially necessary rail services. The railway was required to introduce additional protection at road level crossings when so directed by the Minister, which followed the serious accident at Hixon, Staffordshire, in January of that year.

Private enterprise was just about present in the railways of the 1950s. Here, the English Electric Co's prototype *Deltic* locomotive is heading the 'Shamrock', the 16.35 Euston to Liverpool Lime Street near Weaver Junction on 20 May 1957. Hopes of large sales of these 3,300hp machines to British Railways were translated into a perhaps disappointing order for 22 locomotives, which formed the backbone of East Coast motive power for the next 15 years.
R. Whitfield/Author's collection

Transport Act 1974

Introduction of grants for the provision of freight facilities on railways, dependent upon a consequential reduction in road traffic.

Level Crossings Act 1983

The Secretary of State was enabled to make orders specifying in detail the protective equipment to be provided, and to give authority to alter or replace existing equipment.

Town & Country Planning Act 1990

The Act under which local planning authorities may attach conditions to permissions given for land development, including financial ones, which may be used for purposes such as securing the provision of a railway station and access thereto, or contributions towards that provision (Section 106 agreements). These agreements are being superseded by those made under the **Planning and Compulsory Purchase Act 2004**.

Transport & Works Act 1992

This Act ended the need for railway businesses to promote their own legislation where they required legal powers for proposed actions, such as compulsory purchase; at the very least, organisations such as the British Railways Board needed an annual Bill for a miscellaneous series of works that they intended to carry out. The Transport & Works Act replaced this long-established system with legislation more closely related to the Planning Inquiry.

Today, a formal application to carry out certain works is submitted to the Secretary of State and published in the form prescribed. Depending upon the reactions received, the Secretary of State may cause a local public inquiry to be held so that objections can be heard. Subsequently, the Secretary of State will make an Order, with or without modification to that applied for, or refuse it.

Where the matter concerned is judged by the Secretary of State to be of national significance, a more robust means of authorisation is available by introducing a Hybrid Bill into the Houses of Parliament. Such a Bill is Private in nature, but has Government backing from the outset. An Order made as a result of this procedure has to be approved by a resolution of both Houses of Parliament, passed on a motion moved by a Minister of the Crown. The Crossrail Bill was introduced on this basis in March 2005.

Railways Act 1993

This Act provided the framework for the privatisation of British Railways. It set up the system of rail regulation and established a licensing regime for the ownership and use of railway assets to provide passenger and goods services, and specified how such licences might be modified. It also established an access regime under which a railway facility owner was required to enter into access agreements with train operators, which allowed the operator to use the owner's facilities. It also introduced franchising of passenger services. The Government was given the right to give directions to all those involved in service provision in times of hostilities or national emergency. Railway operators and others were given the status of statutory authorities for some purposes.

The 1993 Act included amending legislation to the **Health & Safety at Work Act 1974**. This brought the proper operation and safe construction of the railways, their locomotives and rolling stock, and the protection of the general public and railway employees from personal injury and other risks, under the terms of that Act.

Disability Discrimination Act 1995 (DDA)
Requires that reasonable access to goods and services is provided for the disabled, and sets certain specific standards for new trains.

Greater London Authority Act 1999
Gave power to the Mayor of London to give directions and guidance to the Strategic Rail Authority in certain circumstances.

Transport Act 2000
Introduced the Local Transport Plan concept, whereby all local transport authorities must set out their policies for the promotion and encouragement of safe, integrated, efficient and economic transport facilities. This Act also established the short-lived Strategic Rail Authority. The duties of other bodies were also amended.

Railways & Transport Safety Act 2003
Reorganisation of British Transport Police and replacement of the Office of the Rail Regulator by the Office of Rail Regulation. Creation of the Rail Accident Investigation Branch and Railway Safety Levy and incorporation of COTIF into British law.

Railways Act 2005
The main elements of this Act are:
● Abolition of the SRA and the transfer of its principal functions to the Department for Transport (or the devolved administrations).
● Strategy, finance and the awarding of franchises to become the responsibility of the Department for Transport, the Scottish Executive and the Welsh Assembly.
● The Secretary of State will set out what Network Rail is expected to deliver for the public money it receives through access charges and grant.
● Transfer of safety policy, regulation and enforcement functions from the HSE to the ORR.
● Transfer of the SRA's responsibility for consumer protection licence conditions to the Office of Rail Regulation.
● Changing the role of the Rail Passengers Council and abolishing the local Committees.
● Amending railway closure procedures.
● Reducing the powers of Passenger Transport Executives and giving equivalent powers to Transport *for* London.
● Provision to introduce franchising of rail replacement bus services.
● General enhancement of the powers of the Welsh Assembly and, particularly, the Scottish Executive.

A wheelchair being unloaded from a Class 170 First North Western train at Grange-over-Sands on 13 July 2002. The train is the 11.49 Manchester Airport to Barrow-in-Furness. *John Glover*

Regulations

Fire Precautions, Sub-Surface Railway Stations, Statutory Instrument 1989/1401

In 1989, the Secretary of State made regulations under s12 of the **Fire Precautions Act 1971**. These apply at stations which have platforms which are wholly or mainly enclosed in a tunnel or building, and are below ground level.

The Regulations state *inter alia* that a proper means of escape should be provided and kept clear of obstructions, that there should be means of fighting a fire and giving a warning, and that parts of the premises should be separated by fire-resistant construction. Also specified are the fire-resistant qualities required in wall and ceiling cladding.

In organisational terms, station employees should receive training, a contingency plan should be prepared, smoking (by anyone) must be prevented, staffing and supervisory levels should be specified, and that full records be kept. This followed the King's Cross fire on London Underground in 1987.

Railway & Other Transport Systems (Approval of Works, Plant & Equipment) Regulations (ROTS) 1994

HSE approval required for bringing any new and altered railway works, plant and equipment into use. For the first time, this included locomotives and rolling stock.

Railways (Safety Critical Work) Regulations 1994

These Regulations require that staff undertaking such work are competent and fit, and make arrangements for the external scrutiny of such records.

Carriage of Dangerous Goods by Rail Regulations 1994 & 1996

These Regulations establish a framework to control the carriage of dangerous (eg explosive or flammable) goods on any railway. The Regulations establish a 'chain of responsibility' and aim to ensure that everyone in the chain understands his own role and responsibilities. They cover the design, strength, construction, suitability, labelling and marking of freight containers, tank containers, tank wagons and ordinary wagons so used, as well as their initial certification and periodic maintenance by a competent person. They also include provisions on safe loading, segregation, fire and explosion, and information instruction and training of crew, etc.

Health & Safety (Safety, Signs & Signals) Regulations 1996

These assign colours to signs of different types. Red signs refer to prohibitions, danger alarm and fire-fighting equipment, Yellow signs give warnings, Blue signs refer to mandatory actions or procedures, and Green signs are used for items such as emergency escape and first aid.

Rail Vehicle Accessibility Regulations (RVAR) 1998

These are to ensure that disabled people can get on or off regulated rail vehicles in safety and without unreasonable difficulty, be carried in rail vehicles in safety and in reasonable comfort and, in the case of wheelchair users, to do so while remaining in their wheelchairs.

Railways (Safety Case) Regulations 2000

These Regulations made under the **Health & Safety at Work (etc) Act 1974** require every railway operator to prepare and secure acceptance of a 'Safety Case'. This is a prerequisite for the issue of a licence to operate. The Safety Case demonstrates that the operator has the ability and commitment to adequately control risks to the health and safety of employees and the general public. There are three kinds of 'railway operator': Infrastructure controllers, Train Operators and Station Operators.

Railway Safety Cases are to be replaced by Safety Certificates.

Other Regulations include those which transpose Community Directives into British law, notably the **Railways Regulations 1998**.

Regulations with no specific railway connections include:

● **Transfer of Undertakings (Protection of Employment) Regulations (TUPE) 1981**

● **Control of Substances Hazardous to Health (COSHH) Regulations 1988**

● **Reporting of Injuries, Diseases and Dangerous Occurrences Regulations (RIDDOR) 1995.**

APPENDIX C
EUROPEAN LEGISLATION

Present approach

With a quality European railway system the aim, the Commission's third railway package of 2004 proposes to open up international passenger services to competition within the European Union in 2010. It thus seeks to complete the integration of the European railway area and stimulate rail transport.

The Commission is also proposing to improve the rights of passengers using international services, establish a certification system for locomotive drivers and step up the quality of freight services. This further series of measures is intended to revitalise the railways in accordance with the guidelines set out in the White Paper 'European transport policy for 2010: Time to decide'[1].

These measures add to the framework in place since the Directives of the first railway package of 2001 and the measures of the second railway package undergoing final adoption (Directive on railway safety, rail agency, opening up of the freight market). The first railway package allowed the regulated opening up of international goods transport.

The second railway package aims to speed up this process and extend it to national goods transport operations (cabotage). In addition, it improves safety and allows greater interoperability, as a result of a number of specific directives and the setting up of the European Agency for Rail Safety and Interoperability based in Valenciennes (France).

European Regulations, Directives and Decisions

Regulation 1191/69: Public Service Obligation
The State must compensate railway undertakings if it requires them to provide unprofitable passenger services in the public interest.

Directive 91/440: Development of the Community's railways
This Directive provided for the separation of railway infrastructure and train service provision (accounting compulsory, organisations optional), securing management independence, improving financial structures and limited open access for international goods transit. The whole of this legislation was aimed at the international markets.

Subsequently amended by **Directive 2001/12**, to require also the separation of accounts and no cross-subsidy between passenger and freight, separation of licence issue plus capacity and charging functions from railway service providers, and extend competition in the international freight market.

Further amended by **Directive 2004/51**, which extends the scope for open access to domestic freight traffic from 2007.

Directive 95/18: Licensing of railway undertakings
Criteria and procedures for the issue, renewal and amendment of licences for railway undertakings to carry out operations covered by 91/440.

Subsequently amended by **Directive 2001/13**, setting out requirements for the independence of the licensing body.

Directive 95/19: Allocation of railway infrastructure capacity and the charging of infrastructure fees
Non-discriminatory allocation of infrastructure capacity according to published national priorities and the development of access charging criteria for services covered by 91/440. In Britain this saw the establishment of the International Rail Regulator as licensing authority. But see **Directive 2001/14**.

Directive 96/48: Interoperability of the trans-European high speed rail system
Interoperability may be defined as the effort to render the various national rail systems of the Member States compatible and operational. For instance, vocational qualifications for train drivers are completely different from one Member State to another, and depend largely on the companies themselves.

The aim of this Directive is to establish the conditions to be met for the Technical Standards for Interoperability (TSI) of the high speed network for infrastructure and rolling stock.

Subsequently amended by **Directive 2004/50**, which is aimed at facilitating international services, creating an internal market, and contributing generally to interoperability.

In Britain, the high speed network will consist of:
- London St Pancras to the Channel Tunnel (CTRL).
- London Euston to Glasgow Central via Trent Valley, to Liverpool Lime Street, to Manchester Piccadilly via Stoke-on-Trent and via Crewe, Carstairs to Edinburgh.

[1]COM(2001)370 of 12.09.2001.

- London King's Cross to Edinburgh direct.
- London Paddington to Bristol via Bristol Parkway and via Bath Spa, Bristol Parkway to Cardiff Central.

Directive 2001/14: Infrastructure capacity allocation, access fees, network statement, safety certification and regulation

Replaced Directive 95/19 in full. It covers domestic and international services (excluding only suburban and stand-alone regional local passenger networks). It requires the publication of a detailed network statement including conditions of access, details of access charges for the use of that infrastructure (and associated performance requirements), and capacity allocation methods. Charges need to cover the direct costs of provision as a minimum, but may be higher to reflect scarcity. The allocation of railway infrastructure capacity includes the principles of scheduling and use of train paths, and the length of time such operator capacity rights remain in force. Where there are insufficient train paths to meet operator demand, the infrastructure manager must carry out an analysis of options. Requirements for safety certification are specified and regulatory bodies are established. The length of access contracts is limited.

Directive 2001/16: Interoperability of the trans-European conventional rail system

This Directive sets out to establish the conditions to be met on the conventional (non-high speed) parts of the system so designated, concerning design, construction, putting into service, upgrading, renewal, operation and maintenance. This leads to a minimum level of technical harmonisation to make interoperability possible.

Directive 2002/49: Assessment and management of environmental noise

Regulation 881/2004: Establishment of a European Railway Agency

To support the implementation of Community legislation on technical matters, including the TSIs (Technical Standards for Interoperability). These cover:

Structural sub-systems
- Infrastructure
- Energy
- Control and command and signalling
- Rolling stock

Operational sub-systems
- Maintenance
- Environment
- Operation
- Users

Directive 2004/35: Environmental liability with regard to the prevention and remedying of environmental damage

Directive 2004/49: The Railway Safety Directive

This Directive sets out principles for safety and provides for the preparation of common safety targets (based on risk assessment) and common methods of assessment. The content of safety certificates is specified, as are requirements for staff training and safety management including accident investigation. There are some amendments to Directives 95/18 and 2001/14.

There are many more Directives with an actual or potential impact on the railways, for example the Working Time Directive and the Non-Road Mobile Machine Directive.

The new St Pancras International station is taking shape. The interim arrangements have Midland Main Line services using what will later become the Channel Tunnel Rail Link domestic service platforms. Here, a MML Class 222 'Meridian' unit stands in Platform 12 on 23 August 2005. *John Glover*

Acknowledgements

A book of this nature covers many facets of a huge field, with some of which any individual may be well versed, but others less so. From the beginning, therefore, I was only too well aware that the help of others would be needed, and indeed many people have offered me a lot of support.

Intriguingly, though, differences of opinion do arise as to what certain terms mean, which may be down to evolution over time, regional differences, or both. Readers will doubtless have their own opinions, too. I have tried to steer a middle road and used those definitions which I felt to be the most likely; consequently, the responsibility for what appears here is mine alone.

I am particularly indebted to the following, many of whom are fellow members of the Strategic Rail Forum of the Chartered Institute of Logistics and Transport in the UK. My thanks start with those to the present Chairman of that group, Mary Bonar FCILT, who worked her way assiduously through many of the contractual and legal aspects. Peter Ashton, Dr Martin Higginson FCILT and Malcolm Pheasey FCILT all gave meticulous consideration to definition after definition, each making some very constructive suggestions according to his own detailed knowledge of the industry. John Chapman FCILT and Jeremy Drew FCILT put me right on matters of freight and economics respectively, while Michael Woods FCILT contributed the section on level crossings, courtesy RSSB, and tidied up many loose ends. Walter Turner kindly put his expertise in matters electrical at my disposal and Iain MacLauchlan checked the section on European legislation. Bob Breakwell generously offered an overview of the whole.

Finally, I was delighted that Chris Green FCILT was able to offer a foreword to what I hope will be a useful and perhaps even a mildly entertaining book.

Bibliography

A Guide to Rail Freight, Railtrack, 1999.

abc Railway Technology. B. K. Cooper. ISBN 0 7110 2266 6. Ian Allan Publishing Ltd, 1994.

Acts of Parliament, Statutory Instruments and European Directives, as noted individually.

An Economic History of Transport. Christopher I. Savage. No ISBN. Hutchinson & Co, second edition 1966.

Balfour Beatty website.

British Railway Track – Design, Construction and Maintenance. Geoffrey H. Cope (ed). ISBN 0 903489 03 1. Permanent Way Institution, sixth edition 1993.

British Railway Track, Vol 9 Track Terminology. I. W. Ellis. ISBN 0 903489 05 3. Permanent Way Institution, 2004.

British Transport Law by Road and Rail. G. A. Bonner. ISBN 0 7153 6000 0. David & Charles, 1974.

Carriage of Dangerous Goods Explained part 3: Guidance for Rail Operators and Others Involved in the Carriage of Dangerous Goods by Rail. ISBN 0 7176 1256 2. HSE, 1996.

Department for Transport website.

Glossary terms for those involved in Combined Transport Initiatives, Baker Rose, 1993.

Gloucestershire Warwickshire Railway website, 2004.

Little Black Book UK European Railway Cost Benchmarks 2004-05. Franklin Andrews, Construction Economists.

LMS Diesels – Locomotives and Railcars. E. V. Richards. ISBN 0 901115 76 2. RCTS, 1996.

Manual of Firemanship Book 4: Incidents involving Aircraft, Shipping and Railways. ISBN 0 11 340584 7. Home Office, 1985.

mda Railway Object Name Thesaurus website, 2004.

Metro Rule Book. Tyne & Wear Passenger Transport Executive, June 1979.

Network Rail Annual Return, 2003-04.

Network Rail Annual Return, 2004-05.

Network Rail Jargon Buster, 2001.

Network Rail Technical Plan, 2004.

Passenger Rail Industry Overview, Office of Passenger Rail Franchising, June 1996.

Rail Safety and Rail Privatisation in Britain (paper), Andrew W. Evans, 16 June 2004.

Rail Safety and Standards Board website.

Railway Track Diagrams (series of five), Quail Map Company, Exeter.

Regulations for Train Signalling and Signalmen's General Instructions, British Railways, 1972.

Rule Book, British Railways, 1970 and RSSB, 2003.

Standard Codes for Telegrams, BR, 1958 and as amended.

Strategic Rail Authority Glossary of Terms.

The Devil's Guide to the Railway Industry website, 2004.

The Dictionary of Transport and Logistics, David Lowe. ISBN 0 7494 3571 2. Kogan Page, 2002.

The Railway Clearing House in the British Economy, 1842-1922, Philip Bagwell. SBN 04 331037 0. George Allen & Unwin, 1968.

The Wordsworth Railway Dictionary, Alan A. Jackson. ISBN 1 85326 750 3. Wordsworth Editions Ltd, 1992.

TOPS manuals 1986 and 1987, British Rail.

Transport and Public Policy, K. M. Gwilliam. George Allen & Unwin, 1964.

Two Centuries of Railway Signalling, Geoffrey Kichenside and Alan Williams. ISBN 0 86983 541 8. Oxford Publishing Co. 1998.

World Metro Systems, Paul Garbutt. ISBN 1 85414 191 0. Capital Transport Publishing, second edition, 1997.

Where it all began . . . One of a series of plaques affixed to the boundary fence at Dartford station; photographed on 29 January 2001. *John Glover*

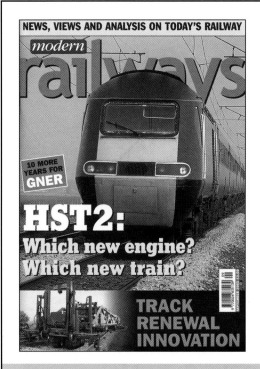